Frederick W. Headley

The Structure and Life of Birds

Frederick W. Headley

The Structure and Life of Birds

ISBN/EAN: 9783337849160

Printed in Europe, USA, Canada, Australia, Japan

Cover: Foto ©Andreas Hilbeck / pixelio.de

More available books at **www.hansebooks.com**

THE STRUCTURE

AND

LIFE OF BIRDS

BY

F. W. HEADLEY, M.A., F.Z.S.

ASSISTANT MASTER AT HAILEYBURY COLLEGE

WITH SEVENTY-EIGHT ILLUSTRATIONS

London

MACMILLAN AND CO.

AND NEW YORK

1895

PREFACE

THE aim of this book is an ambitious one. It attempts to give good evidence of the development of birds from reptilian ancestors, to show what modifications in their anatomy have accompanied their advance to a more vigorous life, and, after explaining, as far as possible, their physiology, to make clear the main principles of their noble accomplishment, flight, the visible proof and expression of their high vitality. After this it deals, principally, with the subjects of colour and song, instinct and reason, migration, and the principles of classification, and, lastly, gives some hints as to the best methods of studying birds. The field is a wide one, but this is not in every way a drawback. Specialisation has its evils as well as its advantages. Many of our best ornithologists write admirably of the life and habits of birds, but leave out of sight their anatomy and physiology. Thus they separate things which in nature are mutually dependent. The anatomists and physiologists, on their side, limit themselves sternly to their own departments. Their works,

too, are often over-elaborate for those to whom
ornithology is not the main business of life. Many
people, however devoted to the subject, have not
the time for the proper study of Dr. Gadow's great
work, which, moreover, being written in German, is
a sealed book to numbers of English readers. For
the study of bird anatomy they are often thrown
back upon the good but insufficient treatises written
for the use of medical students. Natural History
books, describing the lives of birds, are many, and,
not a few of them, first-rate, though, curiously, there
was not, to my knowledge, any English book in
which a general review of the known facts and of
the problems of migration had been successfully undertaken, till the appearance of the second volume
of Professor Newton's *Dictionary of Birds,* containing
a very able article on the subject. There are several
books in English treating of flight. Of these
Professor Marey's *Animal Mechanism* seems to me
the best. But some of his most instructive experiments have been made since its publication, and an
account of them is to be found only in his later and
larger work, *Le Vol des Oiseaux.* It has been my
wish to bring the work of the anatomist and physio-
logist into connection with that of the student of
flight and that of the outdoor naturalist. With this
object I have made some investigations and observations which, I believe, may lay claim to originality,
and I have consulted the best English, French, and
German books upon ornithology, as well as a number

of papers to be found in the Proceedings and Transactions of learned societies. Wherever it has been
possible, I have verified what I have learnt from
books by the methods explained in the concluding .
chapter. Discussions with mathematicians, in particular with Mr. T. J. Bowlker and Mr. R. C. Gilson,
to whom my most cordial thanks are due, have
greatly helped me in dealing with the difficult
problems of flight. Mr. A. H. Macpherson has
very kindly put at my service the results of some
of his observations on the song and on the migration
of birds. I have also to thank Mr. F. E. Beddard,
without whose encouragement I should not have
begun this work. In important cases I have
mentioned in footnotes the source to which I am
indebted for facts or theories, and at the end of each
chapter I have given a list of some of the best books
and papers on the subject treated of. Those of my
readers who wish to proceed to a more special study
of any of the different branches of ornithology will,
I hope, find these references an assistance.

On many parts of the subject I have delivered
lectures to the Haileybury Natural Science Society.
In this book I have followed much the same lines, in
the hope that it may prove useful to lovers of birds
here and elsewhere. Technical terms, except such as
are unavoidable, I have dispensed with, and, as far as
possible, I have explained difficulties, never, inten-
tionally, wrapped them in the obscurity of big words.
There is only one species of ornithologists with whom

I have no sympathy—the species represented by a boy famous in fiction, whose fondness for birds always led him to throw stones at them. It includes many varieties and sub-varieties, but all its representatives are either random slaughterers or cold-blooded exterminators. I would urge my readers to oppose them by joining the *Society for the Protection of Birds*.[1]

The illustrations are, nearly all of them, by Mr. Prendergast Parker, who has taken great pains to make them accurate and really illustrative. Professor Howes has very kindly watched their progress and in a good many cases provided the specimens from which they were drawn. I am much indebted to him for this great assistance. Dr. Hans Gadow, Mr. W. B. Hardy, Mr. Gilson, and Mr. Macpherson have been very kind in reading proof-sheets, and I wish most warmly to thank them for the great service they have thus rendered me.

[1] For particulars about the Society address the Hon. Secretary, Mrs. F. E. Lemon Hillcrest, Redhill, Surrey.

CONTENTS

CHAPTER X.

CHAPTER XI.

CHAPTER XII.

CHAPTER XIII.

CHAPTER XIV.

CONTENTS

CHAPTER XV.

CHAPTER XVI.

CHAPTER XVII.

LIST OF ILLUSTRATIONS

b

THE
STRUCTURE AND LIFE OF BIRDS

CHAPTER I

INTRODUCTORY

A BIRD seems to have more life in him than any other living creature. A Swift will outpace the fastest racehorse. Migratory birds arrive unexhausted after a flight of hundreds of miles. An Ostrich will leave behind the horseman who pursues him. The Penguin swims as if water were the native element of birds. And this vitality shows itself in many other ways, notably in the brilliant colours of the plumage, as in the Bird of Paradise or the Peacock. Sometimes, as in the Argus Pheasant, there is great richness of colouring without any gaudiness. Even when there is neither brilliancy nor richness of hue, but the plumage is of the very soberest, there is often such a brightness about the eye and the general air of our birds that their plainness passes unnoticed. Their leading characteristic is not their dull colouring but

E
B

their grace and sprightliness. Not even the most dazzling and ethereal of Humming-birds surpasses the Wheatear in beauty. High spirits are another sign of vitality in most if not in all birds. The Thrush will sing by the hour together for pure jollity. With our English birds this is the common way of giving expression to hilarity. Some foreign species hold most elaborate dances, and in all lands the fights among the cock birds in spring are signs of exuberant life. To find food and meet the actual needs of the day seems easy enough, so that there is a large surplus of energy to devote to pleasure or rivalry.

There is nothing in nature more wonderful than the instincts of birds—for the present we must use this much-debated word without explanation—nothing, perhaps, that presents more interesting problems. Take, for instance, the migratory instinct. The Swallow travels to the south of Africa to spend the winter and returns in spring to build her nest, often in the very chimney where she reared her brood the previous year.

The nests are in many ways interesting, from their beauty, from their wonderful variety—birds belonging to the same family often building quite differently—and from the fact that young birds have to build their first nest without any instruction. Take again the extraordinary instinct of the Cuckoo, and the still more extraordinary instinct of her infant progeny. Then, too, there is the death-feigning and wound-feigning instinct. All these, however much they may be studied, can never lose their interest

The bodies and brains of birds are suited to their full and varied life. Their circulation is rapid, their temperature higher than that of mammals, their lungs, though small, are probably the most efficient in the animal kingdom, their bones and their muscles have been adapted for purposes of flight, running, or swimming, they have brains that are, comparatively speaking, highly developed.

And yet the bird is a near relation of the lizard. He is descended, unless nearly all our great authorities are at fault, though not from any existing reptile, yet from ancestors that were definitely reptilian. And yet how enormous is the difference between these descendants from the same stock! For the two lines must meet if we trace them upward far enough.

A lizard is limited to earth, and even there his gait is an undignified shuffle. True, he slips with unsurpassed nimbleness into his hiding-place on a hot day when the sun has warmed his sluggish blood. But though he be the fastest of lizards, many a bird of no great size is a better runner, and could, without having recourse to the magic of wings, easily distance him in a race of more than a few yards. His forehead is low, hardly rising above his nose, showing, if other evidence were wanting, that his intellect is feeble. Indeed, in this respect, he is hardly above the boa-constrictor who mistakes his blanket for a rabbit and swallows it. His blood is cold, and when the thermometer sinks a little below the freezing-point he torpifies. In the winter he merely exists, while the bird lives. He eats but little and digests slowly— a sign of the sluggishness of his whole life. Both in body and in brain he presents a striking contrast to the bird. But the evidence of anatomy is irresistible. From lizard-like ancestors the bird is descended. A reptilian fore limb has been modified and adapted for flight, two of the five fingers having disappeared during the process, and one of the remaining three having shrunk almost to a mere rudiment. The breast bone has attained wonderful dimensions for the attachment of the muscles of flight. The hind leg has been much strengthened so as to make the quadruped a biped and keep the wings from dragging in the mire. The back has been stiffened, since an approach to rigidity is required for flight, and, perhaps still more, for the nearly horizontal carriage of the body in walking. A long neck, snakelike but more supple than a snake, brings the ground within easy reach of the longest-legged of the race. The scales have become feathers. The part of the brain in which the higher faculties reside has grown, so that the forehead rises high. The eye has become large and has acquired a wonderful keenness of sight. The three-chambered reptile's heart has become a four-chambered heart, and untold advantages have thereby been gained. The lungs have not been enlarged, but their effectiveness has been many times multiplied. In many cases the heavy bones have become hollow and are filled with air. The teeth are gone, but a gizzard or muscular stomach, better placed and equally efficient, has taken over their work. The gastric juices are stronger and equal to dealing with hearty and frequently recurring meals. All this—better heart, better lungs, better digestive apparatus—means higher temperature, comparative superiority to external conditions, greater vitality, and greater enjoyment of life. And the changes from first to last have not been additions of new organs, but adaptations of existing materials.

The differences between a bird and a reptile are so striking, they lie so much on the surface, that we are in danger of seeing the differences only and passing over the resemblances, some of which are obscure and require a minute knowledge of anatomy. But there is no reason why the pedigree should be taken on trust. Much of the evidence that enables us to trace it is easily intelligible.

After trying to make clear the development of the bird from reptile ancestors, I shall go on to describe (1) his structure in more detail and the work done by the different organs, (2) what cannot be dissociated from his structure, his life and habits.

CHAPTER II

THE SKELETONS OF BIRD AND REPTILE

The Fore Limb

I WILL now put the skeletons of a bird and of a lizard side by side and compare them. Everywhere there are striking contrasts, but since the power of flight is the prominent characteristic of birds, or of most of them, the fore limb shall be the starting-point. At the outset it will be necessary to learn the names of the bones that compose it, taking them first in the lizard, since there they are more easily made out. The first bone is the Humerus, or upper-arm bone (HU, fig. 1). Then follow two which lie side by side, one slender and one stout. The former of these is the Radius (R), and is described as being præaxial in position—*i.e.*, in front of the axis, the axis of any part of a limb being an imaginary central line drawn through it lengthwise; the other is the Ulna (U), and is postaxial or behind the axis. These terms, præaxial and postaxial, should be thoroughly under-stood, because, in all the transformations which they

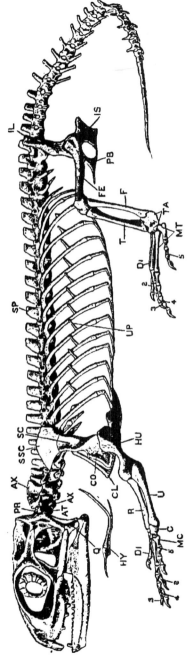

FIG. 1.—Skeleton of Hatteria Lizard.

AT, atlas vertebra; AX, axis vertebra; C, carpal bones; CL, clavicle; CO, coracoid; D 1, 2, 3, 4, 5, digits; FE, femur; F, fibula; HU, humerus; HY, hyoid bone that supports the tongue; IL, ilium; IS, ischium; MC, metacarpals; MT, metatarsals; PB, pubis; PR, pro-atlas probably a partly developed vertebra; Q, quadrate bone; R, radius; SC, scapula; SP, spine; SSC, supra-scapula; T, tibia; TA, tarsals; U, ulna; UP, uncinate process.

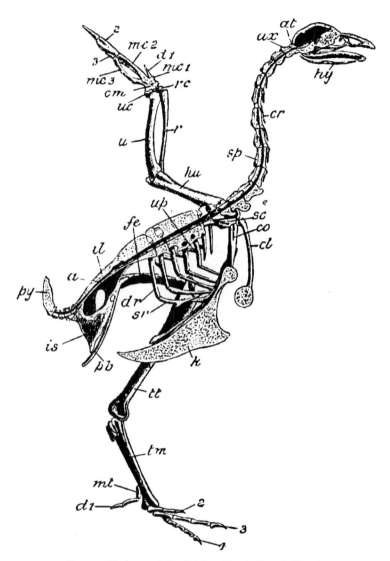

FIG. 2.—Skeleton of Fowl (after Marshall and Hurst).

A, acetabulum ; AT, atlas vertebra ; AX, axis vertebra ; CL, clavicle ; CM, carpo-metacarpus ; CO, coracoid ; CR, cervical rib ; D 1, 2, 3, 4, digits ; DR, dorsal rib ; FE, femur ; HU, humerus ; HY, hyoid bone that supports the tongue ; IL, ilium ; IS, ischium ; K, keel of sternum ; MC, 1, 2, 3, metacarpals ; MT, first metatarsal; PB, pubis ; PV, pygostyle ; R, radius ; RC, radial carpal ; SC, scapula ; SP, spine ; SR, sternal piece of rib ; TM, tarso-metatarsus ; TT, tibio-tarsus ; U, ulna ; UC, ulnar carpal ; UP, uncinate processes.

undergo, bones remain, relatively to each other, in the
same position.   Hence it often happens that to observe
carefully the position of a bone is the best way to
discover what bone it is.   The wrist now follows, consisting of two rows of bones called Carpals (C, fig. 4a),
with a central one (CE) wedged in between the two,
after these the five Metacarpals,
the bones of the hand (MC).
Next to them come the finger
bones, each division being
called a Phalanx (D 1, 2, 3,
4, 5).   The thumb has two
phalanges, the second digit
three, the third four, the fourth
five, and the fifth three.   And
at the end of each digit is a
claw.   Apart from its being
featherless, nothing less suited
for flying can be imagined.

If we turn now to the bird
we shall find that the Humerus (HU, fig. 2) has broad-
ened, especially at the nearer
end, and is covered with great

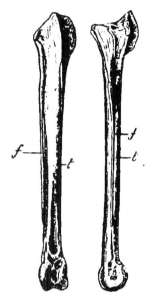

FIG. 3.—Tibia and Fibula of
Fowl.

F, fibula; T, tibia.

protuberances, good evidence that powerful muscles
spring from it and are attached to it.   Till we come
to the fingers, there will be a striking increase in the
length of the various bones.   A bird's wing would be
an outrageously long leg for a lizard of equal weight
and bulk.   When the long radius and ulna are extended, the elbow-joint allows of no turning motion.
As is essential for flight, they are held stiff whatever

strain is put upon them. The Radius is a very slender bone, the Ulna much thicker, with small but well-marked projections at the points where the great feathers grow. Of the nearer row of carpal bones there are only two (RC and UC), whereas there are three found in the lizard ; in the bird the small intermediate one has disappeared, and also the central bone

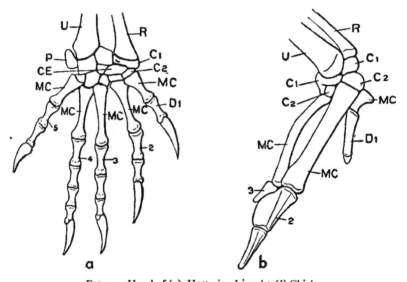

Fig. 4.—Hand of (*a*) Hatteria Lizard ; (*b*) Chick.

c1, near row of carpals ; c2, farther row of carpals ; ce, central bones—there are often two ; d 1, 2, 3, 4, 5, digits ; mc, metacarpals ; p, pisiform bone, originally a tendon ; r, radius ; u, ulna.

beyond it. Of the more distant row there is not a sign in the mature bird, but, if we examine the skeleton of an embryo, it may be made out. In a young chick there are still two free bones to represent it (C 2, fig. 4). In the adult these have been fused with the Metacarpals beyond. The tendency to fusion, or, as it is technically called, ankylosis, is found in many parts of the bird's skeleton, and may be regarded as a most marked characteristic. The bone formed by the fusion of the farther row of carpals with the metacarpals forms a broad slab on which rest many of the most powerful feathers of the wing. Its compound nature is described by its name of Carpo-metacarpus, or wrist-hand bone (CM fig. 2). Of the five metacarpals only three remain, and these three are fused together at their bases. Farther on they separate and can be easily distinguished. The first is only a slight pro- jection from which the thumb[1] springs, the second is long, strong, and nearly straight, the third after de- scribing a curve fuses again with the second at its farther end. The very short thumb consists of two phalanges only, the last being very small. It fre- quently has attached to it a claw suggestive of reptilian ancestry. The second and third digits are far away at the ends of their long metacarpals, attached firmly one to the other so that neither can move separately. The second is formed of three phalanges, of which the first is broad and plate-like, the last very minute ; the third digit is insignificant, with only a single phalanx. In digits I and II the final phalanx is often missing. The two united fingers have some slight power of movement, which many birds turn to account ; but in no part of the hand is there what can in any ordinary sense be called a joint. The wrist-joint, also, has much changed its character. It allows the hand to move freely towards the place where the fifth digit (or

[1] I am taking it for granted for the present that this digit corresponds to our thumb. See p. 42.

"little finger") should be. The up-and-down movement that the lizard has, and that we have in our
wrists, has almost disappeared : when the wing is
extended, it does not exist at all ; when it is flexed,
some movement of the kind becomes possible. The
fusion of one row of carpal bones with the metacarpals has no doubt helped towards this rigidity
which is so important to the wing. At the shoulder-
joint there is always the utmost free play.

A bird's bones combine in a most remarkable way
lightness and strength. It is popularly supposed that
all birds, or at any rate those which fly much, have
all their chief bones hollow and marrowless. This is,
however, a fallacy ; some of the best flyers—*e.g.*, the
Swallow—having even the Humerus solid. But whether
pneumatic or not, the bones are always fine in the
grain and strong.

The chief results of the changes that the fore limb has
undergone may now be summed up. (1) It is of most remarkable length. (2) It is at one time rigid, at another
flexible, according as rigidity or flexibility is required.
Contrast with a bird's hand a lizard's with its waggly
fingers. And how neatly and comfortably the wing
folds, when it is to be put to rest upon the body, in the
form of a Z. (3) There are broad surfaces of bone
to support the feathers. (4) Strength is combined
with lightness. (5) The loss of two metacarpal bones
and two fingers has been a gain, since the present
hand formed of three united metacarpals and two
united fingers (I am disregarding the insignificant
" thumb ") is more efficient for purposes of flight than
a hand with five fingers could well be.

The Breastbone and the Bones that meet at the shoulder-joint.

A powerful wing would be of no use without powerful machinery for moving it, and a lizard with a bird's wings would be no more able to fly than any

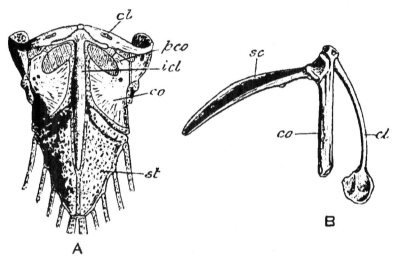

FIG. 5.—(*a*) Sternum of Iguana, with interclavicle, coracoid, precoracoid, and clavicle.
CL, clavicle ; CO, coracoid ; ICL, interclavicle ; PCO, precoracoid ; ST, sternum ;
(*b*) Coracoid, scapula, and clavicle of fowl.
CO, coracoid ; SC, scapula ; CL, clavicle.

ordinary lizard.   In the bird's skeleton the enormous breastbone suggests a great deal.   They must be strong muscles which have so strong and big a bone to which to attach themselves.   No two things can be more unlike than the breastbones of the bird and the lizard, and the same may be said of the associated bones.   In the lizard the whole apparatus is flat and weak. Its chief component, the Sternum (ST, fig. 5a) or breastbone, is a level expanse with ribs attached to its margin. Down the middle may be seen running a thicker and stronger bone, which throws out a branch on either side, so that the whole makes something of a T shape. This bone is called the Inter-. clavicle (ICL), and it will be seen that the Clavicles (CL) or collar-bones converge upon it. This inter-clavicle was formerly thought to correspond to the keel, the high, projecting ridge upon a bird's breast. But this is not the case, for the interclavicle is a membrane bone—*i.e.*, a hardened ossified membrane—while the keel of a bird's breastbone originates from cartilage or gristle. There is also a bone called the Coracoid (CO) running from the shoulder-joint to the fore part of the sternum, and this bone in the lizard divides into two, the fore part being called the Pre-coracoid (PCO). Both parts are thin and weak. At the shoulder-joint the Coracoid and Clavicle are met by another bone, the Scapula (SC) or shoulder-blade, which with the Coracoid forms the socket. The Scapula is a thin expanse of bone approaching close to the back-bone, to which it is attached by muscles. The upper part, the Supra-scapula, consists of gristle or cartilage not completely ossified. In the bird all this has been metamorphosed, though the materials are in the main the same. There is the sternum with a high ridge added which ossifies—*i.e.*, becomes bone—from a different centre. In the young bird the keel is at first mere gristle, which at a certain point begins to ossify, and the process continues till the bone of the keel meets and joins the bone of the sternum proper.

The Coracoids have become much stronger, while the Precoracoids and the Interclavicle have disappeared. The Scapula is formed of sound bone from end to end. In shape it has grown long and blade-like—in the chapter on Flight I shall explain what advantage has thus been gained—and it is fastened to the back-bone by muscles firmly, but in a way that allows a great deal of free play. And while maintaining their positions relatively to one another the various bones have much changed their attitudes. If we look upon the shoulder-joint as the fixed point, the sternum begins farther back, and, consequently, the Coracoids slope forwards instead of backwards, in order, with their other ends, to reach the joint, towards the formation of which they contribute so much. And the bird is much deeper-chested than the lizard : therefore they must slope not only forwards but upwards. With all these changes they retain their slope outward. Scapula and Coracoid form an acute angle, opening towards the tail, whereas, in the lizard, the angle formed opens towards the head, or, sometimes, one bone continues the line of the other. The clavicles, moreover, have not the slope backward towards the shoulder-joint that is so marked in many lizards ; they point upward and outward. The most important result of all these changes is that a firm pivot has been found on which the wing can turn— a firm pivot (1) because of the great strength of the Coracoid ; (2) because both it and the Clavicle have a marked outward slope ; and (3) because they buttress each other.

The Ribs.

The ribs have very remarkable cross-pieces, called Uncinate—*i.e.*, hooked—processes (UP, fig. 2) that spring from about the middle of their upper part and slope backwards and upwards. These uncinate processes, no doubt, serve to strengthen the chest, and, apart from this, they possess a singular interest. They are common to all birds, but absent in nearly all reptiles. In a very few lizards they are found— *e.g.*, in the Hatteria, a native of some of the islands of the New Zealand group, and now so rare that it may be in danger of extermination (fig. 1). It will be seen that each rib has a joint at a point considerably nearer to the sternum than to the backbone, the two parts being spoken of as the dorsal ribs (Latin *dorsum*, the back) and the sternal pieces respectively.

The Hind Limb.

In naming the bones of the leg, the genius of the older anatomists for seeing resemblances where it is difficult for us to see any has run riot. The larger of the two leg bones is the Tibia or flute, the smaller one is the Fibula or brooch (F, fig. 1, 3). The Acetabulum, as they called the socket of the thigh-bone, is a happier name. Strictly the word means a vinegar-pot, and it is used of any cup-shaped vessel. A bird's Acetabulum (A, fig. 8) is remarkable. If you look at a skeleton in a museum you will see that the cup has no bottom to it. The bottom was formed of membrane, not, as in mammals and most reptiles, entirely of bone, and it has vanished.   But ankylosis or fusion is perhaps the most marked characteristic of a bird's leg.   There are the same bones as in the lizard's leg, if we could only see them—viz.: Femur (FE, fig. 2) or thigh-bone, Tibia (T), Fibula (F), two rows of Tarsals or ankle-bones (TA), four of the lizard's five Metatarsals (MT), though of one of the four only the farther end (MT$_1$, fig. 2) remains, and four of his five

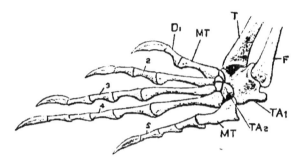

FIG. 6.—Hatteria Lizard's left hind foot.
D 1, 2, 3, 4, 5, digits; F, fibula; MT, metatarsals; T, tibia; TA1, two bones fixed, represents near row of tarsals; TA2, distant row.

digits.   The Femur has not undergone so much change, but the Tibia and Fibula (fig. 3) are very different from the corresponding bones in reptiles. The latter has nearly vanished ; it is a slender, almost needle-like bone, attached to the side of the Tibia and not reaching to its farther end.   In many mammals too the Fibula is but a remnant.   The way to make certain, in the skeleton of any animal whatever, which bone is the Tibia and which the Fibula, is to imagine the limb extended, as it is in the lizard, outwards from the body ; then the Tibia is præaxial and the Fibula

C

postaxial. But if we look for the bird's tarsals they
are not to be seen. The disappearance of the nearer
row is to be accounted for in this way : the bone we
have just called the Tibia is really the Tibia plus the
nearer row of tarsals which have been fused with it, and
its proper name is Tibio-tarsus (TT, fig. 2). This has
been made out clearly in the leg of the embryo bird.
The farther row of tarsals has also no separate existence. They have been fused with the Metatarsals.
In the young chick each row of tarsals has one large
separate bone to represent it. In the mature bird,
directly below the Tibio-tarsus comes another long
compound bone, the Tarso-metatarsus. At the farther
end of this, deep grooves show that it is made up of
three bones—the second, third, and fourth metatarsals.
Of the first metatarsal there is only the afore-mentioned
remnant (MTi). All these things are very difficult to
remember. One plan is to go over them again and
again till in time they become familiar. A better plan
is to remember the names Tibio-tarsus and Tarso-
metatarsus, which explain the most difficult points.

The four digits or toes possessed by most birds are
the first, second, third, and fourth. The "great toe"
is dwarfed by the others, and has only two phalanges ;
the second has three, the third four, the fourth five.
Thus the numbers run in regular progression—2, 3, 4,
5. In lizards the five toes, each attached to its
independent metatarsal, are always present, and they
have respectively 2, 3, 4, 5, 3 or 4 phalanges. The
correspondence in numbers is very curious. No bird
has a fifth toe. Domestic fowls, Dorkings especially,
often have a supernumerary "toe," which is really a

skin formation, and no more a toe than a caterpillar's hind " leg " is a leg.

The whole limb is very different from a lizard's ; it is longer and stronger and fitted for an upright carriage. The strong Tibia is well able to do its own work as well as that of the Fibula, which has almost disappeared. The bird stands on his toes, which are strong and springy, and jumps lightly into the air in order to start his flight. Length of leg is to many species of vital importance, and the elongation has been to a great extent effected by the large development of the metatarsals. The fusion of the two rows of ankle-bones with the longer bones above and below was, I think, necessary for the effective working of the machinery by which a bird is enabled, even during sleep, to grip his perch firmly (see p. 166). Moreover, without all this fusion of bones, would the luxury of standing on one leg be a possibility for him ?

The horse's leg presents remarkable points of resemblance to the bird's. In both, the Tibia relieves the Fibula of all its work. In both the Femur is short, so that the knee-joint is high and easily remains unnoticed ; in the bird it is hidden among the feathers. In both the ankle-joint is raised high above the ground.

The Skull.

In a way, the skull is the most bird-like part of the whole skeleton. It is light, not only because of the thinness of its walls, but because of its many air-cavities. Even birds which have their long bones solid have the skull pneumatic. Lightness is of the

utmost importance. Otherwise, how could the head
be supported at the end of so long a neck? But
muscles get tired with prolonged exertion, however
slight the exertion may be, and to provide against
this there are, between the spines of the vertebræ of
the neck (SP, fig. 2), elastic ligaments similar to that
which is so enormously developed in the horse's neck
to support his ponderous head. These ligaments hold
the neck in position when it forms an S. In the Swan
they are but slightly developed, hence perhaps the
ease with which he erects his neck straight as a flag-
staff. Even when there are ligaments to relieve the
muscles, the skull is the place where aëration of bones
is desirable if anywhere. Its great size compared with
that of the lizard, and, consequently, the great size of
the brain, I have already pointed out. The skull, too,
illustrates better than any other part of the skeleton
the tendency to ankylosis, or fusion of bones. Even
in a very young bird this has already proceeded a long
way. The skull seems to be made up of a shell of
bone almost without suture. It is really composed of
scores of different bones, the boundary lines between
which may be seen in the embryo. And how are these
to be studied? It is possible to go through them and
learn them up as one does for an examination. But
for such studies it is usually the imminence of the
examination, not the interest of the subject, which
supplies the stimulus. Without this stimulus, to a
mind that has not as yet the patience wanted for
scientific investigation—the patience to collect facts,
even if the clue to them and the interest of them may
not be found till years after—there is something barren

and unsatisfying in, for instance, the isolated fact that
a certain bone in a certain part of the skull is called
the Squamosal (SQ, fig. 10).   Something is wanted to
give point and interest to such dry fragments of anatomical knowledge, some strange variation in the bone
in question in different classes of animals, or a theory
as to the origin of the skull, so that the memory may
not have to deal with what abhors it more than anything
else—viz., isolated meaningless facts.   There is much
pleasure to be got by putting the wing of a bird and the
fore leg of a lizard side by side, and observing the
changes that have made a fuller and more vigorous
life possible to the bird.   The same kind of interest
may be found in a general comparison of the skulls.
But since it is difficult for human weakness to maintain this during the slow groping progress through
the labyrinth of bones, I shall pass over this part
of the subject without going into any detail.   There
is, however, something of a clue to the labyrinth.
Göthe discovered one which will lead us some way,
though not nearly so far as he imagined.   The skull,
according to him, was simply an expanded vertebral
column, all its chief bones being vertebræ, the name
given to the series of bones which combine to form
the neck, backbone, and the bony skeleton of the
tail, all included in the term vertebral column.
This is one of the great ideas which advance science.
Even if it had turned out entirely unfounded, still
something would have been learnt in the process of
testing it.   But this theory has not proved to be without foundation.   There is no doubt that the skull is
made up partly of vertebræ.   But, so far, the difficul-

ties have been insurmountable when it has been attempted to show how many vertebræ go to the skull, or to find in a bone of the skull parts that correspond to the easily distinguishable parts of a vertebra. The skull as yet presents many unsolved problems. For the present we must make a guarded statement that vertebræ to some extent enter into the formation of it. The bones of the jaw and those connected with them present problems of hardly inferior interest. But it will be time to give some account of them when we come to the subject of the embryo bird.

The articulation of the skull with the neck will be described in the next chapter.

The Vertebral Column.

The bird's neck bends with greater ease and freedom than the lizard's. Indeed it outdoes even the suppleness of the snake. If you hold up a snake by his tail, he tries to get at your hand, with a view to biting you if he is of a poisonous kind, by bending upward sideways. He has not much power of hollowing his back, so as to rise without a curve to the side. True, some snakes have much more suppleness in an upward and downward direction than others. If the Hooded Snake is irritated, he raises the fore part of his body so that it forms a double curve or S shape. But even he cannot make by a long way so decided an S as a long-necked bird, and the reason is that in the bird the bones which form the neck articulate with each other differently, by a joint which is a marked improvement on the reptile's joint. The

latter is a ball-and-socket.   At the hinder end of each
vertebra there is a protuberance, rounded on its upper
side but nearly flat below, which fits into a hollow in
the vertebra behind.   The fact that the protuberance is

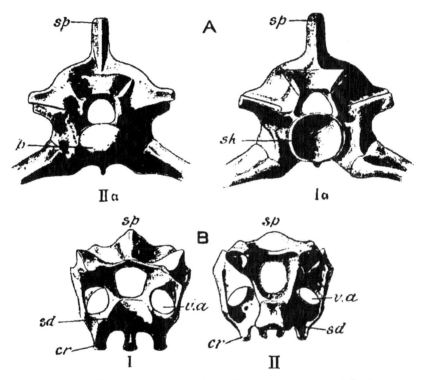

FIG. 7.—(*A*) Two vertebræ of Snake.   (*B*) Two neck vertebræ of Eagle.
I. Anterior end.   II. Posterior.
B, ball; CR, cervical rib; SD, "saddle"; SK, socket; SP, spine; VA, tunnel through
which vertebral artery passes.

not a perfect ball but has its underside flattened limits
the freedom of movement, and, in addition to this, each
vertebra bears a spine (SP, fig. 1) upon the top, the spine
of one being very near to that of the next, and thus
a further limit is put to movement up and down.   The

joints in a bird's neck resemble two saddles laid
crosswise one upon the other, so that the pommels
of one face at right angles to those of the other, the
upper saddle being, of course, upside down.   In the
bird's neck the " saddles " are so arranged that at the
hinder end of each vertebra the pommels are at the
top and bottom, while at the front end they are at
the sides.   Thus the two vertebræ will slide over
one another sideways, or up and down, in the same
way that two saddles will slide when they are laid
upon one another in the way which I have described.
And the upright spines in a bird's neck are small and
far from one another, so that they do not hinder the
movement (SP, fig. 2).

The backbone of the bird has been so much modified
for purposes of flying and walking that it presents a
difficult study.   The vertebral columns of reptiles and
mammals are divided into well-defined regions—the
regions of the neck, breast, loins, pelvis, and tail.   In the
bird, fusion or ankylosis has gone on to such an extent,
and the pelvis has extended so far backwards and
forwards, that it is a most perplexing problem how to
map out the backbone.   I shall not attempt this here.
The subject does not seem to be of first-rate importance;
in studying the views held by various great authorities,
not very much of the principles of anatomy would be
learnt, since it is admitted that there is no essential, no
morphological difference, to use the technical term, between a neck vertebra and a thoracic or breast vertebra.
They are corresponding organs, in slightly different
places and slightly modified, a breast vertebra being
defined as one which has attached to it a rib that

unites with the sternum, and as the neck vertebræ
bear small undeveloped ribs this is not an important
distinction. These neck ribs, short thin straight bones
pointing backward, can be seen in fig. 2 (CR, cervical
ribs) ; the two bases of each are fused with the vertebra, and between them runs a tunnel through which
the vertebral artery passes. Besides this, the fore
limb has in some cases, very possibly, moved backward, since the neck varies very greatly, far more
than the backbone, in the number of vertebræ that
compose it.[1] Where, then, is our fixed point ?

I have already described the way in which the neck
vertebræ articulate. The next point to notice is their
large number, sixteen or seventeen being not un-
commonly found ; the Ostrich and the Swan having
considerably more : even small song-birds have not
less than ten. With mammals seven is the almost
invariable number, the neck of a Giraffe and of a
Hippopotamus being alike in this. A bird's neck,
to be supple and more than snake-like, must clearly
have a great many vertebræ. In the lizard eight is
the normal number.

By far the most noticeable feature about the remainder
of a bird's vertebral column is its stiffness, due to the
fact that the vertebræ have become ankylosed together.
But it is quite erroneous to describe the bird's backbone as being throughout its length a rigid rod. In
all the specimens I have examined it bends, at a point
just in front of the pelvis, with some freedom to either

---

[1] The question is discussed by Max Fürbringer in his
Morphologie und Systematik der Vögel, of which there is a good
summary in *Nature*, 1888–89.

side, and in all there is some flexibility upwards and
downwards.   But the amount varies much in different
species.   The tail vertebræ are very different, and, in
the freedom with which they move upon one another,
approximate to those of the neck.   Were it not so,
birds could not do what they may easily be seen to do
while flying—move their tails for purposes of steering
or to check themselves suddenly.   The Pygostyle,
the large bone which supports the tail, consists of a
number of vertebræ fused together (PY, fig. 2).

The Pelvis.

The bird's Pelvis, at its anterior end, roofs over
the backbone.   It is formed of three bones, which
in different classes of animals assume forms so
different that they are often difficult to recognise.
The difficulty, however, will be got over, if we bear in
mind what I have already explained, that bones,
however much they may change their form, yet keep
the same position relatively to each other.   One of
these bones, the Ilium (IL, fig. 8) attaches to the backbone, and by that it may be recognised.   Its peculiarity in the bird is that it unites with so many vertebræ
both before and behind the hip-joint, fusing with
them and making this part of the backbone absolutely
rigid.   The two remaining bones assist the Ilium to
form the socket of the hip-joint, and they must be
distinguished by their positions relatively to it.   The
Pubis forms the lower front of the socket (PB), the
Ischium (IS) the hinder part.   The former projects a

very little way forward and a long way backward, a slender bar of bone, united for part of its length with the Ischium. To discuss here whether this is all

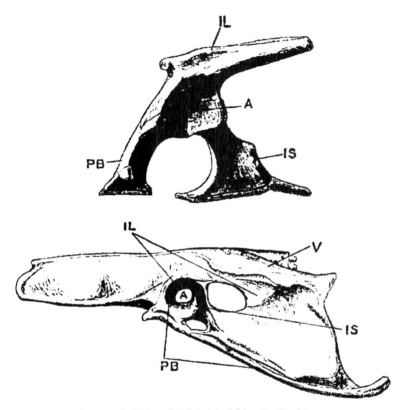

Fig. 8.—Left side of Pelvis (a) of Lizard ; (b) of Bird.
A, acetabulum ; IL, ilium ; IS, ischium ; PB, pubis ; V, vertebræ fused.
In (a) the ischium and pubis slope inwards to meet their fellows from the opposite side.   In (b) all three bones are fused where they meet.   The ilium extends forwards as well as backwards from the acetabulum.

Pubis proper, or whether a pubic "process" has been added, would be out of place. The term process, meaning an out-growth, is a favourite one with anatomists, and is often useful as a name, though, it must be owned, it does not explain much.

Its remarkable form of pelvis is of great advantage
to the bird. It has helped in the stiffening of the
backbone ; it gives room for the attachment of the
large muscles necessary now the quadruped has become a biped ; its backward extension is useful for
the attachment of the muscles that move the tail. The
lizard's pelvis, hanging downward from the backbone,
looks like a different organ. The bones, however,
are the same. The Ilium attaches to the vertebral
column, and the other two can be made out by their
position relatively to it and to each other ; the Ischium
forming the hinder part of the socket in which the
thigh-bone moves, the Pubis the anterior part.

Some Books on the Subject.

Marshall and Hurst's *Practical Zoology*.
Parker's *Zootomy*.
Huxley's *Vertebrate Anatomy*.
Gegenbaur's *Comparative Anatomy*.
Alix's *Essai sur l'appareil locomoteur des Oiseaux*.

CHAPTER III

AFTER all that has been said about the great differences between birds and reptiles, the reader may begin to think that the points of resemblance are few and small, and that the relationship after all may be only a distant one. In reality the evidence of a comparatively near relationship is convincing. But it must not be expected that the resemblances should be as striking as the differences. The latter are due mainly, perhaps entirely, to natural selection working during long ages and gradually suiting the bird's structure to new conditions of life and changing habits. The metamorphosis produced is so great that to the untrained eye the bird has been altered almost beyond recognition. The points of resemblance are ancestral peculiarities that have survived all changes of habit. Not being connected, as a rule, with the new and more brilliant life of the ennobled race, it is only to be expected that they should be comparatively inconspicuous or of the nature of mere rudiments. Before mentioning these marks of reptilian origin it will be well first to explain what is meant by the anatomical terms rudiment, and homology and analogy.

A rudiment is an organ which survives, though it has become wholly or almost functionless. Often it is much reduced in size. The Python has hind legs, the claws of which are sometimes just perceptible through the skin. Men have a muscle for moving the ear forward, but very few are able to use it. The Sea-lion has claws at the end of his toes, but the skin projects far beyond them, so that the claws are absolutely useless. Crabs which live in caves to which no light penetrates have eye-stalks with no eyes on the top of them. Perhaps the most startling rudiment of all is the Pineal body found in lizards, birds, and mammals, and believed to represent a central eye.

Two organs are said to be analogous when their functions are the same ; they are homologous when they are the same in nature and origin. The wing of a bird and the wing of an insect are analogous to one another because they do the same work. The origin of an insect's wing is not known for certain, but there is no doubt that it is not a fore-limb. The relationship, therefore, is one of analogy only. The wing of a bat is only analogous to the wing of a bird ; it is not homologous, for, besides the fact that all five fingers are found in it, it is supported by the leg as well as the arm. There is a small fish called Periophthalmus Kölreuteri, which suns itself upon rocks with only its tail in the water.[1]

[1] See Professor Haddon's paper, *Nature*, January 17, 1889. The fish soon died when its caudal fin was coated over with gold-size. See also Professor Hickson's *Naturalist in Celebes*, p. 30.

The organ of respiration it then uses is in the tail, and cannot, of course, be a gill, though it is doing the work of one. In one and the same animal we sometimes have analogous organs. For instance, a caterpillar has only three pairs of legs properly so called. The hind "legs" before mentioned are only growths of the skin, and do not survive beyond the caterpillar stage. On the other hand the tails of all vertebrates are homologous, however different the purposes for which they are used : the new-world monkey's for climbing, the porpoise's for swimming, the kangaroo's as a leg, the giraffe's and many others as fly-flappers, the bird's for guiding his flight. Many fish have a swim-bladder, which is filled with air and gives them buoyancy. This organ was thought by Darwin to be the same organ as the lungs of mammals. If so, it would have been a paragon example of homology. Unfortunately, it is an outgrowth from the back of the alimentary canal, whereas the opening to the lungs is from the front. By an extension two organs in the same animal are said to be homologous ; for instance, the Humerus is homologous to the Femur, the corresponding bone in the hind limb. To prove relationship we must look for true homologies, as mere analogies prove nothing.

Here are some of the most striking features common to birds and reptiles.

(1) A single condyle or rounded projection in the skull fits into a cup-like hollow in the centrum or thickened base of the first or Atlas vertebra, which is so short as to be hardly more than a ring of bone. At one point in the rim of the cup there is a notch, and

this is filled by a projecting tongue from the second or Axis vertebra, called the odontoid process, which thus completes the cup. All mammals have two condyles. The great freedom with which a bird moves its head is due to the way in which, by its single condyle, it articulates with the vertebra.

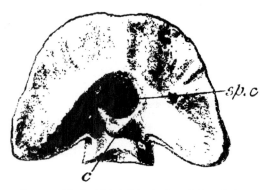

FIG. 9.—Skull of bird (Rhea) viewed from below.
c, condyle ; sr.c, entrance of spinal cord.

(2) The lower jaw articulates with a bone called the Quadrate, which may be easily recognised. It roughly resembles a St. Andrew's cross. To the two lower and shorter arms the lower jaw is hinged. To the outside corner of the outer of these is attached a long thin bone, which connects with the upper jaw. The outer of the two upper arms fits into a hollow in the bone called the Squamosal. In mammals the quadrate is represented by an insignificant bone, the Annulus of the ear (fig. 10, see p. 135).

(3) In mammals the centra, the strong bases from which spring the arches of the vertebræ, have between them plates of bone, called Epiphyses, which are

easily distinguishable. These are absent both in birds and reptiles (fig. 11).

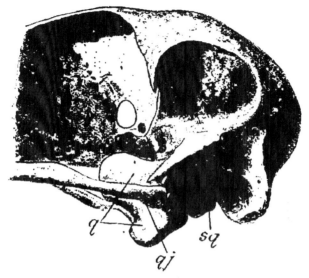

FIG. 10.—Side view of head of Rhea.
Q, quadrate ; QJ, quadrato-jugal, hindmost component of bone connecting with upper jaw ; SQ, squamosal.

(4) The coracoid bone is present. In man there is only a small remnant of its upper end. It is well

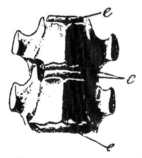

FIG. 11.—Part of vertical column of Rabbit.
E, Epiphyses, applied to anterior and posterior end of centrum of each vertebra.

developed in the Duck-billed Platypus, the lowest of mammals, with a decidedly reptilian anatomy.

D

(5) Birds have a single coracoid; in reptiles it is divided into two, the coracoid proper and precoracoid. But in the Rhea we find a very conspicuous, though rudimentary, survival of the latter, and in the Ostrich the bone is complete.

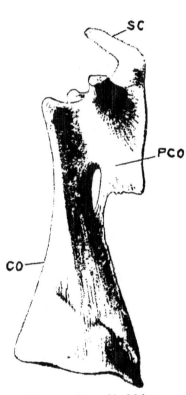

FIG. 12.—Coracoid of Rhea.
co, coracoid; pco, precoracoid; sc, capula.

(6) The bird's feather corresponds to the horny coating of the reptile's scale. The snake moults, when, as we say, he "sheds his skin."

In 1861 there was found in the Lithographic Stone at Solenhofen in Bavaria the form of an animal very different from any that had ever been seen either alive or as fossils. This stone belongs to the Jurassic system and, consequently, was deposited in the Secondary or Mesozoic period, and long, too, before that period was concluded. Here was a feathered creature preserved in the form of a bas-relief, with the detail standing out so distinct and clear, that something even of the minute structure of the feathers might be seen. As Sir Richard Owen showed, it was a bird of a very primitive form. The fossil is now at South Kensington. In 1877 a more perfect example of a bird of the same species was found and is to be seen at Berlin.

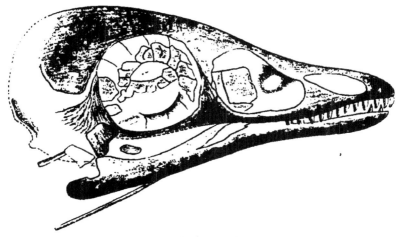

Fig. 13.—Head of Archæopteryx.

This ancient bird was about the size of a rook. His tail was long, consisting of twenty vertebræ, at least the twelve hindmost bearing a pair of well-developed

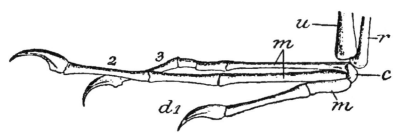

Fig. 14.—Part of wing of Archæopteryx.
c, carpal bone ; D, 1, 2, 3, digits ; M, metacarpal ; R, radius ; U, ulna.

feathers. His breast-bone seems to have been keeled. His wing was strong and well-developed, the humerus remarkably big at the near end, the bones of the fore-

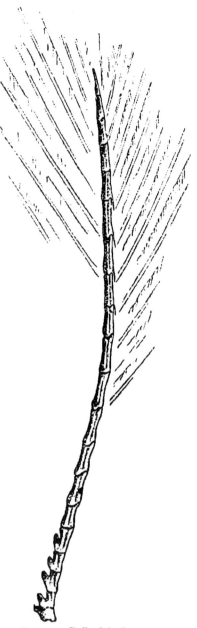

FIG. 15.—Tail of Archæopteryx.
(All three figures after Dames.)

arm were long and strong, the hand had three fingers, each bearing a large claw, and it and the ulna supported a number of large feathers, which seem well suited for flight. The bill was short. The jaws were furnished with teeth, the upper one with many, the lower one with three on each side.

Our first thoughts on looking at this creature might well be, " It must be a feathered lizard." The long tail and the teeth at once suggest this. But there are many things which prove it to be a bird. (1) The three-fingered hand.[1] True, the three metacarpals have not become fused, and the second and third digits are separate. Besides this, each of the fingers bears a big claw. But in many existing birds a claw is found on No. 1, in a fair number on No. 2 as well, in the young Ostrich on all three. The third digit has not been reduced to a single phalanx. But this is no great barrier. In birds of our own day the final phalanx is often lost on digit 1. (2) The length and strength of the humerus and forearm remind one much of existing birds. (3) The acetabulum or socket of the thigh joint, seems to have been closed only with membrane. (4) Scales, not feathers, are found on all known lizards.

There are some interesting points which, if reptilian, are also avian. The vertebræ seem to have

[1] Dr. Hurst (*Natural Science*, October, 1893) has boldly tried to show that archæopteryx had really more than three fingers, and that one or two with larger stronger bones have left no impression on the stone. But when even the delicate forms of the feathers are preserved, it is wonderful that there should be no trace of these bones either in the Berlin Archæopteryx, or in the one at the British Museum.

been bi-concave, *i.e.*, the centra presented hollows at either end. This is a form of vertebra found in very primitive reptiles, *e.g.*, in the Hatteria lizard.

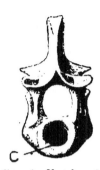

FIG. 16.—Vertebra of Hatteria Lizard.

c, centrum ; it is am- phicœlous, *i.e.* con- cave at each end.

It is also found in Ichthyornis, a fossil bird of more recent date than Archæopteryx. And what is far more strange, the Gull, a highly special- ised, a thoroughly modernised bird, has some of its dorsal vertebræ con- cave behind, thus conforming to an old reptilian type, and one almost bi-concave, which thus carries us back to reptiles of a still more primitive form.[1] In teeth, as I hope to show presently, there is nothing unavian.

It would be very interesting to know how this bird lived. Of one thing we may be certain—he was a poor flyer. With its three long unconnected fingers the wing must have been a weak one. Prob- ably he fluttered, rather than flew, from bough to bough, his long tail serving as a parachute, and his claws may have been used when he was young, as Mr. Pycraft has suggested, and also when he was moulting, to aid him in climbing, as the young Hoatzin uses his now.

Since the discovery of Archæopteryx the fossil bones of many birds of far later date have been found in the cretaceous rocks, and also in the rocks of the most recent geological periods, the Tertiary and

[1] See W. K. Parker on Opisthocomus Cristatus, *Proc. Zool. Society*, vol. xiii. part 2.

Quaternary. Some of these were of gigantic size, larger even than the Ostrich. Like Archæopteryx, they had teeth. In Hesperornis, to take one example, these are very reptilian, in the way they are set in a long hollow in the jaw, in the absence of root and of cement on the neck of the tooth, in the way they were changed, a young tooth being formed on the inner side of the base of the old one. But by this time birds had lost their great length of tail.

Here it will be instructive to mention the discovery in existing birds of what were supposed to be the rudiments of teeth. If you take the beak of a Parrot and macerate it well, you can separate the horny beak from the bone beneath. The horn is only a form of epidermis and, therefore, we should expect to find skin underneath. Skin is found and on it papillæ, small pimple-like elevations, similar to those found beneath a horse's hoof. They nourish the growing and quickly wasting beak. And these were the "rudimentary teeth" which so much interested the zoological world. But here, as often, a false theory by stimulating investigation has led the way to the true one.[1]

There are some very remarkable points of agreement between crocodiles and birds. The ordinary reptile has only three chambers to his heart. The crocodile's heart, though still a very imperfect organ, has four see p. 284). He has a gizzard and habitually swallows stones to aid in digestion. His lungs are far more elaborate structures than those of a lizard.

---

[1] See Bronn's *Thier-Reich*, vol. "Aves," p. 501.

The socket of his thigh-joint is not completely closed with bone : in the skeleton of the crocodile as in that of the bird, the cup of the socket has a hole at the bottom, the membrane which was there during life having disappeared. Several of the ribs have uncinate processes.

These resemblances, to which others might be added, do not prove that the crocodile is the ancestor of the bird. The heart and the gizzard were probably developed independently after birds and crocodiles had arisen from some common and more primitive stock. It would be unwise to say that birds are descended from any existing class of reptiles. But the facts justify us in drawing the inference that birds and reptiles are related; that they had common ancestors with less of specialised character than either of themselves, and that from these ancestors each class has developed in accordance with its own mode of life. In the same way Englishmen and Chinamen come from the same stock ; neither race is descended from the other. The Darwinian theory of the descent of man is that if you trace upward the pedigrees of men and monkeys, the lines will meet, not that men are descended from monkeys.

BOOKS ON THE SUBJECT.

See at the end of Chapter II.

Also Newton's *Dictionary of Birds*, " Fossil Birds " ; Pycraft, *Nat. Science*, November and December, 1894, " Archæopteryx " ; Owen, *Philosophical Transactions*, 1863, " Archæopteryx."

CHAPTER IV

CONNECTING LINKS

THE supply of connecting links can never equal the demand. The discovery of the Ornithorhyncus brought to light a connecting link between mammals on the one side and birds and reptiles on the other. It lays eggs ; it has a beak like a bird's ; its anatomy is highly reptilian, and it suckles its young. Geology shows us an animal, evidently akin to the Horse, with four toes, and thus we are able to put the Horse down as a near relation of the Rhinoceros and the Tapir. But the mending of one gap does not prevent the existence of others. It often seems even to call attention to them. Remains of extinct animals have been found which certainly to some extent bridge the gulf between birds and reptiles. Such evidence of relationship is very valuable, but it is easy to mistake its nature. These fossil reptiles, in so many ways birdlike, must not be looked upon as the ancestors of birds. Nor do they, like the Ornithorhyncus, carry us back to a low unspecialised type. They are only connecting links in this sense, that they show that some undoubted reptiles much resemble birds, that reptiles may develop into very birdlike creatures, and so, that birds themselves may have had a reptilian origin.

In the Secondary or Mesozoic period, there were upon the earth Pterodactyls or wing-fingered animals, also known by the name of Ornithosaurians or Bird-lizards. Some very perfect specimens of these have been found in the lithographic-stone at Solenhofen in Bavaria. England and America have produced pterodactyl bones and almost complete skeletons, the latter country some of enormous size, and thanks to the labours of great anatomists—among them Professors Huxley and H. G. Seeley and Sir Richard Owen —we now understand a great deal about these flying reptiles, and can form a fair notion of how they lived.

On looking at a restoration of one of these ptero-dactyls, one's first thought is, that it is their wings which prove them to be nearly related to birds. This requires to be closely looked into, and what was said above about analogy and homology must be borne in mind. The wings of birds and pterodactyls are similar in function, but in their structure they are very different. They are analogous but not homologous. A bird's wing contains three fingers. The first is very small, the second is far the biggest and strongest, and to it the third is immovably attached. Dr. Hurst [1] has tried to show from the evidence of the Berlin Archæopteryx that these three digits are not the first three, but that the two united ones are the fourth and fifth. For this view, as far as I can see, no evidence is to be found in the Berlin Archæopteryx or anywhere else. But when he maintains that the generally accepted view, that the

[1] *Natural Science*, October, 1893.

little digit is the thumb, and that the other two are Nos.
2 and 3 respectively, is unsupported by evidence, he
seems to me to be stating what is undeniable. When
he goes further and argues that they are Nos. 3, 4, 5,
he is flying in the face of facts. In the embryos of
the Swift and Tern several good observers have seen
a fourth unmistakable metacarpal on the ulnar side
(*i.e.* the side on which in our hand the little finger is)
and in the embryo of that extraordinary South
American bird, the Hoatzin, there is a remnant on
the same side of a fourth finger though the metacarpal has disappeared. There are, then, only two
alternatives : the surviving digits are either 1, 2, 3, or
2, 3, 4. Now the Emeu has only one, the central one
of the three, and all analogy would lead us to believe
that this is the third of the original five and not the
second, since, when reduction proceeds very far with
the digits of birds' feet, or with those of the fore or
hind feet of mammals, they are lost, as far as can be,
symmetrically, not in lopsided fashion. And since it
is the ulnar side of the wing on which mainly the
strain falls in flight, it is not likely that all the weak-
ening would go on on this side and all the strengthening on the other. Moreover, in the embryo Hoatzin
there has been found beyond the so-called "thumb,"
besides vaguely suggestive cartilage, a bone, small yet
solid and well defined, that may be a trace of the true
thumb that has disappeared.[1]   In any case, the bird's

---

[1] See Leighton, *Tuft's College Studies III.*, on " The Develop-
ment of the Wing of Sterna Wilsonii," and W. K. Parker,
Trans. Zool. Soc., Part 2, April, 1891, on " The Morphology of
Opisthocomus Cristatus."

wing is very different from the pterodactyl's. To the support of the latter only one finger, often called the ulnar finger since it articulates with the postaxial side

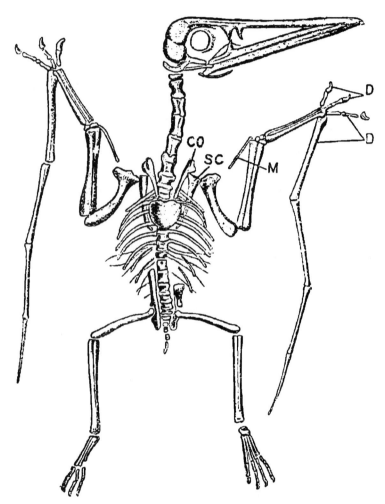

Fig. 17.—(1) Pterodactylus Spectabilis, from lithographic-stone, Bavaria.

of the arm, contributes, and this one may be either No. 4 or No. 5. The settlement of the question depends upon the nature of the small bone which can be seen

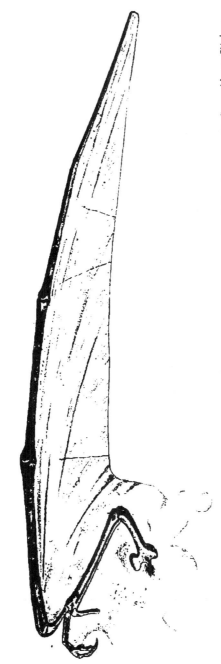

FIG. 17.—(2) Wing of Rhamphorhyncus gemmingi, Bavaria, from the cast of the fossil at South Kensington.   CO, Coracoid ; D, Digits ; M, possibly the 1st Metacarpal, or sesamoid, i.e. originally a tendon ; SC, Scapula ; no trace of a clavicle has been discovered.

projecting from the wrist, and which may be a remnant
of the first metacarpal or only a sesamoid bone [see Fig.
17 (1)]. The wing is a great sheet of membrane supported by this ulnar finger, which was of enormous
length, and also by the leg and tail. Thus, whereas
two fingers united help in the formation of the bird's
wing, only one forms part of the pterodactyl's, for the
other three are little clawed appendages of no use in
flight. Whether these fingers in the bird be Nos. 3 and
4, or 2 and 3 makes little difference. There are two,
not one only, and there is no sign that the smaller one
is likely to disappear, and the larger one being No. 2
or 3 does not correspond to the pterodactyl's ulnar
finger which is No. 4 or 5. The two together form a
short stout bone that contrasts forcibly with the pterodactyl's finger of which the one striking characteristic
is its length. Besides the question of fingers the whole
build of the pterodactyl's wing is different. It gets
its expanse from its great membrane. The bird obtains from its feathers its spread of canvas, while the
pterodactyl has no feathers at all. Its wing, formed by
a membrane stretched from the arm to the leg and to
the tail, was more like a bat's wing than a bird's. But
here again there is an important difference. All the
bat's digits except the thumb help to support the wing,
in the pterodactyl only this one ulnar finger.

We must, therefore, look for other evidence of the
kinship of pterodactyls to birds. Take the head first.
The pterodactyl had a large brain-case and, for a
reptile, an extraordinarily high forehead. The orbits
of his eyes were large. The bones of his skull were
light and became fused together at an early age.

His teeth, as I have explained above, do not separate
him from the bird. In fact, it is far more a bird's
head than a reptile's. Proceeding now to the long
bones we find that many of them have a very
remarkable feature ; they have undoubted air cavities.
These two points—the birdlike character of the skull,
and the aeration of the bones—are, I think, the most
important of all. When they are combined with power
of flight we can infer from them other characters of

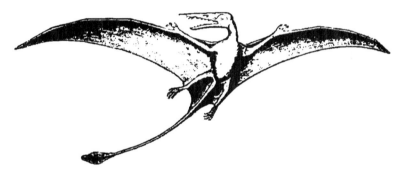

Fig. 18.— Pterodactyl, Rhamphorhyncus phyllurus restored (after Marsh).

which no direct evidence is obtainable, and principally
this—the pterodactyl must have been a warm-blooded
animal. Flight requires great vigour such as is not
found in any cold-blooded creature. Flying-fish can
hardly be said to fly, nor can the so-called Flying
Dragon. Its wings are merely parachutes. Moreover
no animal that we know of combines a highly-developed
brain with cold blood. Among existing animals, birds,
who on the average have a decidedly higher temperature than mammals, have, very many of them,
pneumatic bones. It is true that the same tendency
to pneumaticity is found in the bones of the Dinosaurs,

of which I shall speak soon. But these also may have been to some extent warm-blooded.

The fact that existing reptiles are cold-blooded, while birds have high temperatures, is really no barrier between the two classes. There was once a Python at the Zoological Gardens which laid eggs, and for six weeks sat upon them, at the end of which time they were addled, or, at any rate, the young snakes in them were dead.[1] But the python had not "sat" in vain, for every day her temperature was taken by experts, and also that of a male python hard by who was subjected to the same conditions. The female had an average temperature of 89·07° F., the male of 86·03° F. The maximum temperatures were for the female 92·8° F., for the male 89·8°. But the great difference between warm and cold-blooded animals is that the former do not change their temperature as that of the air changes. The female python was once 16·7° warmer than the surrounding air, the male never more than 11·6°. In a similar case observed in the Jardin des Plantes in 1861 the female's temperature once rose 38·7° F. above that of her surroundings. She-pythons, therefore, when incubating are not altogether the sport of atmospheric changes. Even in mammals temperature varies very much, the small ones having as a rule the hottest blood. Those of large bulk range between 97½° and 98½°. The sheep is said to have a temperature of 104°. The Echidna sends the thermometer only to 82⅔°, and the Ornithorhyncus only to 76¾°. In birds the range is considerable,

[1] *Proceedings of the Zoological Society*, 1881, "The Incubating Python," by W. A. Forbes.

from slightly over 100° F. to 112°. This highest figure is attained by some Passerine birds : Hawks and their allies are never much above 109°, and Gulls rise only a little above 104°. Whether these recorded temperatures are in every case quite exact may be doubted. When the subject is a wild animal, the use of a clinical thermometer is difficult. In the case of the python the results are quite dependable, though the thermometer, laid between the folds, no doubt registered a lower temperature than it would have in the mouth. With other animals fresh experiments are needed. But even as it is we may be quite certain that the figures given are nearly right, though there may be an error of a half or even a whole degree. The conclusions we arrive at, then, are—(1) that there is no hard and fast line to be drawn between warm and cold-blooded animals, and, consequently, our warm-blooded birds may be related to our cold-blooded reptiles ; (2) that pterodactyls, in respect of their temperature, were birdlike rather than reptilian. Before leaving this subject, an objection raised by Sir Richard Owen must be met. He maintained that pterodactyls must have been cold-blooded since they had no feathers to prevent the escape of heat from their bodies. But the temperature of the body has comparatively little to do with external coverings, and depends mainly upon its power of generating heat and upon the regulating apparatus by which it adapts itself to changing conditions.

We will now go on to other points which prove the relationship of pterodactyls to birds, or prove, at any rate, that they have developed separately on very similar lines

E

(1) The head of a pterodactyl is put on at right angles to its neck like a bird's. The head in most reptiles continues the line of the neck.

(2) The sternum or breastbone is broad and has a crest in the middle. This is just what might be expected where great strength is required in the fore limbs and the parts connected. The mole also shows a great development of breastbone : for burrowing this is as necessary as it is for flight.

(3) The scapula is thin and blade-like, and the angle it makes with the coracoid is less than a right angle.

(4) The ilium, the bone of the pelvis that unites with the backbone, is produced both ways, in front of and behind the thigh-joint. This is eminently characteristic of birds.

Altogether the pterodactyl is so near to being a bird that we must, before leaving the subject, briefly show why he is after all a reptile. (1) The hand has at least four fingers, all but the last of these bearing claws; (2) there are no feathers ; (3) the ischium and pubis are at right angles to the ilium, instead of running parallel as in birds ; (4) the pelvis is weak, so that it is extremely unlikely that he could walk upright. In spite of their presumable intelligence and high temperature, in spite of their power of flight, pterodactyls were still reptiles. Many species of them, some not larger than sparrows, others with a span of twenty-five feet from wing tip to wing tip, lived and throve when reptiles were the dominant class upon the earth, and, no doubt, they preyed upon lizards, birds, and mammals.

At the same time there were Dinosaurs, or, as Professor Huxley has called them, Ornithoscelidæ—*i.e.*, bird-legged animals. With wonderful enterprise and zeal, skeletons of these enormous animals, weighing

FIG. 19.—Dinosaur, Iguanodon Mantelli (from a photograph by Dollo of the specimen in the Brussels Museum).

tons, have been collected by Professor Marsh and his assistants in North America. Almost certainly they had the power of walking upon their hind legs, their tails helping to support them. In some species, the nearer row of tarsals or ankle bones is

E 2

fused with the tibia, the stronger of the two leg bones.
All species seem to have been tending towards this
birdlike fusion.   The pelvis is very like that of birds
in its form and in its strength.   The ilium extends
far in front of and behind the thigh joint, and the two
other pelvic bones, the ischium and pubis, extend
downwards and backwards.   If the pelvis of a dinosaur and an emeu be put side by side, the resemblance
is most striking.

Had the pterodactyl had the legs and hind-quarters
of the dinosaur, it would have been still more birdlike
than it is.

Some of the Literature of the Subject.

Besides books mentioned at the end of Chapter II, a number
of papers by Professor H. G. Seeley, Hutchinson's *Extinct
Monsters*, and Huxley's *Vertebrate Anatomy*.

CHAPTER V

THE PROCESS OF CHANGE FROM A REPTILE TO A BIRD

WE have now decided that birds have sprung from some reptilian stock, though not from any existing order of reptiles, and unless we are prepared to differ from the great majority of biologists, we must hold that this has been brought about mainly by the struggle for existence. All animals multiply rapidly, and, if there were no check, this would continue in geometrical ratio, till there would be enough of a single species to people all the earth. Thus, if one pair left two pairs of young, these two would leave four pairs, and those four eight, and so forth. Linnæus calculated that an annual plant producing two seeds in a year would after twenty years have a million descendants. And as every plant produces many more than two seeds—a horse-chestnut tree, for instance, many thousands—every real instance would be far more telling than this imaginary one. The elephant has very few young. Darwin's estimate allows it six in all, born while it is between the ages of thirty and ninety, its term of life being estimated at one hundred years. Yet with these data he calculates that "after a period of from 740 to 750 years there would be nearly 19,000,000 elephants alive, descended from the first pair."

This marvellously rapid increase of all species was one of the two cardinal facts on which his theory of the origin of species was based. The other was the constant tendency to variation. The progeny are very like, but never exactly like their parents. He took his instances mainly from the domesticated animals, because sufficient evidence had not then been collected from wild nature. All the domestic pigeons—the Fantail, the Pouter, the Dragon, the Carrier, the Homer, the Runt, etc.—had been derived from one wild stock, the Rock Dove. The breeder had performed equal wonders with cattle and horses, and during the many thousands of years that the world had been peopled with animals and plants, nature had been doing what the breeder had begun to do only some centuries ago. She had been constantly weeding out those that were less fitted to live. The rocks bear records of thousands of extinct species that have made room for others. Darwin, as I have said, assumed that variation occurred in wild species as among domestic animals. But until this assumption had been proved true, clearly the theory rested upon an insecure foundation. Many observations have now been made, and any one who wishes for a detailed account of them may find it in Dr. Russel Wallace's *Darwinism*. He shows conclusively that in wild species there are two principles working side by side : the principles of

heredity and variation. In form and character the offspring take after their parents, but in almost every case
there is some slight discernible difference. The individuals that have variations that fit them better for
life survive, those that have injurious, or, in some
cases, those that have only useless variations or none
at all, perish. Thus are produced new species, one
useful variation after another being accumulated by
Natural Selection. The sickly and those who are
unsuited to their surroundings have no chance, for
the law is mercifully ruthless.

The facts that I have stated seem to prove much.
The struggle for existence is indisputable, and evolution through Natural Selection seems almost beyond
dispute. But when we come to investigate more in
detail how it has acted, we are met with great difficulties. A living man of science has said that for the
explanation of the brilliant colours of the butterfly
Darwin's theory is but a barren formula. It may
be that only his own imagination is barren. Later
on, in a chapter on colour and song, I hope to
show that colour is, at any rate, connected with
Natural Selection. The particular difficulty that
confronts us when we try to trace the evolution of
birds is that the development of wings would have
been useless, and worse than useless, unless accompanied by other changes. And just as he who builds
a Latin verse conceives a master stroke and puts into
his line, that before was tame and commonplace, a
purpureus pannus, then suddenly, to his dismay, finds
that his brilliant emendation has ruined the grammar
and the sense, so we may imagine a reptile, that

hitherto had passed muster in a mediocre world, ruined by the splendid acquirement of flight, unaccompanied by the other variations without which it would be indubitably fatal.   What if wings had been fully developed so that the fore limbs could no longer be used in walking, while, as yet, the hind limbs had not grown strong so as to make the quadruped a biped?   What if the long legs, so necessary to many wading birds, had not been matched by the length of the neck?   How would such a Tantalus on stilts have reached to the ground to get his food? What would the large expanse of wings have availed, if the muscles to work the wings had not been developed in a corresponding degree?   How would even the fully developed muscles have been equal to a strain so hard, and often so prolonged, had not the heart been so improved that the arterial and venous blood, the fresh and the exhausted, could be kept separate? And what would have been the use of a first-rate heart without first-rate lungs to aerate the blood that was to feed the whole body?   And without an excellent digestive apparatus how could any other part of the system be vigorous?   And without the power of sitting firmly on an elevated perch when asleep, the newly-gained power of flight, the dismay of all enemies during the day, might only have put off the hour of capture and destruction till the night.   This is one of the greatest difficulties which the theory of evolution presents, but it is not insurmountable.   To begin with, variations are almost always small.   We must not imagine the sudden development of a perfect wing. Moreover, slight variations are perpetually occurring ;

it cannot be too strongly insisted upon that they are
not occasional but unceasing, so that it is highly
probable that two, that would be useless unless they
appeared simultaneously, might occur together in the
same individual. It is only reasonable to suppose
that some of the reptiles from which our birds have
sprung were born not only with a fore limb that,
fringed with scale-like feathers, might act as a make-
shift for a wing, but also, by a happy coincidence, with
hind legs stronger than those of their contemporaries.
Quite apart from such coincidences, a very slight
power of flight, due to a modification of the fore limb
not sufficient to incapacitate it for walking, would be
highly advantageous to the birdlike reptile, or reptile-
like bird. When menaced by a snake as he sat upon
a tree, he would flutter to another tree, perhaps feebly,
descending much as he went, his wings acting as a
clumsy parachute. Still, he would save his life. Here,
then, is a stage in advance accomplished. Why
not after this a development of the hind limbs, making
an upright posture possible? And when this was
attained, why not a further development of wings?
And why should not an improvement in the internal
organs follow closely upon the visible changes?
The fact is that in this case it does not seem necessary
to assume an absolute simultaneity of variations.

But supposing it is held by any one that modifications arising singly could not have advanced the
reptile to a bird, and that for simultaneous variations
we must not trust to mere coincidence, we must appeal
to what is called correlated variation. Many instances
of this are given by Darwin. Cats, which are entirely

white and have blue eyes, are generally deaf. Pigeons
with short beaks have small feet, and those with long
beaks large feet.   In wild animals the right and left
sides always vary very nearly in the same way.   The
front and hind limbs often vary together, and even the
jaws and limbs.   He maintains that parts which are
homologous—for instance, arms and legs—often show
similar tendencies.   Length of arm in men generally
goes with height, and if a child has long hands, people
infer that it will be tall.   Possibly, then, through corre-
lation the lengthening and strengthening of the fore limb
might be accompanied by a lengthening and strengthening of the hind limb.   Of course, it cannot be looked upon
as an invariable law that variation follows the lines of
homology.   The fore legs of a giraffe have altogether
dwarfed the hind legs.   The tendency of such variation has been to lift the giraffe's head higher, so that
in times of drought, when other cattle were dying of
hunger, he might browse on the higher branches of
the trees.   A corresponding growth of the hind legs
would have been waste of material, and possibly this
may have caused the weeding out of those whose hind
legs developed *pari passu* with their fore legs.

The difficulty of tracing back the course of development is undeniably great in the case of any animal, and
he who attempts it is apt to lay himself open to ridi-
cule.   The cautious exponent of evolution takes refuge
in generalities.   It is more ingenuous, and in every way
better, to face the difficulties, while at the same time
confessing that much more evidence is wanted from
fossil remains before we can fill in the blanks.   At
present the position of the evolutionist is somewhat,

but by no means entirely, like that of a man who, knowing nothing of the facts of English history, should
attempt to infer them from the character and peculiarities of our existing institutions.   Many and ludicrous
would be his errors.   The evolutionist is saved from
many mistakes by the geological record, which, however fragmentary, is a safe guide as far as it goes.
And if Sir Richard Owen, when presented with a
single bone from New Zealand, was able to some
extent to describe the giant bird of which it had
once formed part, is it not possible that, by the help
of animals, fossil or still existing, evolutionists have
drawn a picture of the primitive ancestors of our
present species that is at any rate not far removed
from the truth ?

BOOKS ON THE SUBJECT.

Darwin's *Origin of Species.*
Wallace's *Darwinism.*
Weissmann's *Essays on Heredity*, and *Romanes Lecture.*
Miss Buckley's *Winners in Life's Race.*
(The literature of the subject is endless.)

CHAPTER VI

FORM AND FUNCTION

Digestive Apparatus

WHAT is the cause of the wonderful vitality of birds? How is it that the Golden-crested Wren, apparently so weak and helpless, can fly all across the North Sea from Norway? What are the processes of life that go on within the bird and make it so different from its lethargic reptilian ancestors? To these questions I hope to give some answer in the present chapter.

To begin with, a bird has a very large appetite, and a reptile a very small one. I have found twenty-two acorns in the crop of an unusually small wood-pigeon, and this was probably quite an ordinary meal to him.[1] They had not made him torpid, like a boa-constrictor after his weekly rabbit. He was flying with all his usual vigour when the shot brought him down. To speak of an animal as an engine, the supplies of fuel

[1] As many as sixty-three have been found. See Badminton Library, *Shooting*, p. 229.

must be large and pretty constant if much work is to be done. Little appetite, little energy, is a rule that holds throughout nature. In his book on the Crayfish, Professor Huxley has a very instructive illustration of what life is. He compares a living creature to a wave in a river which remains always in the same place, being caused by a rock, or something of the kind, near the surface. A still more striking illustration of the same thing is a jet of water in a cataract which, except for slight variations, always keeps the same shape. The wave and the jet of water are at no two moments that you look at them made up of the same materials. Every moment a fresh supply of water as it reaches the same point assumes the same shape and appearance. So it is with the living creature : he may look the same from year to year, but the atoms of which he is built up are not the same. And if he is to be vigorous, an animal must change his constituent atoms rapidly. The large appetite, therefore, of a bird is to be looked upon as a proof of strength and energy. Of course, the appetite alone, without proportionate digestive power, would be worse than useless. The apparatus of digestion must be first-rate, and to the investigation of this apparatus we must now proceed.

In man the saliva plays an important part. In birds, however, the glands which secrete it are small, and the secretion from them, probably, has but little chemical effect upon the food, only helping to soften it. Though the small development of the saliva glands is their chief feature, they vary in size in different birds, those of the Woodpecker being

comparatively big.[1] In all birds the gullet or
œsophagus is large. In many, especially in seed-
eaters, it opens out into a great expansion, with
thickened walls, called the crop, which reaches a
high development in the pigeon. In this bird it is
marked by irregular ridges, and in the breeding season
the cells of the mucous membrane that line it give off
the peculiar cheesy substance known as " pigeon's
milk," with which the young are fed. The crop secretes
no special digestive fluid : it is mainly a storehouse
in which the food is kept till the stomach is ready to
deal with it. The glands found there are only the
ordinary glands of the mucous membrane. Still it
must not be supposed that the food which passes
from the crop is in the same condition as that which
enters it. During its stay there it is acted on by what
saliva has been shot upon it, by water, by the watery
secretion of the mucous membrane, and by the warmth
of the body. Though the crop is not nearly so much
developed in birds of prey, yet in some of them it has
been found equal to hard work. In owls, for instance,
the contraction of the walls strips the skin off their
prey after the under-skin has been weakened by the
secretions, and then the well-known pellets consisting
of hair, feathers, and bones are thrown up.[2] The
South American bird, the Hoatzin, so remarkable for
the two claws on each of its wings and for having the

[1] His tongue, which he can shoot out almost as far as a
chameleon shoots his, is armed with backward-pointing bristles,
and the sticky saliva poured upon it adapts it still further for
fishing out insects from under bark.

[2] See Bronn's *Thier-Reich*, vol. *Aves*, p. 672.

keel developed only on the hinder part of its breastbone, is remarkable also for its highly muscular crop
with furrows and ridges, by means of which it squeezes
out the juices of leaves.   In some birds the crop is
altogether wanting.   In Cormorants, Flamingoes, and
Pelicans only a very small expansion, that might
easily escape notice, has been found.   In all fish-
eaters it is either, as in those just mentioned, very
slightly developed or non-existent.   The two most
striking points about a Cormorant's gullet are its
great size and its elasticity.   Just below the mouth it
opens out to form a spacious pouch with very thin
walls.   Below that it narrows but very slightly before
there comes the very small expansion representing the
crop, and its walls are there just a trifle thicker.
When the bird is lucky enough to secure a long and
thick fish this great tube of nearly uniform size is
ready to receive it.   There is no contraction at any
point sufficient to hinder its downward progress.   A
crop narrowing down at its lower end to a small tube
formed of strong walls would be out of the question in
a fish-eater.   In diving-birds, fish have been found
with their heads partly digested, while upon their
bodies, which had not yet reached the stomach, the
process had not yet begun.   This must inevitably be
so, since nothing is more remarkable than the narrow-
ness of the band within the area of which lie the
digestive glands : a fish of any length cannot possibly
come under the influence of the juices all at once.
Nearly all the stowage room for the cormorant's
large meals is in the ample gullet, and great demands
are made upon it.   One of these huge feeders was

once watched by an apparently trustworthy observer, at a repast which lasted for an hour and a half. Each time that the bird rose after diving, he saw the flash of a small fish and the jerk of the neck with which it was swallowed. And the total number of fish disposed of he estimated at one hundred and eighty. However small they may have been, it must have required a very large gullet to accommodate them.

The stomach has two compartments, very different in their structure and function. There is the fore part, or Proventriculus, which is highly glandular, and the hinder part, which has no glands, and to which, when it is very muscular, as it is in many birds, the name of gizzard is given. The proventriculus secretes strong acid juices from its glands, and some kinds of food, such as meat, may, certainly in mammals, probably in birds, be partly absorbed here, the peptone, as it is called, that is formed from them, passing into the blood vessels that are separated only by a very thin membrane from the cavity of the stomach. It has been thought that the process is that called Osmosis, which is as easy to illustrate as it is difficult to explain. If a bladder containing peptone be held under water, a large quantity of the peptone will make its way out into the water, while the bladder will be distended by the water which has made its way in. Peptone is quite exceptional among solutions of organic matter in the readiness with which it passes through the walls of a bladder. White of egg, for instance, has been tried in the same way, and hardly any of it has escaped.

The absorption of food into the blood-vessels is a

process quite different from Osmosis. The living membrane has a power of selection : it is like a sieve which can let big molecules pass, while it can reject smaller ones. Each cell seems, like an Amœba (of which more presently), to have the power of choosing out and swallowing what it wants. In the same way plants select their food from the ground. Much of the everyday work of nature is too subtle for science to explain.

When the food has penetrated into the blood-vessels it is no longer a foreign substance, but having been thoroughly assimilated has become part of the bird itself. As a rule, however, the process of assimilation is not completed in the proventriculus. The food passes on to the second compartment of the stomach, the walls of which, in seed-eating birds especially, are very thick and strong, being formed of muscular fibres which radiate out from two tendons running down the centre of each side. No less powerful mill would be equal to the grinding of acorns, and even this would be insufficient did not the bird swallow stones which, like molar teeth, break up the food as the muscles contract and relax. So necessary are such molars, that where no stones are to be had birds have been known to swallow hard stonelike seeds, for instance those of the wild prairie rose (Rosa Blanda) which fulfil the same purpose. I have seen stones of portentous size which had been taken from the gizzard of an Emeu. In birds which live on flesh the walls of the stomach are very weak, so that it does not deserve the name of a gizzard and, moreover, no stones are swallowed, nothing of the nature of teeth being

F

necessary. Every one is familiar with the toughness
and solidity of a chicken's gizzard. When the
stomach of a Hawk or Cormorant is set beside it, the
contrast is very striking.

In some birds, all of them fish-eaters, the stomach
has a small third compartment posterior to the
gizzard. The entrance to it is guarded by a flap of
skin or, in the case of the Darter, it is furnished with
thick hairlike formations which at the entrance are
especially long. The purpose both of the flap of skin
and of the hairlike growths seems to be to shut out
all food that has not become thoroughly fluid.[1]

On leaving the second compartment of the stomach,
or the third compartment if there is one, the food
passes into the smaller intestine, where the process of
digestion is completed. The duodenum, the first part
of the smaller intestine, is a U-shaped loop, and in it
lies a great whitish gland called the Pancreas. The
liver is a much greater gland within the two lobes of
which lie the hinder part of the proventriculus and the
fore part of the gizzard. The liver and the pancreas
both pour upon the food in the duodenum the juices of
digestion. The work of the pancreatic juice is, mainly, to
break up starch and convert it into sugar, since starch
as long as it remains starch is of no use to the body as
food, and to emulsify fat, i.e. to dissolve it into fine
globules. The bile—the juice secreted by the liver—
is slightly alkaline and extremely bitter. It is impossible here to describe its exact working. When the
bile and the pancreatic juice have together done their

[1] See Bronn's *Thier-Reich*, vol. "Aves," p. 609. There Dr.
Gadow speaks of it as the Pylorus Magen

work, the process of digestion is complete, and the food goes to build up the living animal. The wonderful process mentioned above is in full swing here; the chyle, that part of the food which consists of emulsified fats, passes into the lacteals (to be described later on) through the villi, small creases in the coat of the intestine, the rest into the blood-vessels, and so, in either case, on to the heart. All refuse is carried into the large intestine, any return from which is prevented by a valve.

Before leaving the subject of digestion, I wish to show how important an organ the liver is to birds. For purposes of flight their weight is reduced as much as possible, but in some good flyers the liver is extraordinarily heavy. In the Tern it is $\frac{1}{20}$ of that of the whole bird, in the Swallow $\frac{1}{18}$, in Vanellus Cristatus, a kind of Lapwing, $\frac{1}{14}$, in the Smew $\frac{1}{11}$. In all these it forms a far larger fraction of the whole than in man. And how account for the great differences? The Smew is mainly a fish-eater and also the Tern. But in the fish-eating Heron the liver is said to be remarkably small. In the common Fowl it contributes rather less than $\frac{1}{26}$ of the total weight, suggesting that seed-eaters depend comparatively little on the liver and more upon the gizzard. But in corn-eating pigeons we find both large gizzards and large livers. And the liver of the flesh-eating gizzard-less Kestrel is lighter than that of the Fowl, only $\frac{1}{36}$, in fact, of his total weight, while in the Tawny Owl it is less than $\frac{1}{43}$. These facts are very perplexing. Dr. Gadow in quoting them remarks that they are untrustworthy, since·they must be affected by the con-

F 2

dition and recent diet of the bird. But, even when we allow for inaccuracies due to this, the differences are startling.[1]

The Heart and Circulation.

Every part of the body is nourished by the blood. Only through the agency of the blood can food and air make good what is lost by wear and tear.

The heart is a force-pump which drives the blood to all parts of the body, and, when it returns impure and loaded with used-up material, sends it to the lungs to be purified, after which it is despatched all over the body again. On the voyage much of it passes through the kidneys, which help the lungs to purge it of the waste of the tissues. The essentials of an efficient heart are that it should be strong, and that it should keep the pure blood separate from the impure. These two essentials are found combined in the hearts of mammals and birds. They are strong muscles: that part at least of them which forces the blood through the arteries is remarkable for its strong thick walls. And, thanks to the perfection of the machinery, the blood which has been purified in the lungs is never mixed with the impure blood which is coming from the body.

The heart is divided into right and left chambers by a division through which there are no doorways. The right and left chambers are each divided into two,

[1] See Bronn's *Thier-Reich*, vol. "Aves," p. 681. The figures, as I have quoted them, are very nearly exact. For simplicity I have disregarded small fractions.

but there are openings from the upper into the lower which may be closed by valves. The two lower chambers are called ventricles and the two upper ones auricles. Before explaining the working of the valves, I shall trace the circulation of the blood. The left ventricle, which is the strongest and most muscular part of the heart, opens into the aorta, the largest of all the arteries. Thence it is distributed into branch arteries and from these into smaller branches : these, in turn, lead into smaller channels called capillaries, varying in diameter, in man, from $\frac{1}{2000}$ to $\frac{1}{1500}$ of an inch. It is when it reaches these extremely minute vessels that the blood does its work of nourishing all the tissues of the body. The capillaries unite to form larger vessels called veins, and these finally form two great trunk veins which carry the blood into the right auricle. From the right auricle it passes to the right ventricle. Thence it is driven into the lungs, from the lungs it passes into the left auricle, and thence into the left ventricle where the same process begins again. Thus the blood in, the right chambers of the heart can reach the left only through the lungs : that in the left can find its way to the right only through the arteries and veins of the body. The pure arterial blood is all on the left side, the impure venous blood on the right. The former may be known by its bright red colour, the latter is blue-black. The following diagram will make clear the course of circulation.

When the blood has passed through the arteries into the capillaries and from them into the veins, it finds a new contrivance to assist in driving it on. In

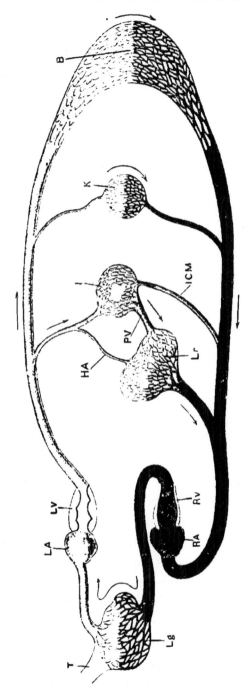

FIG. 20.—Diagram—drawn by Professor Howes for his pupils and copied by his kind permission—to explain the circulatory system of birds. The right and left sides of the heart are separated in order to show that the blood makes only one circuit though it passes twice through the heart in the course of it. The arrows show the direction in which it flows. The venous blood is represented dark, the arterial light. The large vein which brings the blood from the intestines to the liver divides again into capillaries which connect with those into which the hepatic artery branches; in reptiles, but not in birds, there is a similar system in the kidneys. B, body; HA, hepatic artery; I, intestines; I.C.M, inferior-coccygeo-mæsenteric venous system; K, kidneys; Lg, lungs; Lr, liver; LA, left auricle; LV, left ventricle; RA, right auricle; RV, right ventricle; T, trachea.

the veins of the limbs are valves which prevent any
backward flow.   Every movement must tend by
pressure to move the blood forward or backward, and
it will be urged forward since no other course is open.
The places where these valves are in the human arm or
hand can be seen if a finger be pressed upon a vein
and then passed downwards along it in the direction
of the capillaries, thus tending to cause a backward
current.   Little knots will be seen at intervals,
marking the places where the passage of the blood
is checked by the pouchlike valves.   Birds have
fewer of these valves than mammals, but more than
reptiles.

Besides the veins there are other channels in all
parts of the body along which a current is setting
towards the heart.   These are the lymphatics, so
called because they contain a pale watery fluid.   They
differ from veins (1) in that the capillaries from which
they spring end blindly, *i.e.* do not connect with
arteries, (2) in having in their course numbers of
glands through which their contents must pass.   Their
main function seems to be to assist the veins in
carrying on the drainage of the body.   Some of the
lymphatics, however, have a special function and a
special name.   They are called lacteals from the
milky nature of their contents, due to food containing
fat, and their duty is to carry the chyle to the heart
from the smaller intestine round which their capillaries
form a network.   Like the veins they are provided
with frequent valves preventing any backward flow,
and eventually they pour their contents, in birds, into
the two trunk veins which bring the blood from the

right and left sides of the head, in man into that from the left side only.

The great difference (its significance will be made clear in chap. viii.) between the circulatory systems of birds and mammals is this—in mammals the aorta arches over to the left, in birds to the right.

The Valves of the Heart.

When the black blood is discharged into the heart, it has to be sent to the lungs to be purified and to be recharged with oxygen, and the heart by contracting drives it into the pulmonary artery, *i.e.* the artery which leads to the lungs. But unless there is some means of preventing it, obviously the blood will be driven not only to the lungs, but back into the vein which has just carried it to the heart. The right side of the heart, therefore, is divided into two chambers, the passage between them being guarded by a valve which allows the blood to pass from the upper chamber to the lower, but not from the lower to the upper. In the bird this valve is simply a flap of muscle which projects into the ventricle, and which closes the aperture when it is lifted by a rush of blood upwards. In man and other mammals the valve is formed of thin membrane instead of muscle, and consists of three flaps connected with one another and fastened by strings of tendon to the walls of the heart below. This is called the tricuspid valve. It is very curious that the bird's heart should be in most respects so similar to that of man, in this respect so different. These valves remain to show that the two highest classes of animals, mammals and birds, have each separately developed a perfect type of heart from some lower form which allowed the pure and impure blood to mix. On the left side of the heart also the passage between the upper and lower cavities is guarded by a valve. Both in birds and mammals it is formed of two membranous flaps fastened to the walls below by strong cords of the nature of tendons.

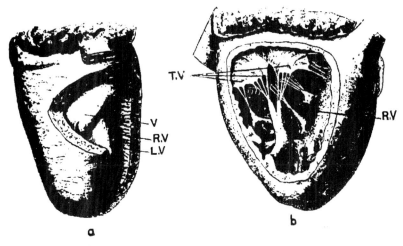

FIG. 21.—(*a*) Bird's heart showing valve between right auricle and right ventricle. (*b*)—modified from Quain—Man's heart showing the same. LV, wall of left ventricle; RV, right ventricle; TV, tricuspid valve; V, valve.

In the human heart it is called the mitral valve from its fancied resemblance to a bishop's mitre. There are other valves as well without which the heart would be very imperfect. There must be some means of preventing the blood when it is driven into the two great arteries, the aorta and the pulmonary, from returning to the heart. The entrance to each, therefore, is guarded by three "semilunar valves," little pockets which look outwards, away from the heart, and, consequently, close against an inrush of blood, but allow an outrush to pass. In a bird of any size they are easy to see.

Some account of a reptile's heart will be found in the chapter on " The Bird within the Egg."

The Blood.

Cut off the supply of blood from a limb, and all its power goes. The muscles lose their sensitiveness to stimulus, and eventually rigor mortis, the stiffness of death, sets in. The life of the whole organism and of each of its parts depends upon the blood. The Jew, who will not eat blood " because it is the life," has dimly seen an important physiological fact.

Blood consists of corpuscles of two kinds, the red and the colourless, commonly called white, and the liquid plasma in which these float. The corpuscles are very minute. It is said that 10,000,000 of the red ones will lie on a space of one square inch. Among birds the Cassowary has the largest, the Humming Bird the smallest. The colourless ones also are always extremely small, though they vary much in size. In shape the red ones, seen under the microscope, are, in birds and reptiles, oval ; in man, round. And the shape is not the only difference. In birds, reptiles, and fishes there is a nucleus, a small roundish body in the middle. In mammals, except in the case of embryos, no sign of this is, as a rule, to be found. Why this nucleus has disappeared, no one has been able to show. It certainly cannot be maintained that there is any superior vitality which we can associate with its

disappearance.   It is easy to connect the reptile's low
temperature with his poverty in corpuscles.

The white blood corpuscle is an object of extreme
interest.   It is simply a cell of granular appearance
with a nucleus.   In shape it is roundish, but when
alive it is a perfect Proteus.   If a drop of blood be

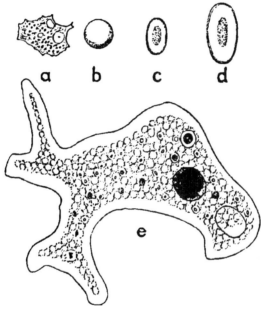

FIG. 22.—(*a*) and (*b*) White and red corpuscles of man from Quain after Schäfer; (*c*)
and (*d*) red corpuscles of Humming Bird and Ostrich after Gulliver; (*e*) Amœba
after Moore.   All to same scale.

taken from the finger and put under the microscope
the white corpuscles are easy to make out, scattered
in comparatively small numbers among the red, but,
unfortunately, they have ceased to move, the change
of temperature, and conditions generally, having
killed them.   But there are one-celled creatures to
be found in stagnant water which closely resemble

them. These are called Amœbæ from their incessant
restlessness. At one moment they may be round,
the next they throw out a limb on one side, the next
that limb is withdrawn and another thrown out elsewhere. Wherever food comes in contact with them
they make a mouth and swallow it. The colourless
corpuscle is one of these simplest of creatures, leading a life of its own within the blood-vessels, but
dependent on the body for the conditions which make
life possible to it. There are several forms of
them, and some, it is believed, do us the priceless
service of swallowing the germs of diseases that find
their way into the blood. The bacillus that has
survived immersion in the strong acid juices of the
stomach is killed, so it is believed, by these small and
half independent organisms. Whether this is so or
not, it is certain that when the blood is thick with
corpuscles, red and white, there is less liability to
disease.

The red corpuscles carry a great deal of oxygen,
and thus they are able to oxidise the tissues, *i.e.* burn
them, for ordinary burning is only a rapid process of
oxidation. If the supply of oxygen is cut off from
it, a fire at once goes out. The oxygen in the blood
keeps up the warmth of the body by slowly burning it.
And in birds, with their very high temperature, the
process is more rapid than in other warm-blooded
animals. The redness of arterial blood is due entirely
to the pigment hæmoglobin in the red corpuscles.
When they lose their oxygen it can be proved by
experiment that they become black, the colour of
venous blood.

The duty, almost the sole duty, of the red corpuscles, is to carry oxygen. It is the work of the colourless plasma to bring food to each part and to carry off the used-up material. The carbonic acid, which is produced by the burning of the tissues, is probably removed, not by the corpuscles, but by the fluid in which they float. At the same time the plasma is busy with other work which falls mainly upon it, the work of carrying in all directions the food-materials which have entered the body, and thus what has been destroyed is rebuilt. It is probable that the various components of the blood divide their functions in the way I have described, but it is quite possible that further investigation may show that the foregoing account requires some modification.

In what part of the body do the corpuscles originate ? In the lymphatic glands corpuscles very similar to, if not identical with, ordinary white corpuscles have been found in process of dividing into two. And it is thought that it is in these glands that the white or colourless kind are produced.

In embryos, and, on occasion, in adults, the spleen, a small red body which can be found in birds attached to the right side of the fore-stomach (Proventriculus) certainly gives birth to many red corpuscles. In the marrow of human bones corpuscles are found intermediate in character between the white and the red, like the former possessing a nucleus, but like the latter having a little of the red hæmoglobin, and these it seems are somehow transformed into ordinary red corpuscles.

Breathing Apparatus and Pneumatic Bones.

A bird's breathing apparatus is of the first order.
When a lark is rising, his wings are beating at the
rate of quite two hundred strokes per minute, probably
much faster.   And yet all the while he sings as if he
were making no great muscular effort.   I recommend
any one who does not appreciate the marvel of this to
try to run up hill and sing or shout at the same time.
Of all those who make this experiment we may quote
what Vergil says of the Greek ghosts in Hades, who
try to raise their war-cry when Æneas appears :—

Inceptus clamor frustratur hiantes.

On the floor of the mouth just behind the tongue is
the glottis or opening into the trachea or windpipe,
a tube formed of rings of bone and gristle which runs
along the neck to its base, where it divides into two
bronchi, which lead, one to the right, the other to the
left lung.   The epiglottis, which springs from the
anterior end of the glottis, and the function of which
in mammals is to close the opening during the process
of swallowing, is very little, if at all, developed in
birds.   Apparently the edges of the larynx, the name
given to the upper end of the trachea, meet so exactly
that no epiglottis or lid to the glottis is necessary.
The larynx has no vocal chords as in mammals, hence
it cannot produce voice, but only raise or lower a note
by bringing together or separating the stiff margins of
the glottis.   The organ of voice is the lower larynx
or syrinx, an organ found in no other class of animals,

situated where the trachea divides to form the bronchi.
I shall describe it later on.

Though a bird has such a splendid "wind," his lungs
are small.   They will be found lying close against the
back, and, if the body is laid down breast uppermost,
under the heart and liver.   They extend from the
first rib to where the kidneys begin, and may easily
be known by their sponginess and their scarlet colour.
It is difficult to measure them exactly, but these are
the measurements as nearly as I could take them
in a common domestic pigeon : length $1\frac{3}{8}$ inch, depth
$\frac{3}{8}$ inch, breadth $\frac{1}{2}$ inch.   This gives for cubic content
$\frac{1}{4}$ inch, for the two lungs together $\frac{1}{2}$ inch.   There is
no reason to suppose that in a Homer pigeon the
dimensions are appreciably larger.   These small lungs
are a wonderful feature in a bird, to whom, under
favourable conditions, a flight of fifty miles in an
hour is no great exertion.   In all birds we find
the same striking contrast between the excellence
and the small size of the lungs.   Though they are
spongy, they have but little elasticity.   When a man
expands his chest, the lungs are distended and the air
rushes in to fill the vacuum caused.   A bird's lungs
vary little in size.   They are prolonged into spacious
air-sacks, the most characteristic part of the breathing apparatus, which renders elasticity of lungs
unnecessary.   These air-sacks are extensions of the
membrane which forms the walls of the bronchi.
The two bronchi we have already described as
leading to the lungs.   They run through the lungs
dividing as they go, and end in these great ex-
pansions by the help of which a bird is able to get

more work, in proportion to the size of his body, out of his exceedingly small and light lungs than a man can out of his far heavier apparatus.   Any one who

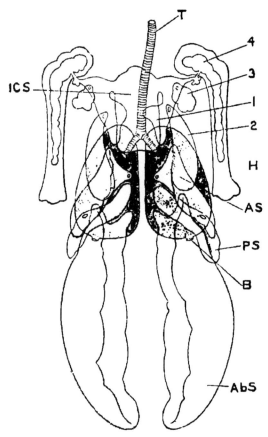

FIG. 23—Diagram after Heider.   Air-sacks excepting the cervical.   The lungs are shaded dark.   Abs, abdominal sack ; AS, anterior thoracic ; B, entrance of bronchial membrane ; H, humerus ; ICS, interclavicular sack, surrounding trachea ; and 1, 2, 3, 4, its extensions ; 2 opens between the pectoral muscles ; PS, posterior thoracic sack ; T, trachea.   See Fig. 25.

wishes to see the air-sacks—and to see them is much better than only to read of them—should take some bird of moderate size, such as a pigeon, cut through the windpipe somewhere in the neck, insert a blowing-tube and tie the windpipe round it with a piece of fine string or cotton, then inflate them. The whole breast and abdomen will be seen to rise and expand. The windpipe should then be tied up and the air-sacks left in a state of inflation. Next the central part of the sternum must be got out of the way. Cut it longitudinally on either side of the keel from the hinder almost to the anterior end. After that remove the viscera very carefully, when the extremely delicate membrane which forms the sacks may be seen, and also the scarlet sponge of the lungs at the bottom of them (the bird lying on its back), and the openings of the bronchi into the sacks. There are nine sacks in all, four on each side, and another pair which have run into one. The hindmost or abdominal pair are very large, and, when the bird is placed upon its back, lie over the kidneys and under the intestines, extending far back behind the lungs. In front of them are the posterior thoracic, and next to them the anterior thoracic, sacks. Then comes the interclavicular sack formed of two which have coalesced. The middle part of this can easily be seen in the angle between the clavicles or wishbones, but it also runs out on either side to the shoulder bones (Fig. 23). The cervical sacks are very small and lie at the base of the neck.

As yet I have only described the minimum of air sacks common to all birds: in many species there are air cavities in the bones, sometimes extending even to the very extremities of the limbs: in some they are found under the skin also, and even in some of the feathers and between the muscles. In a young bird

G

the bones are always filled with marrow, but often as
it grows to maturity the marrow is absorbed, leaving
only a thin dry-looking lining, and the delicate membrane of the air-sacks extends into the cavity.   Thus

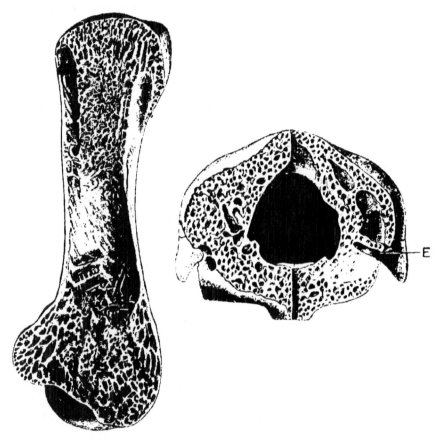

Fig. 24.—Section of (*a*) femur of Ostrich ; (*b*) skull of Carinate Bird.   E, external
opening to ear.   The bronchial membrane lines all the small cavities in the bones.

whenever a bone is hollow (if we except certain
parts of the skull), the cavity connects with the lungs
and is lined with the bronchial membrane.   When the
cavity in the bone is large, thin plates separate from

the inner coat and act as buttresses. Sometimes these buttresses are bound together and a strong network is formed. It is a network like this which supports the beak. In the skull the plates take the form of arches. In all birds without exception, I believe, some of the bones of the skull are aerated, the air being derived mainly from the nostrils and ears. But the beak and some of the bones connected with it are aerated from the lungs. Thither runs from each cervical air-sack a small tube of membrane which lies in an incomplete bony canal under the vertebræ by the side of the vertebral artery. On its way to the beak it throws off branches to the vertebræ of the neck. Every aerated bone has a foramen or aperture through which the bag of membrane finds its way. In the humerus it is easy to find at the end near the body on what is properly the upper side of the bone, but which in the bird's wing, when it is folded, looks backward. The interclavicular sack opens into it. Of all the long bones the humerus is most commonly pneumatic. An easy and interest- ing experiment is to tie up the windpipe of a dead bird, then break the humerus and blow down it through a blowing tube, when the sacks will at once inflate. Indeed wounded birds when their windpipes have been choked with blood have been known to breathe through a broken humerus that has pierced the skin. Other bones that are frequently aerated are the breast- bones, the coracoid, the vertebræ, less frequently the thighbone, shoulder-blade and merrythought. But a good many birds are, as I have said, pneumatic to the very extremities, the Hornbills and the Screamers to the ends of the fingers and toes. The Gannet has large air chambers under the skin, and when these are filled it floats like a bladder on the surface.

The problems connected with the lungs and their extensions are many and difficult, and I shall devote to them a separate division of this chapter (see p. 105).

The Process of Breathing.

It will be well first to say something about the mechanism of breathing in man, and then show how different it is in birds. A man creates the vacuum within him which the air rushes in to fill partly by means of the diaphragm, partly by means of the ribs. The diaphragm is a partition which separates the cavity which contains the heart and lungs from that which contains the intestines. Muscles descend from it to the ribs and stronger ones to the spinal column. When these muscles contract, the lung chamber is enlarged, a vacuum is created, the air rushes in and distends the lungs. Diaphragmal breathing is impossible to a bird since it has no fully developed diaphragm. Indeed the oblique septum, to which the name of diaphragm is often given is apparently so different in its nature and situation that it has been doubted whether we can regard it as the same organ as the diaphragm of mammals. Its arrangement is very complicated. One part lies on the under surface of the lungs and under the cervical air-sacks which, thus, are in a chamber by themselves. The other, the entirely membranous and oblique part, at its anterior end connects with the former along the line of the backbone ; further back it springs from the pelvis.

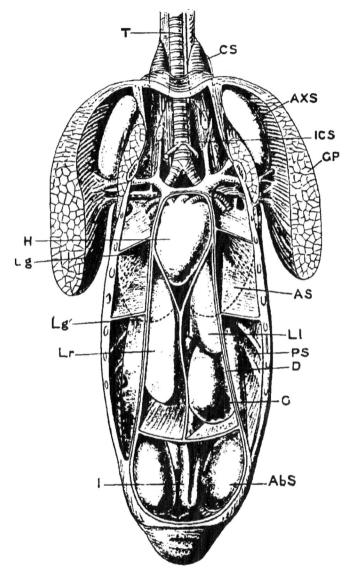

FIG. 25.—Diaphragm of Duck (diagram after Strasser). The sternum has
been removed.

Abs, abdominal sack ; it runs back under the viscera and opens into the lung ;
sometimes penetrates the pelvis and femur : AS, anterior thoracic sack ; AXS, axillary
sack, a pouch of the interclavicular ; CS, cervical sack ; D, diaphragm ; G, gizzard ;
GP, great pectoral muscle turned back ; H, heart ; I, intestine ; ICS, interclavicular
sack, often penetrates keel ; Lg, lung ; Lg', line to which the lungs reach ; Ll and Lr,
left and right lobes of liver ; PS, posterior thoracic sack ; T, trachea.

It forms on either side a sheet which slopes outwards and fastens to the sternum near to its junction with the ribs. Cross-partitions divide the chambers formed between it and the body wall : into these compartments the air-sacks enter, their walls being so thin that it is difficult to separate them from those of the chambers which they line. The diaphragm does not, as in mammals, separate the heart from the intestines. The diagram on page 85 will help to make this description clear.

Obviously a membranous partition like this cannot do the work of the diaphragm of mammals, but that it is homologous to it, *i.e.*, the same in origin, may well be maintained. The difference of position does not disprove this, for it is well known that a muscle may shift its point of attachment so that upon such a question as the nearness of the relationship of reptiles to birds the evidence of muscles does not count for much. Nor is the fact that the diaphragm is muscular in mammals and membranous in birds in any way conclusive. In the apteryx it is strong and fibrous. In a puffin Mr. Beddard found it muscular, and I myself found it very highly so in another bird of the same species. Tendon in fact often replaces muscle. It is certainly possible, on the whole it seems probable, that the diaphragm in mammals and birds may be the same in origin though different in function.[1] It is interesting to find that crocodiles that come near to birds in so many points, are like them also in having an oblique septum.

[1] See Huxley on " Breathing Apparatus of Apteryx," *Proc. Zool. Soc.*, 1882 : article on the " Diaphragm " in Newton's *Dictionary of Birds.*

To return to the subject of breathing, a man breathes not only by means of the diaphragm, but by raising the ribs. This is effected by means of muscles called the external intercostals, which pass downwards and outwards from each rib to the one below it. The contraction of these muscles will raise both ribs, as may be shown by an easy experiment. Take two thin rods of deal and screw them on to a third piece, nail a fourth piece to their other ends to keep them parallel. Join them by an india-rubber band, sloping

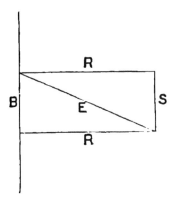

FIG. 26.
R, R represent ribs ; B the backbone ; S the breastbone ; E is the india-rubber band representing the external intercostal muscle.

downwards and outwards and too short to reach without stretching. This will raise the two ribs. There are muscles fastened to the inside of the ribs and from that called the Internal Intercostals which slope downwards and inwards towards the backbone, and therefore act just in the opposite way—*i.e.*, they lower the ribs. When a bird is standing or walking, the breast rises and falls in breathing much in the same way as it does in man, though the great weight of the

breast muscles must make it move less easily.   Owing
to the thicker coating of feathers it is difficult to see the
movements clearly.   When a large bird, a goose or
a crane, utters a loud cry, is the best opportunity.
Then, if he is standing, his breast may easily be seen
to move forward and upward.   When the muscles
relax, the breast will sink and the air will be expelled,
but the latter process will be greatly assisted by the
contraction of other muscles—viz., those that lie over
the abdomen and connect the pelvis and the breast.
The action of these will be to drive the air out of the
great hinder air-sacks.   The chest is loosely hinged
on to the back by muscles near the shoulder joint, so
that very little exertion on the part of the abdominal
muscles will be required.   Take a dead bird and see
how easily the hinder end of the breast works up and
down.   Thus the abdominal muscles in a bird play a
most important part in breathing, in a man they play
a very small one.

But most birds breathe most actively during flight,
and then a different system must be adopted.   John
Hunter, the celebrated anatomist, held that birds did
not inhale and exhale during flight, but merely used
the air which they had stored in their air-sacks.   This
view appears absurd in the face of the fact that they
will sometimes fly hundreds of miles without alighting.
But he was led to adopt it by what is a very real
difficulty—namely, that the movement of the breast in
breathing would seriously derange the machinery of
flight.   The socket in which the wing works is formed
mainly by the coracoid, which is buttressed by the
clavicle.   Both bones are almost rigidly fixed to the

breastbone, from which spring the great muscles which
lower and raise the wing. If the breast were perpetually
moving up and down, a strong stroke, such as flight
requires, would be impossible. M. Edmond Alix gives
what I believe is the right explanation—viz., that a bird
breathes during flight, by moving not its breast, but
its backbone. But he does not explain how this is
effected. After some investigation I have come to the
conclusion that the muscular movements necessary to
flight themselves lend material assistance in the process
of breathing. I have here, therefore, to anticipate
some important points which properly belong to the
chapter on flight. There is a very broad sheet of
muscle, called the Latissimus Dorsi, which arises
from the vertebræ just behind the neck and also
from vertebræ further back, sometimes even from the
pelvis. It attaches to the shoulder bone. When the
wing is lowered in flight, this muscle contracts and
hauls upon the wings, which resist its action since
stronger muscles are pulling them in a different
direction. Since the wings will not give, the body is
lifted towards them, attaining nearly to a horizontal
position. Were it not for this muscle, it would hang
nearly straight down, as you may see by taking a
dead bird and holding it by its outstretched wings.
The Latissimus Dorsi not only keeps the body nearly
horizontal, but expands the air-sacks. For when the
back is raised, the weight of the breast muscles and
the intestines hanging on the ribs will straighten them
out, and so the sacks which lie close under the back
will be distended. This may easily be seen if you
grip the backbone of a dead bird with a pair of pincers,

when the dead weight hanging on the ribs produces the
result described.   And the movement of the shoulder
blades during flight will help to produce the same
effect.   In the down stroke the rotating or twisting of
the wing, by which its front margin is lowered and its
under surface made to look backward, causes a very
slight lowering of the anterior end of the shoulder
blade, and this necessitates a considerable upward
swing of the hinder end, a point that can be best
made out by moving the wing of a dead bird as it
moves in flight.   This raising of the shoulder blade
acts upon the ribs since they are connected with it by
muscle.   They straighten out, chiefly at the joint
which each of them has in its lower half, and so tend
to raise the backbone.   And not only this, but, being
pliable, they bend outwards, and so broaden the roof of
the cage which they form.[1]   Thus in birds, as in the
lobster and crayfish, progression itself aids greatly
the process of breathing.   The external intercostals,
which we saw moved the breastbone forward when
the bird was standing or walking, now play a different
rôle.   During flight the bird's breast is practically
immovable.   The entire weight of the body is hanging on the wings and the wings are pressing inwards
upon the coracoid bones and clavicles which are
firmly fixed to the breastbone.   The dead weight and
the pressure inwards do not allow the breast to move.
Let us see then what will happen when the external
intercostals contract.   It must be remembered that the
action of a muscle is to shorten the distance between
its two ends, and that of the two bones which it

[1] See Fig. 2 on p. 8.

connects that one will move which yields most easily.
Let the accompanying diagram represent two ribs,
the left-hand one being the
anterior of the two. The
contraction of the muscle
will raise the hinder one,
because that will yield the
more easily, the muscular
hinges at the shoulder
joints allowing the hinder
part of the back to rise.
Moreover the backbone of
most birds that I have examined bends downwards
easily, and through a considerable arc just in front
of the pelvis. The raising
of the hindmost ribs which
unite with the backbone
behind the point where the

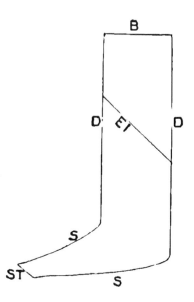

Fig. 27.—B = backbone ; D, dorsal rib ;
E.I., ext. intercostal ; S, sternal rib-
piece ; ST, sternum.

bend takes place, will aid the vertebral muscles in
straightening the back.[1] Wishing to test these conclusions by experiment, I suspended a freshly-killed pigeon
by its wings, and inflated the air-sacks by means of a
blowing-tube. The backbone a little in front of the

---

[1] Other muscles assist. The levatores costarum, which I have
found highly developed in the domestic pigeon, arising from the
vertebræ, then passing backwards and attaching to the ribs some
way down, tend to make the upper part of the rib horizontal,
thus broadening the chamber beneath. The triangularis sterni,
which arises from the inside of the sternum, from its anterior
lateral end, attaches to the sternal rib-pieces, and tends to make
them perpendicular. ·

thigh-joint moved rather more than half an inch, the
movement of the sternum being almost too slight to
measure.   I do not wish to represent this experiment
as one of much value.   However, the conditions of
flight were so far reproduced that the weight of the
body was hanging upon the wings and so hindering
the movement of the breast while leaving the back
free ; it is true, there was none of the pressure—which
during flight must be very great—of the wings upon
the coracoids and clavicles.   But would not the only
effect of this pressure be to render the breastbone and
the bones united with it still less ready to move ?
When a bird flies with his body sloping upward, as
he always does when he wishes to rise, I believe the
process of breathing will be the same, with the
difference that the Latissimus Dorsi will not contract
sufficiently to raise the back nearly to the horizontal.

There is yet another posture which birds commonly
adopt, and in which the problem of breathing does not
seem altogether a simple one.   A chicken sleeps with its
breast resting on its perch.   And gulls, geese, ducks,
and other birds will often lie with their breasts on the
ground.   In this case the movement of the breast is
out of the question, and sometimes ocular evidence
may be obtained that it is the back that moves.   I
have spent a considerable time in watching a Chinese
goose at the Zoological Gardens, while it lay on its
breast and uttered loud and uncouth noises.   The
hinder part of the back rose visibly.   And this was
not surprising, for there was no weight upon the legs,
and it is this of course which makes back-breathing
impossible when the bird is in a standing posture.

But what muscles are brought into play? The muscle that connects the wing with the back-bone will not help us now. We have to depend on the external intercostals, the action of which I have already explained (p. 91) for raising the back. Besides there are fairly strong muscles running along the vertebral column, and these will straighten the back at the point just in front of the pelvis, where, as I have said, there is a joint which allows a considerable rise or fall.

The machinery of breathing, then, in birds is very different from ours. Let us compare the results, remembering that the object of breathing is to oxidise the blood. In all lungs the blood is separated from the air by a very thin membrane which allows the passage-out of carbonic acid gas and the passage-in of oxygen. An experiment will illustrate this. If black venous blood is placed in a bladder and the bladder placed in oxygen gas, the oxygen will find its way into the bladder, and the blood will be arterialised. In fact gases mechanically held in a fluid tend to diffuse into any atmosphere to which they are exposed—*e.g.* the carbonic acid gas in soda water—and gases separated by a dry porous partition diffuse into one another. But the oxidation of the blood is a very complicated process.[1] Here it is enough to say that when air as it comes from the lungs is compared with fresh air, it is found to have gained about 5 per cent. of carbonic acid and to have lost about 5 per cent. of oxygen. This is proof positive of the interchange of gases. Moreover it is

[1] See Huxley's *Elementary Physiology*, Lesson IV.

beyond dispute that the more rapid and complete
the change of air in the lungs, the more rapid and
thorough will be the oxidation of the blood. It is
easy to increase the warmth of the body by taking
long and rapid breaths for a minute or two, and the
increase in temperature is due to the fact that the
blood, carrying more oxygen, burns the tissues more
rapidly.

The lungs proper are never penetrated by fresh
air. There is an amount of air in them which by no
effort can be exhaled. This is called residual air, and
in man averages from 75 to 100 cubic inches. There
is about an equal quantity which may be driven out
with effort, but which remains after an ordinary
expiration. This is called supplemental air. Only
the tidal air (20—30 cubic inches) passes in and out
in ordinary breathing. Thus, taking the largest
estimates—residual air 100, supplemental 100, tidal
30—rather less than ¼ of the air is changed when an
ordinary breath is taken, and the fresh air penetrates only
the trachea and bronchi, and not the minute air-cells
which open from them. The stationary air, residual
and supplemental, carries on respiration. It receives
the carbonic acid from the blood and gives it up to
the tidal air, since it is a law of nature that gases,
when in contact, diffuse into one another. Increase
the volume of the tidal air, and the more rapid will be
the interchange of oxygen and carbonic acid gas between it and the stationary air. If the inspired air is
very poor in oxygen or meagre in amount the process
will be much slower and the whole vitality will be
lowered. In fact the refreshing effect of exercise is due

mainly to the more rapid breathing caused, and the consequent more rapid oxidation of the blood.   Now, we have seen that in birds the air rushes in through the lungs into the air-sacks behind, and that the latter have a capacity many times as great as that of the lungs.   Not only, therefore, does the fresh air penetrate all the bronchial passages on its way to the air-sacks, but expiration also will bring to the lungs a supply of air only slightly vitiated, since it will drive into them the as yet unused air in the sacks.   This fact must be viewed in connection with the known rapidity of a bird's breathing.   According to M. Milne Edwards big birds, when inactive, breathe 20—30 times a minute, small birds 30—60 times.[1] The thick coating of feathers makes it difficult to count a bird's respirations.   In ducks, which I have watched closely, they have been from 18 to 22.   Even this lower estimate makes a bird breathe more rapidly than we do ourselves, for an adult man, when sitting still, averages only 13—15 respirations per minute. In the case of a young horse, according to M. Milne Edwards, the average is 10—12 per minute, of an adult horse 9—10.   In comparing a bird's rate of breathing with that of other animals, we must bear in mind the fact, that exhalation brings air that is practically fresh to the lungs, so that a duck's 18 breaths per minute, taking the lowest estimate, ought to be counted as nearly 36.

It is possible to obtain more accurate evidence of an animal's respiratory activity by measuring the amount of carbonic acid gas given off, for this is, roughly

[1] *Physiologie et Anatomie comparée*, vol. ii., p. 487.

speaking, equal to the amount of oxygen absorbed.
M. Milne Edwards records some experiments of this
nature, the results of which are very striking.[1]   The
amount of carbonic acid gas exhaled by various
animals during a given time was exactly measured,
and then equated to one standard, so that the different
sizes of the subjects of the experiments might cause
no confusion.   Thus, the figures that follow enable us
to compare animals of the most widely separated
classes, in respect of the amount of carbonic acid which
they breathe out ; and since, as I have said, this roughly
corresponds to the amount of oxygen absorbed, it is a
measure of the excellence, or the reverse, of their
breathing apparatus.

The slug ...	...	...	...	2
The snail ...	...	...	4 or	5
The toad ...	...		5 or	6
The frog ...	...		7 or	8
The guinea-pig ...			14 or	15
The pigeon	...		...	20

The pigeon is a good deal ahead of the guinea-pig,
the only other warm-blooded animal in the list.   The
cold-blooded creatures are far behind the guinea-pig.

To sum up, then, a bird's respiratory system is, as
far as we know, much more active than that of any
mammal. As evidence of this we have—(1) the greater
amount of carbonic acid given off; (2) the more rapid
breathing, the effect of which is much increased by the
air-sacks ; (3) high temperature, which could not exist
without thorough oxidation of the blood.

[1] *Physiologie et Anatomie comparée*, vol. ii., p. 534.

Lungs of Lower Vertebrate Animals.

In comparing reptiles and birds in a previous chapter, I said nothing about the lungs, because I thought it would be more intelligible after some account of the machinery of breathing and its working had been given.

If birds really had reptilian ancestors, it would be very odd if existing reptiles had no trace of any development similar to the air-sacks that in birds are so characteristic a feature. There is one reptile that has unmistakable air-sacks—the Chameleon. They are small, it is true, but in their nature the same as the bird's. The snake's one fully developed lung (the other has shrunk to insignificance) is suggestive of a bird's; it is a bag the walls of the front part of which are full of blood vessels. The hinder part is simply a reservoir of air. The same is the case with the lizard's lungs. In crocodiles, they are more complicated, not at all like mere bags as they are in snakes and lizards. In this point, too, crocodiles come nearer to birds than other reptiles. It is curious that the swim-bladder of fishes, like lungs, an outgrowth from the alimentary canal, but, unlike lungs, an outgrowth from its dorsal (or hinder) wall, often has its anterior half covered with blood vessels, while the hinder part is simply a membranous bag. The lepidosirens are fish, which, if left in the mud when their river dries up, become air-breathers ; they have true lungs, pouches opening from the ventral (or front) wall of the gullet, and these are furnished with extensions which have no blood vessels.

H

Thus, air-sacks are not peculiar to birds, though they have turned them to account in a way that is quite unique. How important a part they play in respiration I have already described. But they are far larger than is necessary for this, and we shall now have to consider what other purposes they serve.

Regulation of Temperature.

Our investigations have already made it clear why a bird is warm-blooded. Thorough oxidation of the blood and a rapid circulation bring about the burning of the tissues which is the cause of animal warmth. It must not be imagined that high temperature can be due to a thick coating of feathers. They no doubt help to retain heat, but they cannot produce it. Wrap a lizard up in blankets, and he will still remain cold-blooded. He has not the digestion, the heart, or the lungs that mark the warm-blooded vigorous animal.

We must now try to understand by what means warm-blooded creatures in general, and birds in particular, regulate their temperature. This power is one of the most wonderful things in the constitution of the higher animals. In Parry's Polar Expedition, a wolf was shot, and its temperature was found to be 104° F., while the thermometer was nearly 33° below zero. The greater the cold to which the body is exposed, the more rapid the combustion that is always going on within it, so that its temperature does not rise and fall with the thermometer. But it must always be remembered that extremes, whether of cold or heat, must reduce the vigour of the body by obliging it to make an effort to resist them. In man the ordinary temperature is 98° and a fraction ; a slight rise above this indicates fever, and a slight decline below it shows a failing of the bodily powers. When in health, the body can be exposed to enormous heat without itself growing appreciably warmer. The sensation of heat comes when great effort is required to keep the normal temperature. In the hottest room in Turkish baths the thermometer sometimes rises to 230° F., and some bathers remain there as long as 20 minutes. But this is far below the record. Doctors Fordyce and Blayden were able to remain some time in a chamber heated to 260° F. I have been told that a man who earned his living by feats of this kind, found himself compelled to rush precipitately from a heated oven because some one, who was more scientific than kind, had placed a can of hot water in one corner. Every one knows how oppressive the heat of a hothouse is. The heat of the vapour baths in Russia is said sometimes to rise to 116° F., but between this and 260° there is a great gulf. We have in this a hint as to one method of keeping down temperature—viz., by evaporation. Perspiration, or rather the evaporation, to which it gives rise, lowers the temperature of the body. When the air around is so damp that evaporation is slow, even moderate heat is oppressive. When through long exposure to a burning sun, all the available moisture in the body has been exhausted, there results a feverish heat and an uncontrollable thirst. Under these circumstances, a private soldier will not stop to use his pocket-filter, if he happens to have been supplied with one, but will gulp down the most poisonous filth, though he knows it to be poison. And yet a bird does not perspire at all, and is perfectly at ease when flying under a hot sun. A man, if he is to endure heat, must resemble one of the porous earthenware pots used in India for cooling water. Put them in wind which, however hot, is dry, and, the evaporation increasing, the water cools all the more rapidly, and the sahib's bath will be ready all the sooner. A man's skin is highly porous, being covered with sweat glands, little tubes leading into the skin and communicating with the capillary blood vessels, from which the moisture permeates to the tube and so to the surface. Even when perspiration is imperceptible, a great deal is given off in the course of the day. A bird, on the contrary, has no sweat glands; it must therefore, have some other means of keeping down its temperature. True, some evaporation will go on though there are no pores, for if a bladder full of water be hung up in the air, the water will ooze through. Still, the process is a very slow one, and such evaporation cannot be of much service to a bird.

It is now time to investigate more exactly the various means by which the body rids itself of superfluous heat. The processes at work are evaporation, conduction, radiation. The chilling effect of evaporation, every one is familar with. We are conscious of loss of heat by conduction when we touch cold iron. But the same cause is always at work. By conduction, the air that is next to the body is warmed —*i.e.*, the body gives off heat to the air. Clothes, according to the material of which they are made, vary very much in their power to lessen conduction ; they can never arrest it altogether. Radiation takes

place when heat passes out into the surrounding
atmosphere, not into the particular molecules in
contact with the body, just as the earth radiates out
its heat on a clear starlight night. In man the skin
does most of this work, a much less but still a considerable amount being done by the lungs. Estimates
by different authorities vary considerably, some credit-
ing the lungs with 20 per cent., others with as little as 9.[1]
In birds, the skin undertakes comparatively little of
the work, the lungs and air-sacks far the greater share.
Conduction is much checked by the feathers, though
the bare tracts, called apteria, make the coating much
less impervious than might be supposed. It must also
be borne in mind that owing to the high temperature
of the bird's body, the air will be colder to him than to
ourselves, and, so far, the conditions for loss of heat
by conduction are more favourable. Making all
allowances, the heat given off in this way cannot be
very great ; and, as I have said, owing to the absence of
sweat glands, there is no appreciable amount of evaporation. The work is, therefore, of necessity, thrown
upon the lungs and air-sacks. It is these organs that
by means of evaporation and conduction regulate
the temperature of the bird's body. It must be remembered that, however hot or however cold the air
inhaled, by the time it emerges from the lungs it has

---

[1] Dr. Michael Foster (*Textbook of Physiology*, p. 464, 1883
ed.) writes : " It has been calculated that the relative amounts
of the losses by these several channels are as follows : in warming the urine and faeces about 3, or according to others, 6 per
cent. ; by respiration about 20, or according to others, about 9
only per cent., leaving 77, or, alternatively, 85 per cent., for conduction and radiation and evaporation from the skin."

very nearly the same temperature as the body, and all the heat communicated to the air is withdrawn from the bird. The rapid breathing, therefore, that is natural in flight, will of itself counteract the heating effect of violent exercise. In the same way, since they perspire only through the tongue and feet, dogs maintain an equable temperature when running fast, by means of quickened respiration. It is, probably, as regulators of temperature that the air-sacks have been developed till their cubic capacity surpasses that of the lungs many times : how many, it is difficult to estimate; probably ten times at least. They cannot, as some writers have supposed, do the work of lungs, since the blood vessels in them are so minute as to be of little use, whereas, by exposing their very large surfaces constantly to fresh indraughts of air, they cause a large withdrawal of heat from the body, and for this no other effectual machinery exists. It would be very interesting to discover exactly what amount of aqueous vapour is given off by a bird in breathing, so that we might know whether, in proportion to the size of body, it is more than it is in man. Among other reasons for regarding this as probable, is the fact that a bird's kidneys secrete little or no water, so that of the three organs which get rid of the waste products of the body—the skin, the lungs, and the kidneys—the lungs alone are available for disposing of any great amount of what is fluid. Unfortunately, it is impossible to give any exact figures. As far as I am aware, no evidence on this point has been obtained by experiment.

Books on comparative anatomy are common, and

the smallest points have been investigated and re-
investigated. But comparative physiology is a less
common study. The physiologists, except when wishing to throw light upon human life, have, as a rule,
neglected the life of other animals. In default of
such experiments we must point to the enormous size
of the air-sacks, far greater than is needed for mere
breathing, and also to the rate of respiration, which,
as I have said above, is much greater in a bird, even
when at rest, than in a man.

We have not yet done with the machinery by
which temperature is regulated. There are nerves
which can cause increased warmth in any organ
or part of an organ which requires it, and which
also exercise a general control. If a small artery
be watched, it will be seen to vary in width without
any apparent change taking place in the heart's
beat. To see this, cut a hole in a thin piece of
deal, put a frog's foot over it, and tie the toes
so that it cannot move them. The frog will suffer
some discomfort but no actual pain. If now the foot
be examined under the microscope, the blood will be
seen circulating, as the skin is quite transparent, and
the widening and narrowing of the small arteries may
be made out. The same thing may be seen in a
small artery in the rabbit's ear. When little blood is
wanted in a particular part, the artery which supplies it
is constricted or tightened. When much is wanted, it is
dilated. This is effected by the vaso-motor nerves—*i.e.*
the nerves which act upon the blood vessels—and the
centre from which they act is believed to be the part
of the brain which is called the medulla oblongata

But they do not all centre in this, and the exact part of the brain from which some of them come has yet to be discovered. The vaso-motor nerves not only have local power, but by combined action can affect the temperature of the body generally. They lower it by sending a large flow of blood to the surface; more heat will then be lost through radiation and conduction, and in man by evaporation. Thus exercise at once raises and keeps down temperature—raises it by muscular activity which always generates heat, keeps it down by bringing blood to the surface. In exposure to cold, the blood withdraws from the surface, and protects the vital organs from chill.

It is supposed by high authorities that there are yet other nerves or nerve-fibres, which have more complete power over temperature in that they control directly the amount of oxidation. When a warm-blooded animal is dosed with the drug urari, it behaves like a cold-blooded creature. If the nerves that arise from the medulla oblongata are severed, the results are the same in kind, though not so striking. This cannot be due to the vaso-motor nerves, which only regulate the amount of blood sent along the arteries.

The subject will be more intelligible, when I have made clear what is meant by "behaving like a cold-blooded animal." For purposes of distilling, a chemist puts various substances in a retort and exposes them to heat, and the greater the heat applied the faster the process goes on. A cold-blooded animal has been well compared to such a mixture of dead substances in a chemist's retort. Heat increases and cold diminishes its activity ; when the thermometer goes down a few degrees below freezing, it torpifies.

The warm-blooded animal generates heat within himself, and, in a certain measure, is superior to external conditions. The cold-blooded animal is their slave. It might be thought that fish live through great cold in hard winters. But since water is densest and heaviest when it is at a temperature of 39° F., ponds and pools in rivers are not so cold some way below the ice as might be thought. It is true that when fish die during a frost, it is usually from want of oxygen, the ice not having been broken to allow oxidation of the water at the surface. There is no reason, however, to suppose that fish can stand very great cold any more than other cold-blooded animals It is true of them as a class that they are at the mercy of their surroundings.

It is impossible here to spend more space on so abstruse a subject. I would refer the reader to Dr. Michael Foster's *Textbook of Physiology*, where the subject is admirably handled. He is not there speaking of birds ; but, in this respect, what is true of one warm-blooded animal is probably true, roughly speaking, of all.

Problems connected with the Hollow Bones of Birds.

Not long ago the problems connected with this subject were settled in a very offhand way. The heated air in the air-sacks and bones being lighter than the surrounding atmosphere made the bird a balloon, and so flight was easy. This theory has withered beneath the cruel light of fact. A bird can carry only a very small amount of air in its sacks and bones, and the difference in weight between a few cubic inches of heated or cold air is too infinitesimal to be worth considering. The fact that an eagle may sometimes be seen carrying off a lamb ought to convince any one that the saving of the tiniest fraction of an ounce of weight would make practically no difference. True, air within the bird, whether heated or not, will expand its volume, and lessen its specific gravity,[1] but it could not help it to rise, and this is the real difficulty. Moreover, many birds which fly to perfection, for instance the swallow, have all their large bones solid. If by any means a bird attained the lightness of a balloon, he could not fly. A balloon drifts with every gust; steering is impossible; the wind chooses its course. A machine which is light as air can have no strength to gain a velocity other than that of the air-current in which it moves. The bird-balloon, as light as the wind and as strong as iron, is a figment of the imagination.

What, then, is the true explanation of the aeration or pneumaticity of birds' bones? It is impossible that it can be of use in the regulation of temperature, since the air cannot be expelled from them at will. But the

[1] It may be well to explain what is meant by specific gravity. The weight of water is taken as the unit. When it is said that the specific gravity of gold is 19, it is meant that a cubic foot of gold weighs 19 times as much as a cubic foot of water. Thus, when a bird inflates his sacks with air, his weight increases by the weight of the air breathed in, but his specific gravity is lessened. An average cubic inch of him does not now weigh so much; his weight in proportion to his bulk has gone down.

capillaries in the great expanse of bronchial membrane must help a little to aerate the blood. With a view to discovering the main purpose of pneumaticity, I will briefly set down the chief facts.

(1) Many small birds that are first-rate flyers have either marrow in all their larger bones, or else in all except the upper-arm bone ; the Swift in all with this exception, the Swallow in all.

(2) Most of the big strong-flying birds have a great deal of aeration.

(3) The Hornbills, which according to good observers are very poor flyers, are as pneumatic as any birds or, perhaps, more so than any.

(4) The Apteryx, the wingless bird of New Zealand, has only part of its skull, and no other bones, aerated. On the other hand the Ostrich, Emeu, Rhea, and Cassowary have great hollows in the thigh bones, the vertebræ, the ribs, the breast bone, and the coracoids.

(5) Birds which dive have solid bones, or only the shoulder bone aerated.

(6) Birds which spend much of their time in the water without diving have, at least in all the species of which I have been able to obtain specimens, nearly all the bones solid. The Gulls are the most striking example of this, even the humerus in the Black-headed Gull being solid.

(7) There are great differences between nearly related species—*e.g.* the Gannet has an extraordinary amount of aeration, while its near ally, the Cormorant, has only the humerus pneumatic. The Hornbill is not very distantly related to the Swift, which has singularly little aeration.

(8) The bones of birds that are highly pneumatic are, relatively to their length, larger in girth than those of birds in which the aeration is but slight.

(9) All young birds have solid bones. As they grow to maturity, if pneumaticity is characteristic of the species, the marrow dries up and the bronchial membrane extends into the hollow.

These facts look tangled and perplexing, but I believe it is possible to some extent to unravel them. I will begin by considering the case of the diving birds. Much aeration of the bones would be an inconvenience to them ; as it is, they can regulate the amount of the body that appears above the water, sometimes sinking till no more than the head is visible. Very often it is impossible to see a Red-throated Diver swimming in a mountain tarn. Only his neck stands out above the water, and you cannot distinguish it among the reeds. The Cormorant uses the same device, but he is not equal to the Red-throated Diver in making himself heavy or cork-like at pleasure. This power to vary their specific gravity resides, no doubt, in the air-sacks, which they can at will empty or inflate. Sometimes they help diving birds, it is thought, in another way : those which lie under the skin about the neck and breast of the Gannet may serve as air-cushions to break his fall when he dashes into the sea from a height of over 100 feet.[1]   Aerated bones, on the other hand, would be a hindrance and not a help to a diver, for they would make it harder for him to swim under water. Probably, too, the marrow in the bones serves

[1] See on this point a paper by Mr. F. A. Lucas in *Natural Science*, January, 1894.

a very important physiological purpose.[1] Divers are frequently exposed to great cold when in the water. They are protected against this by a peculiarly thick coat of feathers, and by a deep layer of fat beneath the skin ; and I cannot help thinking that the marrow also helps to maintain their warmth.   In other animals it is held to be the birthplace of a large proportion of the red blood-corpuscles, and unless they are very thick in the blood, a high temperature cannot be maintained. But if the marrow is a factory of red corpuscles, what substitute for this have birds whose chief bones have only a thin lining of marrow from which the output must be small?   Though, as a rule, exposed to less cold than diving-birds, they show in severe weather a very great power of generating heat.   Birds as a class have more red corpuscles than any other animal.   Is the spleen, which in emergencies (*e.g.* when much blood is lost) is a great red corpuscle factory, more developed in birds which have little or no marrow ? The vital organs are sometimes strangely versatile. When an animal's spleen is removed, its work is done somewhere else in the body and no ill effects are felt.

Putting physiology out of sight, I am going now to consider why it is that among birds of powerful flight we find differences so great in the amount of aeration, and why such a poor flyer as the Hornbill is, in respect of bones, so well equipped for aerial navigation.   To put physiology aside, is to assume that if

[1] Physiology is the science which aims at explaining the work done by the different organs of the body.   It deals with all the processes which maintain life.

hollow bones are advantageous to a bird, natural selection can bring it about that they become hollow and that somehow the bird is able to dispense with the marrow. This would be a bold assumption, did we not know it to be an accomplished fact. The bones are hollow, and there is no want of life in the birds.

We shall find that pneumaticity in a bone implies greater girth in proportion to its length, and consequently greater strength ; and that a decrease of weight has accompanied the increase of strength, mainly through the drying up of the marrow, but partly through a reduction, if we allow for the increased size of the bones, in the thickness of the hard osseous shell. I shall give first a few measurements to show that in the case of birds whose skeletons have little or no aeration, the girth of the bones is, relatively to the bulk and weight of the body, considerably less.

Bones highly pneumatic. Girth of humerus.	ins.	Bones very little or not at all aerated. Girth of humerus.	ins.
Screamer	$1\frac{5}{8}$	Logger-headed Duck	$1\frac{1}{16}$
Rhinoceros Hornbill	$1\frac{3}{8}$	Scoter Duck	$\frac{13}{16}$
Golden Eagle	$1\frac{5}{8}$	Nestor Parrot	$\frac{3}{4}$
Vulture Monachus	$2\frac{1}{4}$	Red-throated Diver	1
Marabou Stork	$2\frac{5}{8}$	Spur-winged Goose	$1\frac{5}{16}$

These measurements speak for themselves, even without any exact statement of the weights of the birds ; but the following illustration will do more to explain the problem of hollow bones. The shoulder bones of a Skua Gull, which has scarcely any aeration, of a vociferous Sea Eagle, and a Hornbill, both of which are highly pneumatic, are placed side by side. The

greater girth of the hollow bones in proportion to their
length is at once obvious.   But to bring this out still
more clearly, I have taken the wing bones of the Skua

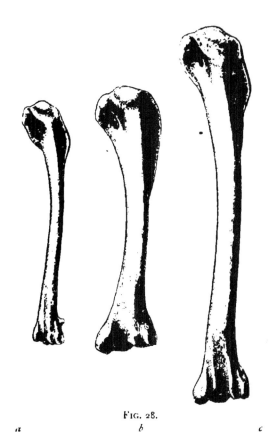

FIG. 28.

a   *b*   *c*

Humerus of Pomatorhine Skua (*a*); Rhinoceros Hornbill (*b*); and Vociferous Sea
Eagle (*c*).   Drawn to scale.

as the standard, and calculated what would have been
the length of the same bones and of the whole wing in
the Sea Eagle and the Hornbill, if they had been built
upon the same lines :

	Girth of Humerus.	Humerus.		Aggregate Length of Wing Bones.	
		Actual Length.	Length proportionate to Girth.	Actual Length.	Length proportionate to Girth of Humerus.
Skua . .	$\frac{25}{32}$ inches	$4\frac{3}{8}$ inches	$4\frac{1}{8}$ inches	$13\frac{3}{4}$	$13\frac{5}{8}$
Sea Eagle	$1\frac{5}{16}$,,	$6\frac{1}{4}$.,	$7\frac{7}{16}$,,	$20\frac{7}{16}$	$22\frac{1}{20}$
Rhinoceros Hornbill	$1\frac{3}{8}$,,	$4\frac{5}{8}$.,	$7\frac{7}{16}$,,	$15\frac{7}{8}$	$23\frac{49}{60}$

Thus, if in the Sea Eagle's humerus length were proportioned to girth, the bone would be more than half an inch longer ; on the same principle the aggregate length of the wing bones would be greater by more than one and a half inch ; the Hornbill's wing would be lengthened by more than eight inches, its humerus by more than three ! If now we take a fine saw and cut the humeri of the Skua and the Sea Eagle from end to end, we shall find that the walls of the latter are not thicker in proportion to the greater girth of the bone. The larger bone, compared with the small one, has a girth two thirds as great again, a thickness of wall only one third as great again.[1] We can now see why small birds have so little aeration. In their case, there would be no great reduction of weight since the exterior shell of the bones forms a great part of their bulk. In the case of a larger bird, with bones many times multiplied in size, but the thickness of the walls increased comparatively little, the removal of the

[1] The girths are in the ratio of 25 : 42 ; while 3 : 4 represents the ratio of the thickness of the walls, the measurements being $\frac{3}{100}$ and $\frac{4}{100}$ of an inch.

marrow will be a great advantage. This will be clear
if we take two cubes, a side of one of which is twice
the length of a side of the other.

Then the face is four times as large and the cubic
contents eight times as large. This will be true of other
figures besides cubes, so that if the average girth of one
bone be double that of another, and if the length also be
double, its cubic contents will be approximately eight

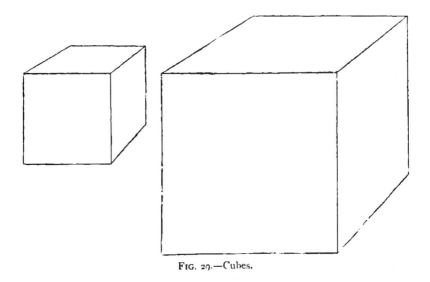

FIG. 29.—Cubes.

times as great; and as the walls do not thicken in proportion to the increased girth, nearly all the enlarged
interior can be filled with air. Clearly, then, a large
bird has much more to gain by dispensing with marrow
than a small one.

Thus the Eagle has gained in point of lightness. It
must also have gained in point of strength, for increased length of wing means an altogether disproportionate increase of work. The longer the wing,

I

the greater the pace at which its extremity will move ; if the velocity is doubled, it is well known that the resistance of the air is far more than doubled, so that an increase of strength is required that is altogether out of proportion to the increase of length. This will be made clearer, when we come to the subject of flight (see p. 175).

The Hornbills are a puzzle. The extreme shortness of the hand bones, a ridiculous anticlimax following upon so grand an ulna and so portentous a humerus, might suggest that they were once better flyers, and that the wing is slowly undergoing reduction. But the mountainous beak seems to show that colossal bones are an ancient heritage of the family, that even feeble flight might have been difficult had they not become hollow, and that existing Hornbills fly quite as well as their ancestors. In either case they have been great gainers by aeration.

The Ostrich and its allies present another difficulty. But here too it may be said that by means of pneumaticity great strength has been combined with lightness in a way that with solid bones would have been impossible.

Any one who wishes to realise the relation, in birds' bones, of slimness to solidity, and of large girth to aeration, should inspect collections such as those at the Royal College of Surgeons, or at the Natural History Museum at South Kensington, where a large number representing different families may be seen side by side. It is easy then to see that big long-winged birds have wing bones thicker in proportion to their length in order to bear the far greater strain upon them, while the aeration of the bones has obviated the natural increase of weight which would have been a serious hindrance. But there remains the perplexing physiological problem : what organ of the body does the work that, in mammals, and, presumably, in birds that have solid bones, is done by the marrow ?[1]

The Kidneys.

In man, as remarked above, three organs—the skin, the lungs, and the kidneys—divide between them the work of eliminating waste products from the body. The skin disposes of a great deal of water and a little carbonic acid ; the lungs of carbonic acid and water, but water to a much less extent than the skin ; the kidneys of urea, uric acid (much nitrogen in both, the débris of the tissues) and water. As these three are allied organs, doing work that is similar, to some extent actually the same, it might be expected that in birds, since their skin is not an excretory organ, the other two would be unusually active. With the lungs we have seen that this is the case. And the kidneys are very large ; they will be found lying behind the lungs against the pelvis—long dark bodies. Yet they do not undertake all the work that they do in mammals. They are very active in excreting urea and uric acid ; but, as is the case with snakes, it is in a nearly solid form, the product of their activity being easily dis-

[1] On " Aeration of Bones " see Fürbringer, *Morphologie und Systematik der Vögel*, especially pp. 47 and 133 ; Strasser, *Morphologisches Jahrbuch* (Leipzig, 1877) ; Dr. Crisp, *Proc. Zool. Society*, 1857. .

tinguishable by its whiteness. Upon the lungs alone must fall the duty of getting rid of superfluous water in any large quantity.

The Nerves.

About the nerves it is unnecessary to say much, since they do not differ very materially from those of mammals. The spinal cord is the great trunk nerve which sends out branches on either side between the vertebræ. It broadens out and forms part of the back of the brain. There is also another system of nerves called the Sympathetic, which lies in front of the vertebral column, and which acts mainly on the intestines and blood vessels, not on the voluntary muscles. It is connected with the spinal cord and so with the brain. Nerves are called afferent and efferent. When any part of the body comes into contact with anything that necessitates prompt action—for instance, red-hot iron— the afferent nerve carries the news to the spinal cord, and so to the brain. The efferent nerve causes the requisite muscular movements. In every warm-blooded animal the nerves are highly developed. Otherwise a highly-organised brain would be of little use. The keenness of sight and hearing for which birds are remarkable shows the perfection of their nervous system. Great strength may co-exist with sluggish nerves, as in a crocodile. But when a Swallow catches sight of a gnat, and in less than a second has taken all the necessary steps—eye communicating with brain, brain directing the proper adjustment of the muscles of wings, tail, neck, and beak—for an unerring dart and snap at the victim, he has proved that he possesses nerves of the first order.[1]

The Brain.

The subject is a very difficult one. It is impossible as yet to impart interest to it by allotting to each part of the brain its special function. Some progress is being made in this by methods of study that are scientific and dependable, but, at the same time, slow and laborious. It is hardly necessary to say that phrenology which mapped out the skull into provinces, like an old and well-known country, not like a half-explored continent, has gone to the limbo where all systems founded on mere guesswork must go.

If a bird's fragile skull be removed carefully, so as to leave the brain uninjured, the posterior part, the cerebellum (*cb*, Fig. 30), will be easily distinguished ; in contact with it at their hinder ends are two large bodies that make up nearly the whole of the top of the brain. These are the cerebral hemispheres, the larger development of which makes a bird's brain so different from a reptile's (*c.h*). In them all the higher faculties reside. If they are severely injured or removed, there is no more intelligence, memory, or voluntary movement. There is only what is called reflex action such as is called forth in a hydra or a coral animal when food touches its tentacles ; they close upon it without consciousness or intention on the

[1] See Coues' *Field and General Ornithology*, p. 257 and onward.

animal's part.   In the same way when the eyes wink
at a sudden flash of light, we call the action reflex.
The Frog, whose cerebral hemispheres are no longer
in their place, will move its foot when it is irritated :
of thus much, lower parts of the brain are capable.

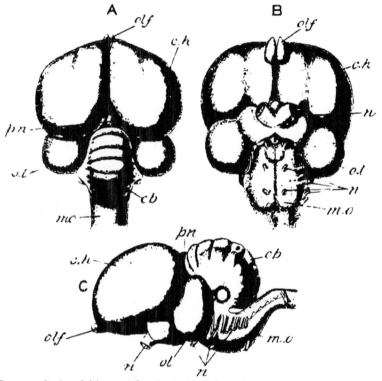

FIG. 30.—Brain of Pigeon (after Parker) ; A from above ; B from below ; C from
left side (×2); cb cerebellum; c.h. cerebral hemispheres; m.o. Medulla Oblongata;
n roots of cerebral nerves : o.l. optic lobes ; olf olfactory lobes ; pn pineal body.

If the whole brain is removed and only the spinal
cord is left, even breathing will not continue.   When
there is much intellectual power, as in man, the
hemispheres are highly convoluted—i.e., they are a
mass of folds and wrinkles.   When the bird's skull is

removed, one is struck with the smoothness of the brain.

The olfactory lobes (olf.), in which lies the sense of smell, are small cone-shaped objects which project from underneath the front end of the hemispheres, their smallness suggesting that birds depend little on this sense. Formerly it was thought that vultures "scented the carrion from afar," but Darwin showed by experiment that this was not the case. He wrapped some meat in paper, and put it near some condors that were tethered in a garden. When it was only a yard off him, an old cock bird "looked at it for a moment with attention, but then regarded it no more."[1] It was pushed closer and closer till at last it touched his beak, when the paper was "torn off with fury."

The optic lobes (o.l.) are many times larger—two rather egg-shaped bodies at the sides of the brain, partly below the hemispheres. Their size suggests, what is really the case, that the vulture finds his food by sight. His eyes sweep the whole country round as he flies, and when he swoops down upon a carcass he is seen by numbers of others who quickly follow.

Towards the back of the brain between and under the hemispheres lies a small oval object called the pineal gland or body (pn.). What may now be its function, if it has any, is unknown. Formerly it is believed to have been a central eye. In the bird's skull, in which the fusion of bones is so marked a characteristic, we should not expect to find any external evidence of this rudimentary organ. But in lizards a hole in the

[1] Darwin's *Journal of Researches*, chap. ix. (p. 133, Minerva ed.).

front central part of the skull bears witness to its existence. In the Hatteria, the now rare New Zealand lizard, this hole is very large. As long ago as 1829 it was noticed that in the Sand Lizard (Lacerta agilis) one of the scales at this point was quite unlike the rest. In 1884 it was first suggested that the pineal body was a rudimentary eye—*i.e.*, an eye that had become functionless. It has now been examined in various reptiles; and partly in one, partly in another, the lens, the retina, and the nerves, all the chief characters of an eye, have been identified. But in one important point, which I shall explain when I come to what are commonly known as eyes, it is the eye of an invertebrate, not of a vertebrate animal. We must go to insects or to crustaceans to find its fellow. In birds it has lost all resemblance to an eye, and it has been covered by the hemispheres which extend over and in front of it. In man it is also present, and Descartes suggested that this mysterious object, about the size of a hazel-nut, might be the seat of the soul.

If the question be asked what any animal wants with two different kinds of eyes, it is not easy to answer positively. We can say that many insects have compound eyes with hundreds of facets as well as simple eyes (ocelli), the latter having, probably, very defective sight, extending only to the very nearest objects. The lower crustaceans have eyes and a central ocellus; but in the higher members of the class, such as the crayfish, the ocellus has been lost. Possibly in vertebrates, before the two eyes as we know them had attained to their present perfection

in focussing, a central eye with a very near range may
have saved its owner occasional hard knocks against
objects close at hand when its superior organs of vision
were gazing upon some more distant scene.[1]

Of the lower parts of the brain, I do not intend
to say much. The medulla oblongata, however (m.o.
in Fig. 30), must not be passed over. It forms the
lowest part of the brain, being really a continuation
of the spinal cord. We have already seen that in it
mainly centre the vaso-motor nerves, which govern the
arteries and so regulate the flow of blood. And
through it pass all of the twelve pairs of nerves
which proceed from the brain, except two, the optic
and olfactory; and these two are not, strictly
speaking, nerves, but prolongations of the brain.
The muscles that move the eyes, the muscles of
the face, the tongue, the larynx, the lungs, the liver,
and stomach work at the bidding of nerves that arise
from the medulla oblongata.

The Eye.

In most essentials the bird's eye is formed on the
same plan as our own. It is a camera at the back of
which is a nerve which expands into what is called
the retina; the retina is sensitive to light, and the
image formed upon it is conveyed by the nerve to the
brain, where the impulse given to the nerve becomes
sensation—where, that is, sight actually takes place.

Before describing the eye more particularly, I wish

[1] For a description of the pineal body see Lubbock's *Senses
of Animals*

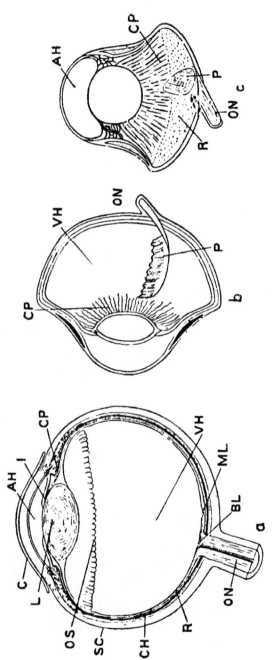

FIG. 31.—(a) Human Eye—after Huxley; (b) of typical bird—after Coues; (c) of owl—after Gadow; AH, Aqueous Humour; BL, Blind Spot; C, Cornea; CH. Choroid: CP, Ciliary Processes; I, Iris; L, Lens; ML, Macula Lutea; ON, Optic Nerve; OS. Ora Serrata, line along which the Retina ends; P, Pecten; R, Retina; SC, Sclerotic; VH, Vitreous Humour. It is important to remember that the Ciliary Processes, like the Iris, form a ring of muscle.

to distinguish sight from mere sensitiveness to light.
Thus much even an earthworm possesses, for when at
night the light of a lantern is thrown upon him he
hurries into his hole. This is quite different from
seeing a definite image of things. With our eyes
shut, we can tell whether we are in a bright light or
in the dark, and the earthworm has no power beyond
this. An insect's compound eye, again, is formed on
quite a different principle from the eyes of vertebrate
animals. It has a number of tiny facets beneath
which are sensitive cells, so that a mosaic picture is
formed. There can be no doubt that eyes of this
description are very inferior to our own. Among
their great defects is this, that they have no power
of adjusting themselves to different distances. To
return to the vertebrate eye. It is a camera with a
biconvex lens in front—*i.e.*, a lens rounded outwards on
both sides. If a lens of this kind (a common magni-
fying glass will do well) be taken and a candle be
held in front of it, an inverted image of the flame
will be thrown upon the wall. The room must be
darkened except for the candle, and you must be
careful to get the right focus—*i.e.*, to hold the lens at
such a distance from the wall, and the candle at such
a distance from the lens, that the image is clear.
The less convex the lens, the further away you
must hold the candle, and *vice versâ*. Here, then,
we have one means of focussing objects at different
distances; we use lenses of various degrees of
convexity.

If the lens is to form a really clear image the light
must fall upon it only from in front; rays from the

sides must be carefully screened off, and of course the box of the camera must be impervious to light. The remaining essential is a sensitive plate at the back of the camera on which the image is formed. All these parts are represented in the eye. The eyeball is the box of the camera ; it is tough and untransparent, and is called the Sclerotic (SC, σκληρὸς = hard), only in front it becomes transparent, and is known as the Cornea (C). Side rays are shut out by a circular curtain, the Iris (I), with a hole in the middle, the Pupil, which can be seen opening and contracting to regulate the amount of light admitted. There is a crystalline lens (L) of great elasticity, which by the action of the muscles which suspend it is made more or less convex so as to focus for objects at different distances. In front, between the cornea and the lens, is a fluid called the aqueous humour (AH), and behind the lens is the less fluid vitreous humour (VII). The rays of light that fall upon the eyes are refracted or bent by the curved surface of the cornea, then by the anterior surface of the lens, and again when they pass from the lens into the vitreous humour. The cornea, the aqueous humour, the crystalline lens, and the vitreous humour may be, therefore, looked upon as making one compound lens. But of the component parts the crystalline lens is far the most important, since it alone has the power of accommodation—*i.e.*, of adjusting itself to different distances.

The sensitive plate at the back of this living camera is called, as I have said, the retina (R). Though thinner than tissue paper, it is made up of nine distinct layers, and it is the hindmost of these on which is formed the picture of the world without. It is made up of very delicate rods and cones—30,000,000 of the former and 3,000,000 of the latter in the human eye, at the lowest estimate. On these millions of sensitive points the image is formed. They extend over the back of the eyeball, but there is a central mark, called the Macula Lutea (ML) or yellow spot, which is the region of clearest vision. The entrance of the nerve is rather towards the nose (ON), and at this point the eye is blind, as a simple experiment will show (BL).

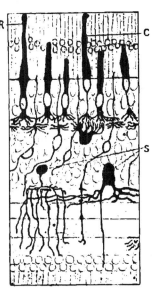

Hold the book at arm's length, close the left eye, and fix the right upon the cross mark, the image of which will fall upon the Macula Lutea. The dot will be also visible. Now move the book slowly towards you, and the image of the dot must at length fall upon the point where the nerve enters the eye. At this moment the

Fig. 32.—Section of Retina of duck (after Cajal); C, Cone; R, Rod; S, cells of supporting tissues.

+

dot will disappear, then again at a nearer distance come again into view, as the image of it gets once more clear of the blind spot. The rods and cones cover the whole of the back of the eye, except this one point. Another experiment shows that it is the hindmost layer of the retina that is sensitive. Let a candle

be the only light in the room. Get some one to hold
it by the side of your eye, and with the help
of a lens to focus the rays upon it. Look at the wall,
which must be uniformly coloured. The shadows of
the blood vessels which ramify in the retina in front of
the rods and cones will be distinctly visible. Not only
is it the hindmost layer on which light makes itself
felt, but the rods and cones look backward. In the
invertebrate eye the retina looks forward, and its front
surface is the sensitive one. In this important point
the pineal body is the eye of an invertebrate.[1] Behind
the retina is a deep layer of dark pigment, called the
Choroid (CH); in this the rays after passing the sensitive
cells are absorbed. Were they reflected from one part
of the retina to another, any clearness of vision would
be impossible. But it would be rash to say that the
pigment exists for the sole purpose of preventing
reflection. This coloured layer is continued in front, and
forms the round curtain called the Iris, and, besides this,
where the sclerotic or white of the eye passes into the
transparent cornea, it sends out a number of muscular
frills, which lie behind the iris and which are separate
from it except that they spring from the same point ;
for the Iris, like these frills or, as they are called, ciliary
processes (CP), arises, as I have said, from the choroid
and is attached to the sclerotic at its margin close to
the cornea. It is these ciliary processes, consisting of
striated or voluntary muscle, which enable the eye to

---

[1] See Grenacher's *Schorgan der Arthropoden.* Sir John
Lubbock, by an oversight, has stated in his *Senses of Animals*
that the pigment lies in front of the sensitive cells (retina) in
the eyes of vertebrates. This of course cannot be so.

focus. When they contract the choroid is drawn forward, the strain upon the lens is reduced, and, consequently, its surface becomes more rounded. This is the process that takes place when the sight is adjusted for near objects. At the same time the Iris contracts and lessens the amount of light admitted. This wonderful curtain adapts itself to all circumstances : involuntarily, by a reflex action we reduce the size of the pupil when a strong light falls upon the eye ; voluntarily, though habit makes the action unconscious, and by calling into play a different set of nerves, we contract it, when we cast our eyes upon a near object.

It is now time to mention some of the peculiarities of the bird's eye. The eyeball is not so globular as in man ; in front it is much contracted, behind it opens out like a decanter ; the cornea is highly curved. In birds of prey, which see great distances, the front surface of the lens is nearly flat ; in owls, on the contrary, it is much rounded, and at the same time the pupil is very large to admit as much moonlight as possible.

At the back of the eye, springing from the entrance of the nerve, is a peculiar fanlike object, the Pecten, which projects into the eyeball (P). It is full of blood vessels, and is deeply pigmented, like the choroid to which it is akin in structure. It is thought to nourish the vitreous humour ; certainly it does not push the lens forward for focussing purposes as some writers have maintained. Any one who examines it, not in a diagram, but in the eye itself, will find that it is far too limp to produce

any such effect. It is wanting, so far as is known, in
only one bird—the New Zealand Apteryx. It is found
in some reptiles, but always less developed than in
birds. It is odd that it does not interfere seriously
with the access of light to the retina. Besides the
central "yellow spot," which however is not absolutely
central, birds have a second similar spot more towards
the outer side of the eye. It has been thought that,
of the four spots thus possessed by the two eyes, two
are used together for binocular, and two separately for
monocular vision. The retina of a bird or a reptile
contrasts with that of a man in another point : the
cones exceed the rods in number.[1] The nictitating
membrane most people have heard of ; but it is often
imagined that it is the privilege of the eagle alone to
possess it, and that its object is to enable him to gaze
at the sun. As a fact, it is found in all birds and
reptiles. Watch the eye of any bird, and before long
you will see a film pass over it and in a moment vanish.
This is the nictitating membrane, which lies in the
front angle of the eye, and can be found without much
difficulty when the bird is dead. Some birds seem to
have great power of moving the Iris, a movement that
in most human beings is always involuntary, though
sometimes it is caused by nerves which, except for the
force of habit, are believed to be subject to our will. If
a Parrot's eye be watched, the pupil may be seen to
contract till it is quite small, though the light remains
as it was, and though the bird, apparently, continues to

---

[1] See Fürbringer's *Morphologie und Systematik der Vögel*, p.
1069.

look at the same object. Moreover it is maintained [1]
that the muscles of the Iris in the Falcon may be seen
to contract without any alteration in the size of the
pupil ensuing, the outer ring seeming to work separately
from the inner ; it is suggested that the work of this
outer ring is to aid in focussing the eye. I have
watched the eyes of Falcons, Eagles, and other birds of
prey long and carefully, and I do not feel certain that I
have seen this. But an eagle in a cage has very little
need of sudden change of focus. It is far different
when he swoops from a great height upon his prey,
and, no doubt, keeps him clearly in view as he falls
like a thunderbolt upon him. It is certain that the
Iris in birds is highly muscular ; and, moreover, both in
birds and in reptiles the muscle is striated, not smooth
as in mammals. This is evidence that its action is
voluntary, and, perhaps, that it is more powerful. A
natural result of the tightening of the belt of muscle
round the lens would be to round it outwards—*i.e.*, focus
the eye for near objects. On the whole it seems probable that the Iris in birds is not only a curtain to
regulate the amount of light admitted, but that it aids
the ciliary muscles in the work of focussing.

The size of the eye varies very much in different
species, and, as a rule, the power of sight seems to vary
in proportion. Here are some figures which bring
this out clearly.[2] In the Owl, the two eyes cleared of
muscle weigh $\frac{1}{33}$ of the whole body, in the Falcon
$\frac{1}{35}$, in the Woodpecker $\frac{1}{73}$, in the Peacock $\frac{1}{320}$, in the
Goose $\frac{1}{567}$. In the Apteryx, a night feeder like the Owl,

---

[1] See Bronn's *Thier-Reich*, vol. " Aves," p. 434.
[2] *Ibid*, p. 425.

K

the eyes are very small, but the Apteryx is the one bird in which the nostrils open at the end of the beak : it trusts more to scent and touch than to sight.

Birds' keenness of sight is most remarkable. Vultures, as I have already mentioned, descry their prey from enormous distances. A Gannet, flying 100 feet or more above the sea, will distinguish a fish near the surface from the surrounding water which it so nearly resembles, and pounce upon it. It is a common amusement on a steamer to feed the gulls that follow the boat with small pieces of biscuit, which, when thrown, float, often invisible to the human eye, in the wilderness of foam which covers all the wake of the ship. The gulls, flying some thirty or forty feet above the water, will swoop down upon them with unerring aim. Often, when you think they have missed a small fragment, they will at last find it far in the rear of the vessel.

The colours of birds' eyes are very various. In the Shag the Iris is emerald green ; in the green-billed Toucan, light green of the same shade as the beak ; in the Ariel Toucan, like the tip of the beak, pale blue ; in the Black Stork deep red ; in the Eagle Owl red-orange ; in the Javan Fish Owl light yellow ; in the Indian Kite nearly white.

The following examples would seem to show that dark plumage implies a dark shade of colour in the Iris, and *vice versâ*.

	Plumage.	Iris.
Angolan Vulture	Wing coverts white	Pale almost to whiteness.
A Cockatoo	Dark blue	Dark brown.
Ditto	Light blue	Nearly white.

	Plumage.	Iris.
Red-backed Buzzard	To a great extent light brown	Light brown.
Cinereous Vulture	Dusky	Dark brown.
Foster's Milvago	Mainly black	Very dark.
Shag	Dark with green gloss	Emerald green.
Indian Kite	A good many whitish feathers	Nearly white.
Indian Owl	Much of it black	Dark brown.
Flamingo	Light pink	Light yellow.
Javan Fish Owl	Some light brown on nearly all its feathers	Bright light yellow.

But the eye is not always light or dark according to the shade of the plumage. The Crowned Pigeon, whose plumage is a light blue-gray, has eyes of a rich scarlet, just the colour of holly-berries. For the first few months of his life, the Gannet's eyes are almost black, but they soon turn to a pale, almost white, hue, long before he has exchanged the dusky-gray attire of his youth for the snow-white of his maturity. As a rule the Iris is brown in young birds. The brighter tints come with adult years, and in some species they are limited to the male.[1]

The Ear.

I shall first briefly describe the main features of the human ear, then point out the chief differences between it and the same organ in birds. The essential part is in the sidewall of the skull ; and here there is a bony "labyrinth" consisting of three winding tubes of bone, which are filled with fluid (L, in fig. 33). There is

[1] Dr. Gadow (Newton's *Dict. of Birds*, vol. i., p. 230) refers to a paper on this subject by Th. A. Bruhin in *Zool. Garten*, 1870, pp. 290-295, which I have not read.

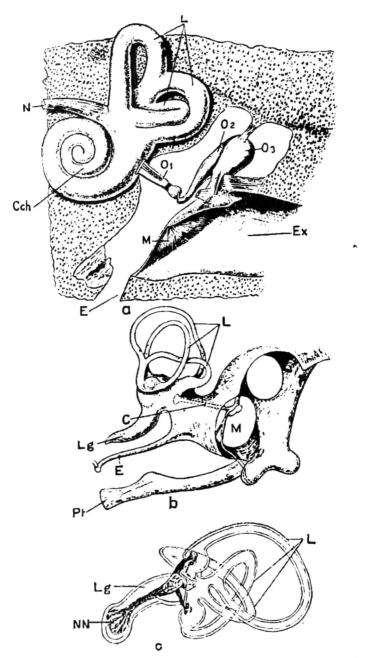

FIG. 33. (a) Human ear—diagrammatic ; (b) ear of Owl, after Gadow ; (c) of Thrush, after Retzius.

c, Columella ; cch, Cochlea ; E, Eustachian tube ; EX, outer opening of Ear ; L, Labyrinth ; Lg, Lagena ; M, Membrane, closing the drum ; N, entrance of auditory nerve ; NN, Nerve endings ; o 1, 2, 3, the three Ossicles, Stapes, Incus, Malleus ; PT, Pterygoid bone.

also a great extension, called, because it is shaped like a spiral shell, the cochlea, and into this too the fluid extends. A membranous bag, also filled with fluid, extends throughout the ramifications of the cochlea and the labyrinth. On the inside of the membranous bag within the labyrinth, at certain points where it is attached to the bony wall, are hairs which are believed to communicate with the nerve of hearing. So far, I have been describing the ear proper. The rest of the machinery has for its object the communication of the vibrations of sound to the fluid in the bony labyrinth, from which they pass to that in the membranous bag which lies in it, from that to the hairs which connect with the nerve. The apparatus for conveying sound vibrations to the labyrinth is rather complicated. There is, to begin with, a membrane which stretches across the external aperture of the ear. When a sound sets the air moving in waves, which we speak of as vibrations, they strike against the membrane. To this membrane and the chamber behind is given the name of the drum of the ear, and on the further side of the drum is the labyrinth described above. Three bones united together have their one end resting against the outer membrane just mentioned, the other against another membrane that at one point takes the place of bone in the bony labyrinth. Thus, the vibrations of the outer membrane are transmitted by the united three bones to the window of membrane in the bony wall of the labyrinth, from there to the fluid in the labyrinth, next to the fluid within the membranous bag, and lastly to the hairs within the bag that connect with the nerve.

A few more points must be mentioned. The bony labyrinth has a second window of membrane, and this, yielding, allows greater vibrations to be imparted to the fluid. In the cochlea, are very peculiar cells, called the rods or pillars of Corti, forming two rows all along the spiral, in all from four to six thousand of them. They lie upon the inside of the membranous bag, following the line along which it comes into contact with the wall of bone. They stand leaning on one another, and rather remind one of the keys of a piano. There are delicate hairs at their ends. It is possible that each of these rods vibrates to a certain note and no other. If you put on a table several tuning forks which have different pitches, and if you set vibrating another, then if one of those on the table is of the same pitch, it also will vibrate. The rest will be motionless and silent. So these rods of Corti have been thought to respond each to a certain note. In the labyrinth there are no similar cells, and it has been suggested that the membrane there is sensitive only to noise as distinguished from music.

It is not known exactly to what part of the brain the nerve of hearing leads—*i.e.* where we have consciousness of sound.

The ear has two openings, the external one with which every one is familiar, and another through what is called the Eustachian tube to the mouth (E). The two tubes from either ear unite and open into the roof of the mouth just behind the two openings from the nasal passages.

I must now describe the main differences between the human ear and the bird's.

(1) No species of bird has what can properly be called an external ear. The Owl has a flap of skin, forming a kind of valve, by which it is said that it can close the ear at pleasure. Certainly it possesses muscles for this purpose. Often the ear valve is larger on one side than the other, the whole skull being at the same time lopsided. During the breeding season, the cock Capercailzie has moments of complete deafness, owing to a fold of skin which becomes swollen with blood and closes the opening of the ear. In other species the flap of skin is very little developed.

(2) The three small bones which in the human ear convey the vibrations of sound from the membrane which forms the outer wall of the drum of the ear to the inner membrane that forms a window in the bony labyrinth are represented in birds by one bone, the columella (C). But it is almost certain that this is formed by a fusion of three, corresponding to those which we find in mammals. It was usual, till recently, to see in the quadrate bone, to which the lower jaw of birds and reptiles is hinged, one of the three bones of the mammalian ear. If these three are combined in the columella, where are we to look for the quadrate in man and other mammals? The best authorities are of opinion that it is represented only by an insignificant ring of bone, called the annulus, which forms a frame for the membrane of the drum of the ear.

(3) In place of the spiral cochlea birds have a slightly curved bone to which the name of the lagena has been given (Lg). It is similar in reptiles.

(4) The absence of the organ of Corti in the bird's ear is a remarkable fact. It is true there is a very

delicate membrane, no doubt sensitive to sound, in the corresponding place. But the distinctive pillars or rods, leaning upon one another and forming arches, are not there. It has been held, as I have said above, that in those cells lies the power of distinguishing nice differences of tone ; in fact, that when we say of some one that he has "an ear for music," we speak of what is supposed to depend on a high development of the organ of Corti. And yet we cannot imagine that birds can be such good singers without having "good ears." Power of appreciation must accompany power of song. The fact is that the ear, whether in mammals or in birds, is an extremely complicated organ about which there is much to learn, and the absence of the pillars of Corti in birds is unexplained.

There can be no two opinions about the acuteness of birds' sense of hearing. It is fine to see an old Heron, put on the alert, at the slightest sound of a human foot, by his wary ears, turn in the direction whence the sound comes his equally wary eye. The Curlew is all ears. The Thrush hears the worm moving beneath the ground and waits for his appearance above the surface.

The Organ of Voice.

As I have said above, a bird's upper larynx at the top of the trachea or windpipe has no vocal chords, and is, therefore, incapable of producing sound though tone may be raised or lowered by it. There is a lower larynx, to which the name of syrinx is commonly given, the mechanism of which is, in all

important respects, the same as that of the human
larynx. There are two membranes corresponding to
those called in man the vocal chords, which can
be stretched tight, and made parallel to one another.
When thus stretched, they are set vibrating by the
passage of the air between them, and a note is produced. The syrinx is in principle a reed instrument,

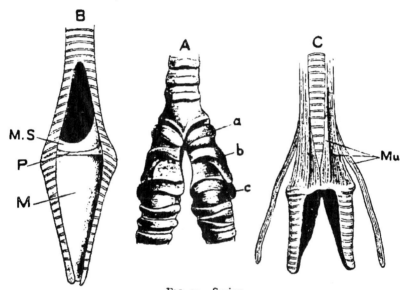

FIG. 34.—Syrinx.

Raven, A with bronchi ; a, b, c, half-rings ; where the two bronchi face each other
there is nothing but membrane. B, side view ; the outer part of the lower end of the
trachea and of the nearer bronchus being cut away ; M, Membranous inner wall of
bronchus ; M.S, Membrana semilunaris ; P, Pessulus ; C, Muscles of Syrinx ; Mu,
Muscles (after Owen).

though, in the relative position of the vibrating membranes thus set edge to edge, it is, as far as I know,
unlike every instrument commonly used. There are
three varieties of syrinx, distinguished by their different
positions in the trachea or bronchi, but I shall describe
only the one which is by far the most common.

Near to the point where the windpipe divides to form

the two bronchi leading to either lung, a bony enlarge-
ment·is found, formed partly from the lower rings
of the windpipe, partly from the upper ones of
the bronchi. The latter on the inner side are of
membrane only. A bar of bone, the pessulus (P in
fig. 34 B), formed where the sides of the two bronchi
meet, passes across the syrinx from front to back.
From this bar a membrane, scalloped like a half-moon
on its outer edge, the membrana semilunaris (M.S. in
fig. 34 B), extends some way across the mouth of the
bronchus. Opposite to it from the outer wall of the
syrinx projects another membrane. On the other
side of the pessulus is a similar crescent-shaped membrane with another facing it. Thus, there are two
pairs of membranes, and there are muscles which can
tighten each pair and make the edges parallel. Many
birds have only two pairs of muscles for this purpose,
one pair passing to the trachea from the clavicles, the
other from the breastbone. But the majority of them
have at least one additional pair of syrinx muscles,
some as many as seven pairs, all having both points
of attachment on the trachea. Long vocal chords
make a low voice, short ones a high voice. Hence
treble notes are characteristic of most birds and other
small creatures. By tightening the chords the tone is
raised, by relaxing them it is lowered. The fact that
birds have so little range of voice seems to show that
the tension does not vary very much. The harsh, gruff
note of the Nightingale, and the abortive attempts of
the Cuckoo, when their vocal time is past, may be due
to the relaxation of the chords.

The chief difference between the syrinx of a songster

and that of an unmusical bird is that the muscles
of the former are, in most cases, more numerous and
stronger. The syrinx of the Skylark is almost a ball
of muscle, whereas the Pigeon's has but very little
to show. But it is very remarkable how muscular a
syrinx some few non-singers have. Among these are
the Crow and the Raven. Perhaps a more striking
instance is that of the Bullfinch who sings very feebly
in the wild state. The hen-bird also, who, I believe,
is almost voiceless, has highly developed voice muscles.
In the cock-bird they have clearly not lost their power,
for in captivity he becomes a splendid vocalist.
However first-rate the syrinx and its muscles may be,
it is wonderful that so small a creature as, for instance,
a Nightingale, can produce such an amount of voice.
Even the Wren sends out a flood of powerful notes.
The Thrush's song is wonderful as a *tour de force*.
If the bird were nothing but a musical instrument, the
volume of sound sent forth would be astonishing ; and
when we consider the variety of functions which its
small body has to perform its musical powers supply
far greater reason for wonder. The air-sacks, no doubt,
are a great assistance. Those great reservoirs of air
must make it easier for the bird to avoid the awkward
crises that come to the untrained human vocalist
when he finds, at the moment his grandest notes are
expected of him, that his voice is becoming thin and
feeble for want of breath. The trachea sometimes
takes strange forms which might be thought to influence the voice. In the Drake, just in front of the syrinx,
it has a big box-like appendage, which looks as if it
might be intended to give the voice greater resonance.

This great air-chamber is entirely wanting in the Duck. Yet the quack of the Duck is loud and sonorous, that of the Drake is thin and without any body in it. In some species of Crane, the trachea winds round about within the keel of the breastbone, which is

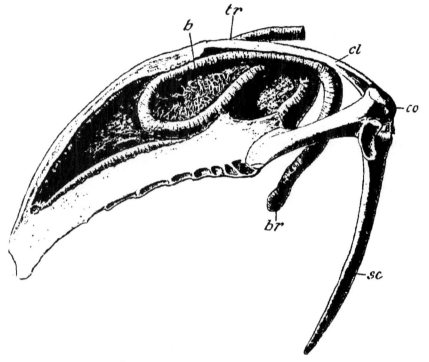

FIG. 35, showing convolutions of Trachea of Mantchurian Crane.
b, Network of bones ; *br*, Trachea dividing into two bronchi; *cl*, Clavicle; *co*, Coracoid ; *sc*, Scapula ; *tr*, Trachea at entrance into keel.

formed of two thin sheets with, in places, a light bony network in between : after all these windings it at length divides and enters the lungs. Cranes have a loud and striking crow, but it is not nearly so striking as the crow of the barndoor Cock, whose windpipe takes the shortest course to the lungs. The whistling

Swan shows convolutions of the trachea very similar
to those of the Crane. Whatever other purpose it may
serve, the long coiled windpipe ensures the thorough
warming of the air before it reaches the lungs.

Muscles and Tendons.

To muscles all movement in the body is due.
When acted on by the motor nerves they contract
and become shorter, with the result that the bone or
other organ connected with them is moved. The
nerve, in reality, gives a series of small shocks which
owing to the elasticity of the muscle, result in one
movement. The diminution in length of the contracting muscle is balanced by an increase in breadth
and thickness. Great as its force is, it is not a perfect
machine. Like a steam-engine it only converts a
fraction of its total energy into work, the rest taking
the form of heat. In a steam-engine the work done
is rarely more than one-tenth of the total energy. In
a muscle, as far as we know at present, it varies from
one fourth to one twenty-fourth.

There are two kinds of muscles: (1) striated or
striped ; (2) unstriated or smooth. All muscles which
we move voluntarily are striated, and it is these which
move most quickly. The unstriated muscles, on the
other hand, which aid in carrying on the processes of·
life in the body, move slowly and are subject to the
sympathetic system of nerves which are not under
the control of the will. The muscle of the Iris in man is
altogether exceptional ; it is unstriated ; its action is in
some cases voluntary, in others involuntary, according

as its activity is due to one or another set of nerves ; it moves with great rapidity, instantaneously enlarging or reducing the size of the pupil.[1] The muscles of the heart, too, are peculiar. Though involuntary, they are striated, and yet unlike other striated muscles.

The amount of contraction possible to a muscle varies with its length ; its strength depends upon its

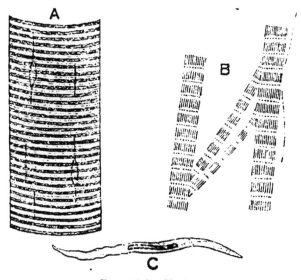

FIG. 36 (after Huxley).
A, Striated muscle of frog ; B, of mammal, "teased out" ; C, non-striated muscle.

thickness. Thus a short thick muscle will have strength, but no great range ; a long thin muscle, great range, but little strength. It has been found that a muscle ·cannot contract more than one-third of its length. It will be important to bear in mind this principle, when we come to consider the varying lengths of the breastbone and, consequently, of the muscles arising from it, in birds with different methods of flight.

[1] See p. 127.

Muscle is related to another kind of tissue which yet in its function is very different. Tendons have no power of contraction. They are merely cords by which, in many cases, the ends of muscles are fastened to the bones. In youth there is comparatively little tendon in the body, nearly all is muscle, and to this is due the springiness of the limbs. In age one of two things happens: either the muscle undergoes a kind of degeneration, fat making its way in among the tissue, as we often see it, in small streaks and flecks, in beef; or else the tendon by which the muscle is attached grows longer, while the muscle grows shorter, an increasing stiffness being the inevitable result. Long tendons, for quite different reasons, to be explained soon (see p. 208), are characteristic of birds. When, as they move, they have to rub against hard surfaces of bone, tendons are protected by little bags filled with moisture ; sometimes they are completely sheathed at these points. Sometimes their working makes grooves in the bones. This can be well seen at the ankle-joint of birds or where the toes spring from the metatarsals. Tendons themselves, in some cases, change their nature, and become sesamoid bones as they are called. Such bones are, for instance, the knee-cap, the pisiform bone, a small bone that can be felt on the outer side of the wrist, and the marsupial bones of the kangaroo.

Bones.

Much has been said on this subject in the opening chapters (see especially Chapter II.), and in the

present one under the head of " Hollow Bones."
For what remains the reader is referred to the remarks on " Passive Machinery " in the next chapter.

Ligaments.

Ligaments are like tendons in having no power of
contraction, but, unlike tendons, they are not connected with muscles. Their usual function is to
fasten two bones together at the joint, and to limit
the amount of freedom with which one turns upon
the other. When a skeleton is obtained by macera-
tion—i.e., by leaving the carcase in water till the flesh
is easily removable, many of the ligaments still remain and keep the bones in their proper connection.
There are some which answer very different purposes.
The horse's head is supported by a strong elastic ligament attached to the upright spines of the vertebrae.
The bird, as I shall show in the article on " Passive
Machinery" in the next chapter, has several which
are remarkable for their elasticity, some, if not all, of
these having been originally tendons.

Feathers—Structure and Development.

A feather is a very elaborate appendage. When
we are told that a Peacock's or an Ostrich's plume, or
the wing-feather of an Albatross is an " epidermic
growth," part, that is, of the horny outer skin, we
seem to hear words that explain nothing. There is
another " epidermic growth," the nature of which it is
perhaps hardly less difficult to realise—the horn of a

rhinoceros. But even with feathers, if we begin with the simplest instead of the most elaborate, the difficulty will appear much less, though it may not entirely vanish. A still better plan will be to begin with the scale of a reptile, and show how it corresponds to a bird's feather. The scale proper is formed from the

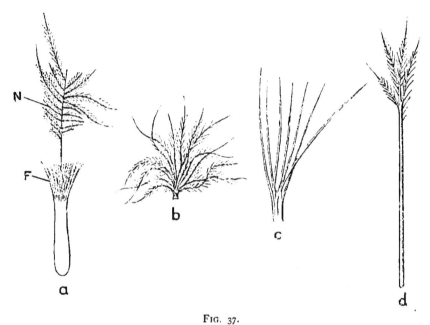

Fig. 37.

(*a*) Feather of Duck, carrying nestling down feather ; (*b*) Nestling down of Thrush; (*c*) of Pigeon ; (*d*) Thread feather of Goose ; (*b*), (*c*), and (*d*) after Gadow ; F, Feather proper ; N, Nestling down.

skin, its horny coating from the epidermis. Where a feather is to grow, there is a little skin papilla or pimple, which corresponds to the scale proper ; the actual feather is formed from the epidermis that covers the papilla, and corresponds to the horny covering of the scale. On the wings of the Penguin, or on the legs of birds of the Ostrich kind—*e.g.*, the

L

Rhea—may be found primitive feathers that are not very different from the scales on the bird's own legs or on a lizard. Birds in general have down feathers among the large ones, and these down feathers are often merely a little fluff at the top of a quill, though sometimes they are almost perfect miniatures of a typical feather. Besides these there are thread-feathers, filoplumes, always growing close to the base of one of the large feathers. Sometimes, like hair, the thread-feathers are perfectly simple and un-branched ; the branches are never more than a very few. The Nightjar has, bordering the mouth, a number of bristles that look like filoplumes, but are really ordinary feathers of which only the shaft remains. There are also found on some birds, notably on some Parrots and on the Heron, powder-down feathers, so called because they shed a fine powder. They continue to grow, and the ends of their branches give off a whitish dust which is at once greasy and dry. What purpose they may serve is quite uncertain.

By the help of these simpler specimens we must try to realise that the most elaborate feather is only a much-divided scale. Such a feather I must now describe, and then try to show how it has grown from a skin papilla. Take a large one from the wing or tail of any common bird. The semi-transparent base is the quill (Q, fig. 38) ; it has two small apertures, one at the bottom, the other at the top, where the branches begin, on the under-surface (U 1 and 2). At the lower one the papilla entered to give the need-ful nourishment, and if a young feather be taken, the quill will be found full of blood (P).

When the quill is dry and hollow, the feather is in most ways a dead thing, but the fact that in some birds there is a change of colour without a moult, and without the loss of any part of the feather, shows that it has not entirely lost life. The stiff rod above the quill is the rachis or shaft (S). It is grooved

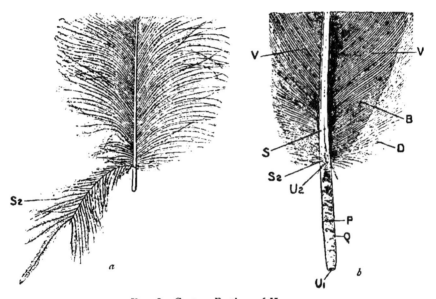

FIG 38.—Contour Feathers of Heron.
(*a*) plume-like feather with little or no interlocking.
(*b*) pennaceous or perfect flight feather.

ʙ, Barb; ᴅ, Downy ends of the lower barbs; ᴘ, dried remains of Pulp; ǫ, Quill; s, Shaft or rachis; s 2, After-shaft; v, Vane formed of the two webs on either side; ᴜ 1, Inferior umbilicus; ᴜ 2, Superior umbilicus.

down the under-surface. The branches on either side are called barbs (B), and the barbs to right and left together form the vane of the feather. The barbs give rise to barbules—*i.e.*, little barbs on either side. The barbules end in barbicels—*i.e.*, still more diminutive barbs. The barbicels belonging to the barbules on the side of the barb that is nearer to the quill

are smooth and hairlike, with only an occasional imperfect hook near the edge of the vane. Those on
the further barbules end, many of them, in perfect
little hooklets. By means of these the barbules of
two neighbouring barbs are locked together.

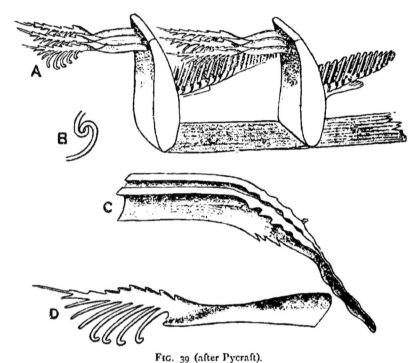

FIG. 39 (after Pycraft).
To show method of interlocking.
A and B, Barbicels running in grooves ; C, Barbule on near side of barb ; D, Barbule
on further side.

If you look at a feather under the microscope, using
a not very high power, you will see that the barbules
on the distant side of the barb are not only hooked
but waved, and the smooth hairlike endings of the
opposite set that meet them are neatly tucked underneath into the hollow of the wave. It is not the case,

as is sometimes stated, that the barbules themselves interlock.   It is the hooklets that fasten one barbule to another, and this they do in such a way that, while keeping a firm grip, they increase the elasticity natural to the material of which the feather is made (Fig. 39A).   The edges of the barbules, that have to be laid hold of by the hooklets of those opposite to them, are folded over.   Below this folded edge is a channel between the two adjacent barbules that lie parallel to one another.   The hooklet keeps hold of the edge, and at the same time is able to move up and down in the channel.   Hence the wonderful play of the vane of a wing or tail feather when pressure is applied to it.   In the softer, partly plume-like feathers the mechanism is not so perfect ; in some cases the hooklets do not exist.   Such feathers are not impervious to air, and they are much less strong and much less elastic.   All feathers, it will be noticed, are concave underneath, a form that adapts them for resisting pressure from below and not from above.

In nearly every case there is a small after-shaft (S 2, fig. 38) arising just below the small pit at the top of the quill.   Generally it is insignificant and escapes notice, unless attention is specially called to it.   In the Pigeon it is minute ; in the Cassowary, on the contrary, it is as large as the main shaft.   It is curious that in the embryo feathers of this bird there is no after-shaft at all.   In no bird except the Emeu does it appear till the feather proper grows, and this has been thought to show that in primitive birds after-shafts were not found.

The development of the feather now demands our

FIG. 45.—Cassowary's feather.

attention. Most birds, before they are fledged, have upon them embryo or nestling feathers, which are very similar to the "downs" of mature birds described above. Beginning the history of one of these from its earliest days, we find first a papilla upon the skin. From the epidermic covering of this springs the nestling feather with a number of thread-like branches, all starting from the same point, so that it is, in fact, a feather with the rachis left out. We may look upon it as a quill split uniformly the whole way round into numbers of narrow pieces ; it does not, like the later feather, face one particular way. Preparatory to this splitting, the epidermic cells over the papilla group themselves round the centre, and their little elevations are indications of the barbs that are soon to appear. When the time comes, the feather proper drives out the nestling feather, and carries it on its tip. The two are not really distinct, but parts of one and the same growth, the real feather with the nestling on the top having been formed even in the egg. The quill does not dry up, so that the

pulp, as it is called, is the same in the nestling down
and the more lasting and stronger formation that
follows it. The change, therefore, bears no resemblance to the shedding of milk teeth and their re-
placement by permanent ones. The early tooth is
driven out by the later one ; the two are not in any
way connected.

After the first moult, the feathers develop without
any nestling " downs " as precursors. Otherwise the
process is not, in essential points, different. The cells of

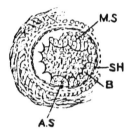

FIG. 41.—(After Gadow). Showing development of feather.
AS, cells forming after shaft ; B, cells forming barbs ; MS, cells forming main shaft ;
SH, horny sheath surrounding whole feather.

the papilla, or rather of the epidermis over it, arrange
themselves starwise. Two of the columns of cells
which cause this starlike formation grow broader and
longer than the rest, and go to make the rachis of the
feather. Two on the opposite side form a secondary
shaft, of which, as I have said, most feathers retain
some trace. At the same time there is a growth
inwards, so that in some cases the bone is reached.
On the ulna the marks of the great wing feathers are
easily discernible.

The cap found on the top of young feathers is
formed from the outermost cells of the epidermis, the

horny tube that overlies the papilla. Of this tube one side only, as a rule, is much developed, the other, that forms the after-shaft, being stunted. The little pit at the top of the quill is the remains of the aperture through which the pulp once forced its way, extending even to the top of the rachis (U2, fig. 38).

The pulp retires when the feather is complete, leaving only a few white flakes in the quill to mark its former presence (P). When the feather is to be moulted the papilla revives.

Varieties of Contour Feathers.

Contour feathers is a general name for the feathers which are visible on the surface and which shape the bird, to distinguish them from " downs," " thread-feathers," and " powder-downs."

The name plumes is generally reserved for feathers which are merely ornamental or a protection against cold. They have not that perfect system of inter-locking that makes the wing and tail feathers air-proof. To the great wing feathers, the name remiges— *i.e.* rowers—is given. Some spring from the hand and are called primaries. The Pigeon has eleven such feathers, six of them attached to the second meta-carpal bone, the rest to the bones of second and third digits. If, as often happens (in the Starling, for in-stance), the outermost is very short, it is called a bastard primary. The " thumb " carries no primary feathers.[1] The rest of the remiges, called secondaries and inner-

---

[1] See p. 42 on the question whether this is really the thumb.

most secondaries, spring from the ulna or the humerus,
The name tertiaries for the latter has now been disused.
The total number of the remiges varies very much, the
Humming-bird having only sixteen, and the Albatross
up to fifty, the variation being found in the secondaries
much more than in the primaries.   Covering the bases
of the remiges are the wing-coverts.   The great flight-
feathers are not originally the hindmost ; by their
enormous development, they push the two rearmost
rows to the lower face of the wing, where, to show
their origin, they still carry the after-shaft undermost.
The large tail feathers are called rectrices or steerers.
They always make an even number, but may be as
few as eight, or, it is said, as many as twenty-four. Somewhere about twelve is the normal. Sometimes they are
useful in distinguishing species.   Thus the Common
Cormorant has fourteen, the Shag only twelve. Shielding
the bases of the tail feathers are the tail-coverts.   In
the same way we speak of neck-coverts and ear-
coverts.

Though feathers are to a great extent dead things,
they are in connection with the living parts of the
body and, so, are frequently moved.   Pelicans may be
seen raising their feathers to dry them after a swim.
An old Hen with chickens raises them in anger.   The
Long-eared Owl lifts his great "ears" to inspire
terror ; the Cockatoo raises his top-knot to add to his
dignity; the Peacock in pride of heart spreads his plumes
or rattles his quills.   The behaviour of the Turkey-
cock is easy to interpret.

To make these movements, there are distributed
generally muscles which move the skin and with it

the feathers. By far the most remarkable of such movements are connected with flight.

It is interesting to put side by side some of the most wonderful forms of feathers, bearing in mind the like origin of all: for instance, an Ostrich's plume, a Penguin's tiny scale-like wing-feather, one of an Albatross's mighty remiges, a Cassowary's plume with its equal shafts, a hackle from the neck of a Barndoor cock, a plume from a Bird of Paradise, a Lyre-bird's tail feather, a spur from a Cassowary's wing (a great wing feather that has lost its barbs so that the shaft alone is left), one of the Motmot's two extraordinary tail feathers, one of the grandest from a Peacock's train, and, to complete the collection, one of the stumpy business-like set with which a Woodpecker props himself as he climbs.

Feather Tracts.

Except in the Penguin the feathers do not cover the whole of the body, but only certain feather tracts. The bare regions are called Apteria, and are sometimes devoid even of down—for instance, in the Woodpecker and the Sparrow-hawk.

Our common birds have most of them a bare tract down the breast, which is very convenient when you wish to skin them. In most sea-birds you have to work through a thick, almost impervious, mass of feathers before you can begin operations. Feather tracts, especially down the neck and back, have been found very useful for purposes of classification.

Moulting.

Moulting, as I have already said, is a reptilian characteristic, and corresponds to the shedding of the horny covering of the scales. It is due to the papilla which once more extends into the quill and causes the feather to fall off. In the Cassowary and Emeu the tip of the new feather extends into the base of the old one, which it carries for a time, but the two are only connected mechanically. They do not, like the nestling down and the feather that follows it, make up one organ. Most birds moult completely in the summer or autumn. Many have a partial moult, at which only small feathers are shed, in spring. It is sometimes stated that migratory birds have two complete moults, one before each migration, but it is probable that none of them shed their great quill feathers more than once. The Cuckoo's main moult is believed to be in spring : sometimes he has arrived in England before its completion. In autumn, after he has left us, the smaller feathers are once more changed. Swifts also, it is supposed, moult in early spring long before they come to us, a slighter moult taking place after their departure. Swallows and Martins moult only once—in very early spring or even in winter—being distinguished by this from the Swifts, which moult twice. With most migrants, as with other birds, autumn is the great season for donning new feathers. Spring is the time when the wedding plumage is put on, and the Ruffs, the Golden Plovers, the Dunlins, the Linnets,

and a host of others come out like different birds.
Ducks and their allies are quite unlike most species·
in this respect. The Mallard, the male of the Wild
Duck, to take an example, gets his fine feathers
in autumn and is in full splendour by October. He
is still wearing these same plumes when the pairing
time comes round. While the eggs are being laid and
sat upon, his plumage is fading, and before long a
moult begins. In June or about that time his faded
finery is shed and replaced by a dull garb very similar
to that of the Duck. Even earlier, towards the end
of May, he drops his big wing feathers, and, since they
all go nearly at the same time, he is incapable of
flight. Till then, he has been a most dutiful partner,
watching over his mate upon the nest, and warning
her if there happens to be danger when she is leaving
it to refresh herself with a bath and food. When his
moulting begins she is left to herself, and often has,
unaided, to take her young ones to the water and
educate them. By the end of July the Mallard is
again possessed of fully grown remiges, but his dull
plumes are still upon him, and it is not till October
that he sheds these, and once more looks his best.
The Duck does not moult till her young ones are off
her hands. Geese, like Ducks, shed their quill feathers
all at once, and, standing, tumbled and helpless, present a truly pitiful sight. It is only some water-birds
who moult in such haste. When the time comes for
it, they are very careful to be on or near the water so
that in case of danger, they may make use of what is
now their only means of escape, their power of
swimming. Mr. Seebohm describes a great procession

of Bean Geese that he saw in the north of Russia,
making for the water when their moult was imminent.[1]
By the time the young can fly, the old birds have
renewed their quills, and they start for the south
together.   Any land bird with such a system of
moulting would be reduced to a sad plight.   He would
be worse off than the Crayfish, who has cast his shell
and, cowering in a hole, waits for the new one to form
and harden.   As far as is known, all birds who are
not at home upon the water, shed their large feathers
at intervals, a pair at a time, one feather from each
side.   In Hawks and other birds of prey, the intervals
are very long, and the process continues nearly the
whole year.   In Homing Pigeons—the breed now in
use for "carrying"—and, I believe, in other pigeons
also, the moult lasts nearly half the year.   About
May the tenth of the eleven primaries counting from
the outermost is lost.   A month later the ninth goes.
By that time the tenth has grown nearly to its full size ;
when the ninth is about half its proper length, the
eighth falls ; the others follow at intervals of from
eight to fifteen days.   In the tail, which has twelve
feathers, the two which are fifth from the sides fall
first.   When the new ones are grown to three quarters
of their full length, the two central ones are shed ; the
remainder fall in this order : the fourth, the third, the
outermost, the second.   The Pigeon suffers much as
the moult approaches its conclusion.   He flies with
difficulty, and is liable to arthritis, commonly known
among Belgian fanciers as *La Maladie des ailes*.
Badly fed birds have a defective moult.   If Pigeons

[1] See his *Siberia in Europe*, p. 287.

after being fed daily are left to pick up their own food, the moult is arrested. Bird fanciers hasten the moult by putting their victims in a dark and rather cold place. Pigeons, which do not pair, put off their moult, and so are in splendid condition for flying. By some process at present not understood in Europe, the Japanese check the shedding of the tail feathers of Cock Chickens, and so produce the enormous growths (ten or twelve feet long) with which we are familiar. The Ptarmigan moults no less than three times in the year. After the nesting season he sheds many of his smaller feathers and becomes gray ; in autumn he moults again, and in winter is arrayed in white, with feathers on his legs supposed to be intended to prevent him from sinking into the snow. A partial moult in spring arrays him in his breeding plumage of black and gray-brown and white. The big wing-feathers are white at all seasons. The claws are shed in July and August, and have grown to their full length again before the bird puts on his winter dress.

The moulting of birds in their first year presents great varieties. In most songsters it begins thirty or forty days after they have left the nest. Hawks and their allies keep their first plumage till next summer. Young Ducks first appear in the same dress as their parents in late autumn. Geese have only down feathers till six weeks old ; after that appear feathers proper, which they shed between September and December. In their second autumn, like mature geese, they moult completely in the space of four weeks. A young bird of aquatic habits can afford to be content with a covering of down for a long time after his birth. A young Partridge has quill feathers big enough to enable him to fly, to some extent, very soon after leaving the egg. These are shed and replaced several times during his first summer and autumn, thus keeping pace with his rapid growth. Thrushes, Blackbirds, and Fieldfares have one complete moult in their first autumn.

Change of Colour without Moulting.

In spring the cock Gray Linnet becomes the " Red Linnet," and appears with a crown and breast of crimson in place of the dull gray of winter, and yet it is certain that no feathers are shed. In captivity he gradually loses his crimson splendours, which fade to ochre-yellow. After the first moult he assumes and retains the dull plumage of the hen. The forehead of the Redpoll becomes blood-red and his throat and breast carmine, equally without the shedding of a feather. The nape and back of the Brambling turn from reddish-brown striped with black to pure glossy blue-black without any moult ; and, to take one more instance, the Blackheaded Gull, in the course of a fortnight, dyes the white plumage of his head black, or, more strictly speaking, a very dark brown. In some cases the explanation is perfectly simple ; the crown and breast feathers of the Linnet have wide gray borders which in spring break off and let the crimson that was before covered up become visible. The same is the case with the Redpoll, Brambling, the Snow Bunting, whose back plumage becomes black in spring, and the Blue Throat. In some of these cases Gätke attributes the change not to a breaking off of the edges, but to a peeling of the barbules. However this may be, he must surely be right when he maintains that in spring there is a rounding off of the ragged edges of feathers. The Linnet's nuptial plumage would be but a sorry garb if the dropping away of the edges left what remained all ragged. A far more remarkable cause of change of colour is the entrance of fresh colouring matter into the feather, which cannot therefore be an entirely dead thing. This is what takes place when the Blackheaded Gull puts on his spring head-dress, the colour, according to Gätke, appearing first at the edges of the feathers and gradually extending till the whole is dyed. In winter the breast of the Dunlin is almost white, in spring it becomes black, the pigment working its way to every part of the feathers through channels as yet undiscovered. By a similar process the head of the Little Gull changes in spring from white with a dash of ashen-gray to black. As in the Linnet in captivity, so in the Herring Gull there takes place a withdrawal of pigment, for the head having been gray in winter becomes snow-white in spring. In these cases no indication of moulting, such as half-grown feathers, is ever found. The plumage of the Wood-sandpiper is an interesting study, since it supplies an example of the influx of fresh colour into the feathers and also of the rounding off of ragged edges. Birds in captivity sometimes show these changes well. This year the Knots at the Zoological Gardens appeared with the chestnut-coloured breasts proper to them in spring, but whether the change in their case is due to the dull margins of feathers being shed or to the influx of fresh pigment, I do not know.[1]

Spurs.

Spurs are outgrowths of bone covered by a horny sheath formed from the epidermis, and, thus, they resemble the horns of oxen and antelopes. The cock's spur is familiar to every one. Some birds, for instance the Double Spurred Peacock, have two on each foot. Spurs are also found upon the wings, for example in the Crested Screamer of South America which is now to be seen at the Zoological Gardens. The Cassowary's spurs, which are really feathers, I have already described. These are found in both sexes, as ordinary wing-spurs sometimes are. All spurs are used in fighting, and well-developed leg-spurs are the privilege of cock birds. We should expect, therefore, to see them, as we do, mainly in those species which are polygamous, and which consequently have an excess of males among whom there is constant war in spring-time. It is with his spur that the game-cock slays his rival.

The Beak.

In the beak the horny covering which overlies the bone is a growth of the epidermis just as spurs are.

[1] On moulting see especially (1) Bronn's *Thier-Reich*, vol. "Aves," pp. 538-542 ; (2) Seebohm's *Brit. Birds*, passim ; (3) Gätke, *Die Vogelwarte Helgoland*, pp. 156-166 ; (4) *Le Pigeon Voyageur*, by F. Chapuis, pp. 103-111. I am indebted to Mr. C. M. Adamson's book *Some more Scraps about Birds*, printed for private circulation

In all birds the upper beak moves slightly, in parrots freely. It is. always growing, but constant friction against hard substances and of the upper against the lower beak prevents this from being apparent. The duck's beak acts as a strainer: the whale, in the so-called whalebone, has a similar instrument which lets the water pass away while retaining the food. The

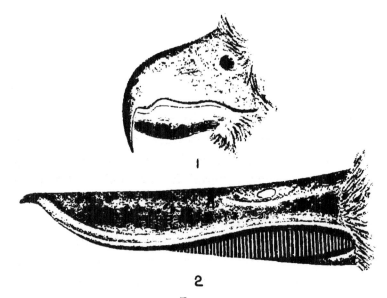

1

2

FIG. 42.
(1), Beak of Falcon showing toothed edge ; (2), of Duck showing strainer.

beaks of Humming-birds are bent or otherwise shaped so as to suit the forms of particular flowers down the corollas of which they dive for the honey. Falcons and other birds of prey have their upper beaks 'cut into teeth, an assistance in tearing their food. And in con-nection with this, it must be remembered that flesh-eating birds have nothing worthy of the name of a gizzard. Hence some tearing of the food is desirable.

Mr. Beddard mentions that the Great Spotted Wood-pecker ate the caterpillar of the Buff-tip moths partially after much pecking.[1] Was this because the conspicuous colours frightened him or because the skin was over-tough ? A Magpie rubbed the hairs off a caterpillar before eating it.   On the other hand a Gannet swallows a mackerel whole.   A Cormorant is only troubled by a whole fish if he happens to swallow him head foremost and so get the fins the wrong way.   He has been known to swallow a Starling with beak and feet and everything appertaining to him, and to attempt to swallow a young kitten.[2] The parrot gnaws his food carefully like a dyspeptic. The great freedom with which his upper beak works enables him to put its long curved point to the front margin of the lower beak when occasion requires.   With this long point he scoops out a Brazil nut when he has cracked the shell like a piece of shortbread.

The beak aided by the long and supple neck takes the place of a hand.   When the forelimbs became wings and the former reptile, now a bird, stood comparatively erect on two legs, some form of hand was clearly necessary.   The parrot uses his feet to lift food to his mouth, but most birds know no hand but their beak. It is also a weapon of offence, many birds being able to give a powerful stroke not unlike that of a snake, and far more promptly administered.   When some members of the *Challenger* expedition visited Penguin " rookeries " they found they must wear thick gaiters

---

[1] *Animal Coloration*, by F. E. Beddard, p. 155.

[2] See *The Home of a Naturalist*, by the Rev. B. Edmondston, p. 77.

to protect their legs from the formidable beaks among
which they had to run the gauntlet. The Woodpecker
pecks a hole in a tree in which to make his nest. His
beak is the hammer with which the Nuthatch, swinging at the hips, cracks his nut. A Thrush may be
seen picking up a snail and dashing it on a stone to
break the shell. The beak is also used to preen the
feathers, even a short-necked bird being able to bring
it to bear on almost any part of his plumage. When
there is an oil-gland at the root of the tail, the bird with
his bill presses the oil from it and distributes it over
his feathers. The Tailor Bird uses it as a needle, and
partly to its skill are due the beautiful nests of many
of our small birds.

The Foot.

It will be enough to mention a few types to show
how the anatomy has adapted itself to different modes
of life. The normal number of toes is four, the fifth
or " little toe" having been lost. The first, as a rule,
points backward. The Emeu, the Rhea, and the
Cassowary have only three, having lost the first as well.
The Ostrich has only two, the third and fourth, and the
latter of these two is small and bears no nail. As in
the horse, it is the middle toe which carries all the
weight. Among English birds the most striking
difference is between the webbed feet of the swimmers
and the separate-toed feet of the perchers, climbers,
waders, and runners. The Gannet, the Cormorant, and
their allies have all four digits connected by the web ;
in most swimming birds the first is free. There are

various intermediate stages before we arrive at separate-
toed feet. In the Dabchick and the other Grebes, the
toes are not connected, but there is on either side of
each a broad expansion of skin. In the Kingfisher
the second, third, and fourth toes are fastened together

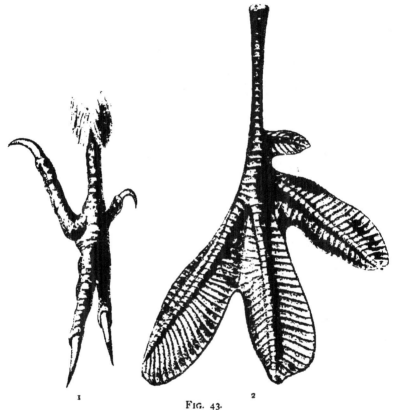

FIG. 43.
Foot of (1), Woodpecker ; (2), Grebe.

for most of their extent. The Woodpeckers, Cuckoos,
and Toucans have a most curious form of foot called
zygodactyle or yoke-toed, the first and fourth toes
pointing backward, the other two forward—a foot
specially adapted for climbing. In the Swift all the

toes turn forwards. The number of Phalanges or segments in each varies very much in different species. Usually the first toe has 2 ; the second, 3 ; the third, 4 ; the fourth, 5. The Swift has in the respective toes only 2, 3, 3, 3. This and the extreme shortness of his legs must account for his inability (if the inability, as is popularly supposed, exists) to rise from the ground. Mr. Howard Saunders denies the correctness of the popular belief, but I am not sure that the bird is not in difficulties when he finds himself among grass of any length.

Perching.

Most of our common birds would soon fall victims to some nocturnal beast of prey, if they had not the power of maintaining themselves on a bough during sleep. To see the machinery by which this is effected, take a bird of some size and cut through the skin at the back of the ankle-joint. We find there, first, two tendons belonging to muscles which have nothing to do with the toes, one of which attaches a little above the foot, the other just below the ankle-joint. As they pass this joint, these tendons spread out and form a sheath in which run several of the tendons that bend the toes, and which are bound together by connective tissue but easily dissected apart. Cutting down deeper we come to other tendons passing to the toes, making the number in all up to seven. Of these the Hallux or first digit (our great toe) has 1 ; the second and third, each, 2 ; the fourth, 1 : while another tendon divides into 3, the branches going to toes 2, 3, 4 respectively. This

branching tendon is the one to which most interest
attaches, and it is easily distinguished from the others :
it lies the most deeply imbedded of all at the ankle-
joint, in a cartilaginous or bony tunnel.   In a great
many birds it connects with the tendon that bends the
Hallux, and the absence of connection or the form of

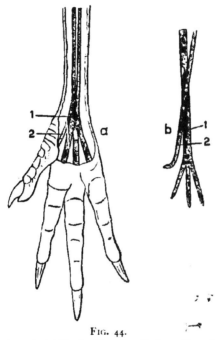

Fig. 44.

Flexor tendons of toes in (*a*) Fowl ; (*b*)—after Gadow—Passerine Bird. (1) deep,
divided tendon ; (2) the tendon that bends the hallux or first toe. In Passerine Birds
they remain unconnected.

connection have been found very useful in classification.[1]   Tracing the tendons upwards we shall find
them passing into muscles that arise partly from the

[1] Some of the chief varieties are well shown in specimens at
the British Museum, S. Kensington, but it is much the best
plan to dissect them out.

top of the Tibiotarsus (drumstick) partly from the lower end of the Femur or thigh-bone. When the leg bends at the ankle, there is a pull upon the tendons, the muscles are stretched, the toes are bent and grasp the perch on which the bird sits. Thus he is maintained in position by his own weight, which bends the leg and so causes the toes to grip. The strain on the muscles is, probably, not great. Chickens and, I believe, other birds rest their breast-bone upon the perch, and so get support nearly in the vertical line in which lies the centre of gravity. The grip of the toes, therefore, is wanted only to steady them. This bending of the toes, as a necessary consequence of bending the leg at the ankle-joint, is not altogether peculiar to birds. A squirrel's toes will open or close according as his leg is straightened or bent. In birds what was once, probably, a trifling or useless feature has been developed in order to supply a vital need. Birds, such as Gulls, which do not sleep upon a perch and are rather ill at ease upon one, have this toe-grip only in a most rudimentary form. I have seen the Black-headed Gull alight on railings, and at the Zoological Gardens, when in a small aviary where they have not much ground to wander over, Gulls will remain perched for some time, though apparently uncomfortable, on the thin bar allotted them. This is no proof, however, that they could sleep upon a perch. Others, which are not ordinarily perchers, are quite capable of adopting arboreal habits. The annual flooding of great tracts of country in Siberia has brought this about in the case of the Snipe.[1]

<hr/>

[1] *Vide* Seebohm's *Siberia in Europe*, p. 147

There is connected with this subject another strange
phenomenon. In many birds a thin muscle, called
Ambiens, arises from the Pelvis just under the thigh-
joint and passes forward on the inner side of the leg
to the knee, before reaching which it becomes a tendon :
it curves round the knee in a little tendinous tunnel
occupied by itself alone, then doubles back on the
outside of the leg and passes into one of the muscles
which bend the toes as described above. It is very
characteristic of birds that a muscle should, by means

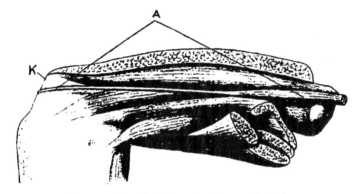

FIG. 45.—Leg of chicken, the side next the body.
A, ambiens muscle ; K, knee-joint.

of a long tendon, do its work at such a distance : but,
curiously, it is not found in by any means all the
perching birds. And, besides, this the same muscle is
to be found in crocodiles.[1] This must not, however, be taken to prove any very close relationship with
birds. The fact that it is found in two families of birds
may help to prove that they are closely allied, but such
evidence is less dependable when we are dealing, not

[1] Refer to *Appareil Locomoteur des Oiseaux* (M. Edmond
Alix), p. 443.

with the relationship between families within the same class, but with the relationship between two classes. In the crocodile the muscle in question appears either not to connect with the toe-flexor muscles or else to be altogether functionless, for when I have bent the ankle-joint of a young American alligator, most probably resembling a crocodile in this point of anatomy, no effect at all has been produced upon the toes.

The habit of standing on one leg is common to many birds. The Heron is well known for it.

> " Nigh upon that hour
> When the lone hern forgets his melancholy,
> Lets down his other leg and, stretching, dreams
> Of goodly supper in the distant pool."

Flamingoes, Storks, and Cranes can frequently be seen in this posture at the Zoological Gardens. It is said to be a restful one, and it must have merits or they would not adopt it. But if the leg be watched it will be seen to be perpetually swaying to and fro. In fact the balance is only maintained by the help of perpetual small muscular adjustments, of which, no doubt, the bird is capable while asleep, some lower part of the brain working when the cerebral hemispheres, the seat of conscious life, are at rest.

Swimming.

People maintain that they have seen from a boat a Shag "flying under water," swimming, that is, by means of his wings. Among the diving birds at the Zoological Gardens there is frequently a Shag, and as he chases the fish in the tank, he holds his wings motionless, just slightly lifted from the body. It is the same with the Indian Darter—he strikes with his legs only. The Penguin, on the other hand, swims almost entirely with his wings. For him swimming is flight under water, the only flight possible to him ; his legs are used only for steering, or for an occasional upward kick to force him downward. The Rough-faced Shag strikes with both feet simultaneously, the Indian Darter's is an alternate stroke, and the same is the case with the Gull. The Swan and the Duck take almost simultaneous strokes with both feet, yet one is always just a little behind the other.

I have already mentioned how various diving birds by driving most of the air out of their air-sacks cause only a small part of their body, or nothing but the neck, to appear above water. Some birds dive to great depths. The Shag begins by jumping up in the water and taking a header, then he strikes hard upward. One was caught once in a crab-pot twenty fathoms below the surface. There is one kind of Penguin which is said to swallow stones for ballast and vomit them up again at the mouth of his burrow on returning.[1] It would be worth while watching long to prove this true or untrue. Certainly a diving bird is in a dilemma if he wishes to descend to a great depth and stop there long. He must take in an abundant supply of air, but this will make him over-buoyant.

Birds which sleep floating upon ponds or tarns

---

[1] *Spheniscus Magellanicus* ; see *Report of "Challenger" Expedition*, vol. ii., p. 127.

are in danger of drifting to the bank and falling victims to any beast of prey. To prevent this ducks and others have the habit of sleeping with one leg tucked under the wing, while with the other they keep gently paddling so that they revolve in a circle. In summer time, when they have had a long day, they will begin this early when there is still some light, and then is the time to watch them. This remarkable habit is a kind of sleep-walking turned to good account, and is, no doubt, perfectly compatible with complete unconsciousness.[1]

SOME OF THE BEST BOOKS ON THE SUBJECT.

(1) Bronn's *Thier-Reich*, vol. "Aves."

(2) Milne-Edwards' *Physiologie et Anatomie comparée.*

(3) Max Fürbringer's *Morphologie und Systematik der Vögel.*

(4) Various articles by Dr. Gadow in Newton's *Dictionary of Birds.*

(5) Michael Foster's *Text-book of Physiology.*

(6) Huxley's *Elementary Physiology.*

(7) Coues' *Field and General Ornithology.*

[See references given in footnotes.]

---

[1] My attention was first called to this interesting point by Mr. Thompson, head keeper at the Zoological Gardens.

CHAPTER VII

FLIGHT

The Wings as Levers, the Air as Fulcrum

ARCHIMEDES was prepared to move the world if he could find a fulcrum for his lever. The problem of flight seems almost equally difficult : the body must be lifted by levers, and the fixed points on which they are to work must be found in the air. But before I show how the bird surmounts this great difficulty, a word about levers is necessary. Levers are rigid rods resting on a fulcrum or fixed point; at another point in the rod is the weight to be moved, and at a third point the power is applied. There are three kinds of levers, the difference lying in the relative position of the three points mentioned. In the first the fulcrum is in the middle, in the second the weight, in the third the power. Of the first we have an example when a poker, rested on the bar of the grate, raises the coal. An oar is an instance of the second ; the boat is the weight, the fulcrum is the water upon which the oar works. And this makes clear an important fact, viz. that the fulcrum is not always an absolutely fixed point, though, of course, the lever would be improved if it could be made so. The third kind of lever in which the power is applied at a point between the weight and the fulcrum is not often used, because it does not economise labour. We have an instance of it in the treadle of a sewing-machine, where the force required is so slight, that economy is unimportant. Wasteful as it seems to be, this third kind of lever is the common one in the bodies of animals. All three classes are represented, but examples of the first and second are comparatively rare. Consequently there have been people who have maintained that the human body is a clumsy machine made on antiquated and unscientific principles. Such an idea shows the danger of a little knowledge. When we use a lever, we wish to move a weight with comparatively little effort, however much we may lose in the speed and amount of the movement. In the levers of the body rapidity is a great object. The arm is a series of levers of the third order, and by their help it can be drawn in quickly, then shot out again to deal a sudden blow. If we try to hold out a weight at arm's length, we then find the weak point of levers of this order. To economise effort with them you must apply the power near to the weight. In the case of the arm, we should require a biceps, springing, as now, from near the shoulder but attaching near the wrist, and this, besides other inconveniences, would entail great slowness of movement. In a bird's wing the leverage which aims at moving a weight with great rapidity is to be seen in its greatest perfection. Very powerful muscles are required, but the muscles are there.

The wing-lever must find its fulcrum in the air. A strong breeze, or, better, a hurricane may give us a notion how this is done. The air, which, when still, seemed to offer no opposition to our progress, becomes, when moving at a great pace, an obstacle through which we must shove our way with effort. It makes no difference whether it is an actual wind that opposes us, or whether it is one existing only relatively to ourselves, being produced by our own rapid travelling. A bicyclist if he rides fast on a calm day is retarded by a breeze due to his own velocity. If there is a light breeze ahead, this may be doubled by the pace at which he rides, so that what to a pedestrian is hardly a breath of air is magnified by the bicyclist into a wind. The resistance of the air, then, increases if we move through it more quickly. But this is only a very vague statement, that gives but little idea of the facts. Some experiments were made by Newton showing that in many cases the resistance of the air increases as the square of the velocity. These experiments depend on the fact that a body, when let fall, gains in velocity for some time, after which it maintains a uniform pace. Nothing but the resistance of the air can check a progressive increase in velocity, and when the pace becomes uniform it is clear that the resistance of the air is exactly equal to the weight of the body falling. Newton took glass globes of equal size, but unequal weights, corresponding to the figures 1, 4, 9, 16. These he let fall from a height, and measured their velocities when each had settled down to its uniform pace. The velocities were in proportion to the numbers 1, 2, 3, 4, but the resistance of the air was, as we have seen, equal to the weights of the globes which were as 1, 4, 9, 16, the squares of the numbers which represent the velocities. Experiments at once more elaborate and more accurate have been made since. Professor Marey concludes from many made by himself, that the resistance increases in a less proportion for velocities between o and 10 metres per second ; when 10 metres per second is exceeded, then the rule of the square of the velocity under-represents the rate of increase of the air's resistance. When the speed attained is very great, in the case of a bullet for instance, Newton's law does not hold at all: the rate of increase of resistance altogether outpaces the square of the velocity. The rate of movement of a wing is comparatively moderate, so that here it might seem that we should be safe in applying Newton's law. There is liability to error, however from another cause. A wing is very different from the glass globes with which he experimented—it presents a concave and irregular surface with rough edges. Such an object passing through the air, which is not a perfect fluid, but viscous, must, like an oar forced through the water, produce eddies, and this complicates the problem so much that our greatest authorities confess that we know very little of the resistance to a surface like that of a wing. It is necessary to say this, since the rule "resistance of air increases as the square of the velocity" is often quoted as if it held true of all surfaces and all velocities. Nevertheless it comes near enough to the facts to be of great value, and probably when we apply it to a bird's wing we understate the rate of increase of the air's resistance.

It will now be well to take a particular instance. Let W A and W B represent the same wing in different postures, *a* and *b* the same point in it. Let *a b* be one inch in length, and A B three times as long. When the wing descends, *a* passes through one inch of air, A through three inches. But the resistance of the air will be, at the lowest estimate, as the squares of 1 and 3—that is, at A it will be nine times as great as it is at *a*. It is by rapid movement of its wings,

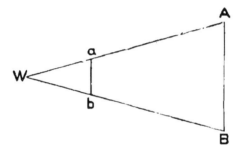

Fig. 46.

then, that the bird obtains a fulcrum on which they can work as levers. However large an expanse a wing might offer it would be useless, unless it were driven through the air at a great speed ; it could not possibly obtain the comparatively fixed point that every lever must have. Though there is still much to be said about the shape of the wing and the way in which the air acts upon it, we have advanced far enough to understand the system of leverage. The weight to be raised is the body of the bird, the power lies in the breast muscles and is applied not far

N

out upon the wing, the fulcrum is at a point not far from the tip. As a fact, of course, the fulcrum is distributed over the whole wing, but since, owing to its more rapid motion, the end meets with far more resistance than the base, we may consider it to be not far from the tip. Here it will be well to mention something that often makes living machinery puzzling. The different parts are not distinct. For instance, when a man breathes, his chest is a suction pump. But there is no separate piston. The walls of the chest, that is, the walls of the pump itself, expand and so cause a vacuum. In the same way we have been speaking of the bird's body as the weight to be raised, of the wings as levers, and of the power as residing in certain muscles. But the muscles in question form part of the body, and they and also the wings go to make up the weight. Nor have we yet done with the complications in which we get involved when we study the wing as a lever. When it is being moved rapidly through the air in order to gain a fulcrum, by the help of which to move the body, the weight is, at first, at the extremity in the shape of the resistance of the air that has to be overcome, while the fulcrum is at the shoulder-joint. When the fixed point has been gained, then the end of the wing becomes the fulcrum, and the body is the weight. But it is only in imagination that we can divide the down-stroke into two such periods. During the whole of it we have at the near end both a weight and a fulcrum, during the whole of it both a weight and a fulcrum at the further end. The body is always suspended from the wings, the ends of the wings never cease to move as they strive, each, for their fixed point. The fact is that the distinction between the fulcrum and the weight is an artificial one. The power applied acts on both ends at once, and if only one moves, or if one moves more than the other, we speak of the weight as being at that end. A weight at the other end which does not give, or gives less, we call the fulcrum. In a bird's wing both ends move, but since the object is to obtain for the extremity as fixed a point as possible and to raise the body, the term fulcrum is reserved for the air. The bald statement, " The air is the fulcrum," is not incorrect, but it leaves out of sight a most interesting process. It is the rapid motion of the wing that wins for it a comparatively fixed point, and throughout the process the air is being moved by a lever that has for its fulcrum the shoulder-joint. The oar, though a lever of the second order, presents the same difficulty, but in a less puzzling form. People who have never thought of the subject are apt if asked what is the fulcrum on which an oar works, to reply " the rowlock." This is as much as to say that it is the aim of the oarsman to displace as much water as possible. It is only, however, by making the displacement of water a preliminary object, that he gains a fulcrum by which to move his boat.

We must now consider the working of both wings at once. In order to understand this we may imagine a boat rowed by oars employed as levers of the same order as a bird's wings. The rowlocks would be in the middle of the boat, and the oarsman would sit on either side holding the oars between rowlock and blade. They would have to face the bows, and this, perhaps, would be the only advantage. But it is quite possible to propel a boat in this way, and such a system of rowing would illustrate what takes place in flight. True, the blades of a bird's "oars" face differently, so that, while they propel him, they at the same time raise or maintain him in the air. But the system of leverage is the same. This diagram is a further illustration.

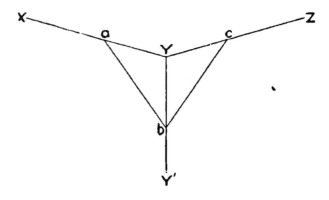

FIG. 47.

X and Z are rigid rods representing the bird's wings hinged at Y to Y Y" the bird's body ; a b and c b are the muscles which lower the wings. The shortening of a b and c b will cause Y Y" to rise, since the air resists the descent of X and Z. After Alix, *Appareil Locomoteur des Oiseaux.*

Horizontal Flight.

Why does a bird advance horizontally when it works its wings up and down ? The common metaphor which makes them oars is picturesque, but may be, as I have shown, misleading. Vergil, who, in describing Dædalus' wings, uses the expression "Remigium alarum," doubtless never intended to commit himself to any theory of flight. If in a scientific work, wings

are spoken of as oars, it must be borne in mind that
they are oars of a peculiar kind. The French are
fond of the terms "vol ramé" and "vol à voiles,"
which have the merit of neatly distinguishing ordinary
from sailing flight.

Wings work by movement up and down. If they
faced as the blades of an oar face, they would be
useless for flight at the rate of fifty miles an hour, since
the stroke would be over before any force could be
put into it. If a boat is moving rapidly—at the rate,
say, of a mile in five minutes—its pace alone brings the
oar in quick to the oarsman's chest, even if he puts

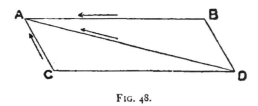

Fig. 48.

little force into it. Hence the importance of "getting
on at the beginning," to use the language of rowing
"coaches," otherwise the happy moment is missed.
Rowing, then, is out of the question for a bird which
is to move at a speed far greater than that of any
boat.

How, then, is horizontal movement gained? To
understand this a knowledge of the parallelogram of
forces is necessary. The proof of the principle involved
will be found in any book on elementary mechanics.
I shall merely try to make clear what is meant. If
two forces act upon a body at one point, they combine
to make one force. If B A and C A are two forces

acting at A, the comparative length of the lines
representing the comparative magnitude of the two
forces, then there results a force which is exactly
represented both in magnitude and direction by D A,
the diagonal of the parallelogram. If, now, we start
with a force represented by DA, we can do in imagination, what often happens in reality, break it up
into two forces BA and CA, or other forces acting
along two other lines, which must, however, con-

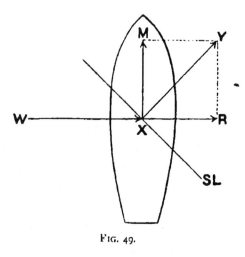

FIG. 49.

verge on A from opposite sides of DA. This fact
is made use of a great deal in sailing. A sail SL is
slung obliquely across the boat, and the wind falling
upon it tends to move the boat in the direction XY,
at right angles to the sail. In the same way when a
stone, thrown slantingwise at a window by some one
standing some way off, but near the wall of the house,
breaks a pane, the fragments of glass are knocked into
the room in a direction at right angles to the window.
To return to the boat, the force XY can be broken up

into two forces, one represented by XM, the other by XR. But the force XR will have little effect since the water offers great resistance to the movement of a boat sideways through it ; at any rate if it has a keel or a centreboard. The force XM will cause the boat to move in the direction she is meant to go. This is an excellent illustration of what happens in the flight of a bird. When the wing is descending its front margin is lower than its hind margin ; it is turned so that the long feathers slope upwards. For simplicity

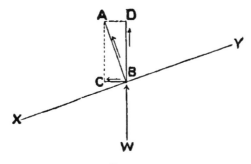

FIG 50.

X Y = section of wing ; X, front margin ; Y, hind margin ; W = wind caused by the down stroke ; BA, resultant force, which is resolved into BC, BD.

we must imagine that the air is quite still. The wing descends with great velocity through it, "making its own wind" like a bicyclist. The resistance of the air will be equal to a wind blowing vertically upward (W in Fig. 50). When it strikes the inclined surface of the wing its force will act in a direction at right angles to it (BA). The force BA may be divided into two forces, BD, which supports the bird, BC, which drives him onward.

Whether Professor Pettigrew's description of the wing's movement agrees with the account I have given, is difficult to say. He speaks of it as working like the screw of a steamer. If this is taken to mean that the surface of the wing during the down stroke has much the same incline as the blade of a screw, the description is no doubt correct : the opposite wing will correspond to a blade of a screw revolving in the opposite direction : both tend to drive the bird forward and, at the same time, lift it, as the descending blades of the screw of a steamer propel and lift the ship. But it is impossible to go beyond this and compare such fractional rotations as the wing is capable of to the complete revolutions of a screw : during the up stroke the wing is certainly not a screw-blade propelling the bird in a forward direction.

In horizontal flight the hind part of the body is raised during each down stroke by muscular effort.[1]

The Bird in Motion—Support Given by the Air.

If a bird flies at a great pace he derives far more support from the air than if he flies slowly. He is perpetually coming to fresh columns of air, each series of which is able to sustain his weight for a moment. If a gull be tied to a string, it is said that he cannot support himself when he comes to the end of his tether, and though some other birds are not under these circumstances reduced to complete help-lessness, the downfall of the gull is a significant fact : since he has no onward movement, the air gives his body little or no support, and, besides this, the air which his wings are beating has rolled in to fill the

[1] See p. 257.

vacuum made by the last stroke and is already in motion downwards. The predicament in which his wings find themselves may be illustrated by the screw of a steamer; till the vessel begins to move on, it churns the same water round and round and gets very little grip. Another illustration will help to explain why the large body surface proves so poor a parachute. Thin ice will often bear a skater who moves rapidly over it, when it would break if he stopped for an instant. A particular square yard has not time to break before he has transferred his weight to another. Or we may put it thus, that he is, as it were, supported by long skates that spread the pressure over a great area. This fact is turned to account by all birds. Though the principle is always at work except when they ascend almost vertically, we see it most clearly when they get up pace and then glide onwards without moving their wings which are fully or partly extended, the body being sloped at a slight angle upwards; when this position is adopted, the resistance offered by the air is very little. The bird cuts edgeways through it, and of the little resistance there is, the greater part acts in an upward direction, or, in other words, supports the bird's weight. Sir George Cayley made some very interesting calculations with regard to this.[1] Experiments had shown that if a flat surface one foot square, a piece of board for instance, be moved forward horizontally at the rate of 23·6 feet a second, the resistance is one pound; whereas if it be held at an angle of 6° to the

---

[1] "On Aerial Navigation," *Journal of Natural Philosophy, Chemistry, and the Arts* (Nicholson's), xxiv., p. 164 (1809).

horizon and moved forward as before, the resistance will be only ⅖ lb. in a direction perpendicular to its surface. If the velocity is then increased to 37·3 feet per second, the resistance will be equal to 1 lb., since, as we have seen, it increases, speaking roughly, as the square of the velocity.[1] Sir George Cayley estimated that the weight and wing area of a Rook were in the proportion of 1 lb. to the square foot. The Rook would therefore maintain his level, if having a velocity of 37·3 feet per second he placed himself at an angle of 6° to the horizon. This calculation has great value since it emphasizes and connects three important facts: (1) if a bird inclines his body at a small angle to the horizon the resistance of the air is much less; (2) the resistance being at right angles to the plane of his body and wings will tend to support his weight; (3) the support given increases enormously with increase of velocity. But it is easy to show that it is inaccurate. To begin with, a Rook does not present a plane surface like a piece of board. It presents irregular concavities which cause the air to offer a far greater resistance; but how much greater, has not been discovered either by calculation or by experiment. Besides this, the whole ⅖ lb. resistance offered by the air will not go to the bird's support. A small fraction of it will oppose his onward progress, the proportion which is thus a hindrance and not a help

---

[1] ⅖ lb. × $\dfrac{37\cdot3 \times 37\cdot3}{23\cdot6 \times 23\cdot6}$ = ⅖ × ⁵⁄₂ (nearly) = 1lb. A mistake in the figures made by Sir George Cayley has been corrected by Professor Roy. See Newton's *Dictionary of Birds*, vol. i., p. 263.

diminishing as the bird's position approaches nearer and nearer to the horizontal. This reduction of waste need not, however, mean an absolute gain. He will have to bear in mind that if he reduces the upward inclination of his body to the vanishing point, his course will be inevitably downwards. When the angle becomes extremely acute, nearly all the resistance comes in the form of support, but this fact will avail him nothing if the total of resistance be too small. Thus the Rook has to make a calculation : if his velocity be so many feet per second, at what angle must he set himself in order not to lose elevation ? This will vary very much with the pace of the bird. The Swift and the Rook are to one another as an express and a parliamentary train : consequently the Swift can venture upon a much more acute angle than the Rook : consequently he will lose pace less rapidly and will be able to glide further.[1]

Mathematical problems are often simplified as Sir George Cayley has simplified this. The complications in Nature are so great that, in many cases, it is necessary to eliminate some of them,

---

[1] It is estimated that the horizontal is to the vertical resistance as the sine of the angle made by the bird's body with the horizon is to the cosine.

Thus if BA represents the bird's body the relative lengths of AC and CB represent the ratio of the horizontal resistance of the air to the vertical resistance.

FIG. 51.

if the problem is to be tackled at all. Every one is familiar with the pipes of different dimensions in arithmetic books which are opened at various times, some of them filling, some of them emptying a cistern, the problem being to discover at what precise time the cistern will be full or empty. Such problems give healthy exercise to the brain, but we must not suppose that the behaviour of water passing through pipes is a thing that can be absolutely predicted. The present calculation shows us general principles. But, since it does not take into account the resistance of the air to such an irregular surface as that of a bird's wing, it does not enable us, in the case of a particular bird, to fix the exact angle at which he must set himself, if he wishes, having attained a certain velocity, to glide onward and maintain his level.

Though the resistance offered by the air to surfaces like those of a wing cannot be accurately measured, yet it is possible to obtain some notion of its amount. If you hold an umbrella so that the inside faces a strong breeze, it feels a great strain, and is likely to give at every point. If, on the other hand, the outside meets the blast, the air passes harmlessly off its slippery convexity. Herr Lilienthal, the German engineer, who has sailed through the air a distance of over 500 yards with only a slight descent, once, as he was carrying his wings to the place of trial, was cheered by the fact that the air gathered in their curved under-surfaces and relieved him of all the weight. If we take a single big wing feather and wave it through the air, we feel that the resistance varies according as we turn the concave or convex surface to the front. The difference is far more apparent when we take the whole wing. Above, a bird s wing is convex, so that it passes easily through the air ; the under-surface is concave and lays hold of it. I am referring mainly to the part of it which is nearest to the body and which forms a kind of irregular cup, its hinder side gently sloping away. Experiments have been made with a view to measuring the resistance of the air to concave surfaces, but the results do not help us much. The irregularity of the wings has not been reproduced, the velocity has been uniform, whereas that of the wing is very different at different stages of the stroke, and no account has been taken of the variation of the curves during flight owing to the elasticity of the great feathers.

The duty of the near part of the wing is to a great extent that of a parachute. Between the strokes, the bird drops, and were it not for these umbrella-like supports, the drop would be greater than it is. The work of propelling is, as we have seen, done mainly by the extremities of the wings, which move with far greater rapidity. It is possible to find approximately the centre of the action of the air—to find a point in the wing so situated that the air shall act with equal force on the near and far sides of it. If the wing were a triangle, this point would be in a line drawn from the middle of the base to the apex, $\frac{2}{3}$ of its length from the shoulder. If it were a rectangle, it would be at a point on the corresponding line $\frac{3}{4}$ of its length out. Professor Marey estimates that in the actual wing it is at a point about $\frac{2}{3}$ of its length from the base. It must vary much in wings of different shape.

But it is not only when we compare base and extremity that the division of labour is unequal. If we divide the wing in imagination by a line drawn down its middle from base to tip, then the front half will do far more work than the hinder half, when the bird is gliding at great speed or moving his wings rapidly through the air. A boat sailing at an angle to the wind with a sail slung obliquely across it supplies an illustration of this. If she moves rapidly, only the forepart of the sail will do much work. The wind is blowing, say, at right angles to the boat. It will strike the forepart of the sail, over all the rest of which there will only be a backward current of air, which has been turned from its course by the forepart. The faster the boat sails, and, also, the nearer to the wind she sails, the truer this will be ; the narrower will be the margin of sail that really works. This is called the law of Avanzini. It holds with regard to the bird's wing, which during the down stroke moves rapidly forward as well as downward, and, of course, shares the onward movement of the whole bird. It is truer of the swiftly moving extremity than of the slower inner part, and this accounts for the remarkable way in which long wings, notably those of the Swift and Gannet, narrow towards their ends. Professor Pettigrew made some experiments which illustrate this. He cut away the hinder part of a Bluebottle's wings and apparently it could fly equally well. In the same way with Sparrows, the removal of the same part of the wing seemed to do little damage. Still to describe the flight after these mutilations as "perfect" is to go too far. No failing may strike the eye. A

FLIGHT

man with his hands tied behind his back may appear
to walk with ease, but in the course of a long tramp,
it would hamper him much.   In stopping, in rising
and till great velocity is attained, a broad expanse of
wing is of use.

For the understanding of gliding flight also, it is
most important to bear in mind the law of Avanzini.
If a bird wishes to descend rapidly, he must partly
flex his wings, so that they may present a less
extended front and, consequently, receive less support.
If he wishes to descend very gradually or maintain
his level or glide upward, he must open his wings to
their full stretch, so as to have the support of as long
a front line as possible.   The amount of work done
by the front margin and, consequently, the trajectory
of his flight will of course vary with the pace[1] (fig. 52).

The principle just explained can be seen at work
in little paper contrivances.   Take a piece of paper
shaped thus

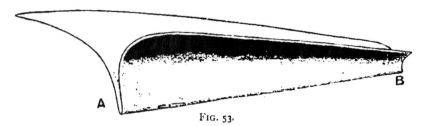

FIG. 53.

Fold it along the line AB so that the two sides slope
upwards.   Put in a pin along the line with its head
near A.   Hold it on a slant with A at the lower end
and let it drop.   It will glide some distance and very
likely show an upward tendency ending in a somer-

[1] See Newton's *Dictionary of Birds*, p. 265.

sault. Then put in the pin with its head near B and drop it as before, but make B the lower end. It will glide by a steep descent to the ground. It is worth while improving the cut and balance of these little toys till they behave properly, for they admirably illustrate gliding flight: when A leads, a bird with wide-spread wings is represented; when B, a bird with wings partly flexed.

Before closing this subject I must refer to the old fallacy that the bird, owing to its hollow bones, is like a balloon. This has been already dealt with in the previous chapter (see p. 105).

The General Shape of the Bird.

If a ship were built on absolutely perfect lines, when she lay at anchor and swung to the tide, the pressure of the stream upon the bows would be exactly balanced by the closing of the waters again at the stern, so that the only force straining at the cable would be due to friction. The case would be far differrent if the vessel presented a flat surface to the current at right angles to it. The lines on which a bird is built are first-rate: its body is not unlike in shape to that of a fish, and investigations have shown that fish are constructed so as to meet the minimum of resistance in passing through a fluid.

Passive Machinery.

The Passive Machinery consists of bones, ligaments, tendons, membranes and feathers. None of these have, like muscular tissue, any power of contraction. Any activity they may show is really due to their being acted on directly or indirectly by muscles.

It will be well first to make some general remarks on the different kinds of joints. Passing over what are called imperfect joints because they allow of very little motion—those between the vertebræ in man are good examples—we have (1) ball and socket joints where the rounded surface of one bone fits into a cuplike hollow in another ; (2) hinge joints where only motion backwards and forwards is possible ; (3) double hinge joints, *e.g.* that by which the thumb articulates with the wrist, or those between the neck vertebræ of birds ; I compared this joint above to two saddles put one atop of the other ; it has been well likened to the articulation between the rider and the saddle ; (4) pivot joints, *e.g.* that between the skull and the atlas vertebra.

In the wing we have examples in full working order only of the ball and socket, and hinge joints. The shoulder joint comes under the former head, and yet it is very different from the types of which we have a familiar instance in the thigh joint, in which a round ball fits into a deep cup. At the shoulder the cup is shallow and imperfect, and the bone which fits into it is not round. The result is that it works with great freedom, so much so that it has sometimes been called

a universal joint. It is at this point only that the wing
turns and twists, when it is fully extended : chiefly at
this point, when it is partly flexed. The other joints
are hinges : had they anything of the "universal"
joint in them, the wing would not have that stiffness
which is indispensable, if it is to stand the pressure
upon it. When the wing flexes some free play in other
directions is possible. It will be interesting now to
compare the elbow joints of men and birds. In man
as in birds the ulna (*i.e.* the hinder or postaxial one of
the two armbones) articulates with the humerus by a
simple hinge joint. The difference lies in the articulation of the radius, the præaxial bone. In man
this moves with considerable freedom, articulating,
as it does, with the humerus by a pivot joint. If
you lay your elbow, forearm, and the back of your hand
upon a table, you can, while still keeping the elbow
immovable, turn the arm so that the palm of the hand
faces downwards. The radius revolves upon its pivot
joint and the hand with it. In the last-mentioned
position it lies across the ulna. It will be useful to
remember that the thumb continues the line of the
radius. When the back of the hand is downwards,
the position is called supination (*supinus* = lying on
the back) ; when the palm is downwards, pronation
(*pronus* = face downwards). In the bird the differences
are great. When extended for flight, the whole wing
is pronated and the elbow joint is immovably stiff. It
is true that if we straighten our arm and then place the
elbow on a table, the hand will not turn so readily as
it did when the arm was bent at the elbow. Still a
great deal of free play remains. In the bird the whole

limb becomes rigid. I think this is due mainly to the ligaments. When the wing is flexed there is much less rigidity, for, to say nothing of the movements necessary to flight, the different parts of the wing must face different ways in order to fold neatly over the body, the upper arm looking upwards and inwards, forearm upwards and outwards, the hand outwards and only very slightly upwards.

The way in which the wrist joint has been modified is remarkable : the hand has very little of the up and down movement that comes to ours so easily, and when the wing is fully extended, none at all. Its only free movement is away from the thumb and towards where the little finger would be. Our wrists are very stiff, if we try to move them thus. This peculiarity in the bird's wrist may be traced to the radius. When the wing is folded the bone slides forward and, extending beyond the ulna, forces the hand into the position described. When the wing is straightened the radius slides back and brings the hand into line with it.

The wing presses with tremendous force upon the bones that support it. When it descends like a flail, with its face during the first half of the stroke looking not only downwards and backwards, but also outwards, there must be great pressure inwards upon the pivot on which it turns. I have in an earlier chapter shown whence this pivot derives its strength. The shoulder is the meeting-place of three bones (the coracoid, the scapula, and clavicle), though only the two former actually help to form the joint. The coracoid and clavicle slope outwards, and it is this outward slope that gives them their power to resist the pressure

inwards, the scapula being useful mainly for hingeing
the back and breast together. A bird with a broken
clavicle is said to be incapable of flight.[1] But the
coracoid is much the stronger bone of the two. Its
broad base is fixed in a long groove in the sternum, to
which it is tied by powerful ligaments, and, besides
this, a strong membrane, covering all the space between
it and the clavicle, binds the two together. If skeletons
representing a number of species are examined, I
believe it will be found that in birds of powerful flight
the coracoids project outwards more than in inferior
flyers. I have no accurate measurements of my own
to give. But I once looked carefully through the
collection of breastbones at South Kensington and
noted down that in the Albatross, the Adjutant, the
Golden Eagle, and other birds that fly well, the two
coracoids made a large angle with each other and
were, at the same time, strong and short : whereas in the
Crowned Pigeon, Game-fowl, Goose, Parrot, Pheasant,
they formed a small angle and were at the same time
in proportion to the size of the bird longer and weaker.
I ought to mention however, that Fürbringer, a very
great authority, holds that the size of the angle made
by the coracoids varies according to the size of the
bird : the greater the bird the greater the angle.[2]
He recognises exceptions to the rule, and these
exceptions will, I think, be accounted for by the
power of flight of the particular species. His rule has,
no doubt, considerable foundation : a big bird takes

[1] Yet some Parrots, whose clavicles are rudimentary, fly well.
[2] See Max Fürbringer's *Untersuchungen zur Morphologic und
Systematik der Vögel*, p. 740.

slower and stronger strokes, the rate of movement of
the further end of the wing increasing enormously with
increase of length, and the resistance of the air increasing out of all proportion to the increase of
velocity.   Thus, in proportion to his weight and bulk,
a big bird will require a firmer pivot for his wing than
a small one.   But the comparatively small inter-cora-
coidal angle in the Pheasant (if I have estimated it
correctly) shows that power of flight as well as size
must be taken into consideration.

The working of the passive machinery may be seen
well in a dead bird.   Only extend the arm, and the
hand is extended!   Only extend the hand, and all the
large feathers are spread!   The radius, as I have
explained, slides back when the forearm is extended
and pulls the hand with it, bringing it into line with
the arm.   Then follows the sudden expansion of the
wing feathers like a fan, effected by means of elastic
ligaments through which the primary and secondary
feathers pass, and which are stretched directly the
angle between the hand and forearm is widened.   The
system of ligaments is elaborate. If the skin is removed
it will be seen that each of the great feathers is fastened
to the bone by a stringy tendinous mass.   Even in
the dry skeleton they leave their mark.   The elastic
ligaments can be made out without any dissection.
One, through which the quill of each feather passes,
can be clearly seen extending from the extremity of
the handbone or metacarpal to the armpit, including,
therefore, all the secondaries, and, with the exception
of those that spring from the fingers, all the primaries.
It is in fact a continuation of a tendon connected with

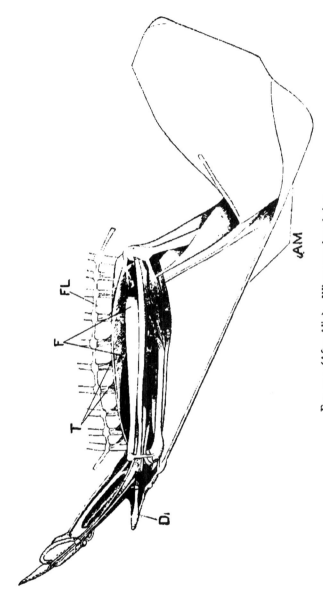

FIG. 54.—(After Alix). Wing seen from below.

AM, muscle and tendon supporting anterior membrane ; D1, digit one ; FL (by mistake for EL), elastic ligament pierced by quills ; F, flexor carpi ulnaris, dividing, as often, into two ; T, tendons passing to quills.

a muscle that arises from the ribs. A little nearer the bases of the quills there is another ligament which, instead of being pierced by them, runs along the lower side only. These two ligaments, according to M. Edmond Alix, get confounded at the hand and elbow, but in Pigeons I have found them running still separate beside the hand.

The above description may possibly have given the impression that the bones and ligaments supplied some motive power. This can only come from muscles. The forearm is put into line with the humerus by muscular effort, and the effort required is greater since the hand is necessarily extended by the same movement, and the extension of the hand requires more force since it involves the stretching of the ligaments in which the feathers are set. Thus, indirectly, the hand and the great feathers are prepared for flight by the action of the triceps muscle that extends the forearm. This must not be supposed to mean that there is no special muscle to extend the hand. There is one for this purpose arising from the further end of the humerus. And it must be remembered that the radius cannot by its sliding movement bring the hand *absolutely* into line with the forearm : the finishing touch must be given by the muscle just mentioned.

It is a marvellous piece of machinery which thus spreads the wings. But what is perhaps the most remarkable thing with regard to the secondaries—the great feathers that spring from the forearm—has yet to be mentioned. They are shifted in such a way that they prevent the passage of air during the down stroke, but let it pass during the up stroke. With this

view each is connected by a little triangle of tendon
with a muscle,[1] which arises from the upper-arm bone
at the end further from the body and attaches its
other extremity to one of the wristbones and also to
one of the metacarpals further on.   Working un-
opposed, it bends the wrist.   When the wing extends,
its resistance tightens up the wrist-joint and helps it
to bear the strain of flight.   When the wing is bent, it
lies in a slightly curved form.   It is straightened out
when the wing straightens, and this, combined with the
sloping of the feathers outwards from their bases, as
they spread, stretches the little tendons that arise from
it and are fastened to the feathers.   These little tendons
slope outwards, away from the shoulder, and passing
under the quills fasten to their further side (fig. 54).
When tightened, they rotate the feathers so that the
near side of the vane is pressed hard against the off
side of the one that overlaps it, thus preventing the
passage of air.   During the up stroke the tendons
relax and the feathers are no longer pressed tight
together, so that the air can now pass through them.

It is worth remarking that though the Triceps
controls the wings from the elbow joint to the hand,
yet that the two united fingers and all the feathers
upon them are not under its sway, but depend upon
their own muscles to extend them, lower them and
raise them—small movements the importance of which
it is so difficult to estimate.   The bastard wing also is
moved by its own muscles.

The wing-area is greatly increased by two mem-

[1] The muscle is called flexor carpi ulnaris by M. Alix; the
cubital antérieur, see p. 412 in *App. Loc. des Oiseaux*.

branes, one of which, called the anterior membrane, stretches from the head of the clavicle to the hand. In the Gannet it is of great breadth, and it is so placed that it makes an almost upright wall along the front margin of the wing, which thus presents a deep umbrella-like hollow, such as a parachute requires. In most birds the membrane is slung more horizontally. In all it is at once stretched, when the wing opens. The other membrane lies behind, in the armpit, and fastens the wing to the side.

The great feathers make some movement, without assistance except from the air. From below they are concave and during the down stroke the concavity is much lessened owing to the pressure upon them. When the muscles cease to lower the wings, the feathers regain their full curve owing to their own elasticity, and their bending thus is equivalent to a slight prolongation of the stroke. Up till this moment they have yielded to the air, they now strike down against it. The result of their action is that the stroke is longer and less violent, and that the strain upon the wing is lessened.

The air lends very material assistance in another movement, to effect which there is, as I have shown, muscular machinery provided. The outer webs of the feathers are very narrow compared with the inner ones. The result is that the air acts much more strongly upon the latter, forcing them upward, so that each feather has the inner side of its vane pressed closely against the one which lies next to it and above it on the side nearer to the body.[1] Thus the shape of the

[1] This interesting fact was first pointed out by Professor Roy.

feathers themselves greatly reduces the work of the muscles and tendons in making the adjustments that are required in order to render the wing impervious to air (fig. 55).

The Active Machinery.

The great muscles of flight lie below the shoulder joint, and yet upon them falls the task of raising the wing. All the great mass of muscle lies behind the joint, and yet the wing must be lowered without being pulled backward. Besides this the muscles can incline the wing rightly for upward flight, for a downward swoop, for a sudden halt; they can adjust it to every varying breeze, to every current or eddy that can be turned to account. In addition to the breast muscles, there are many smaller ones which help in these niceties of adjustment. When we consider the number of these, each with its special office, each giving the wing a slightly different turn from any other, it is extraordinary that Professor Marey should state that "the muscular apparatus of the bird, like that of the insect, has nothing to do with the course of the wing; elevation and depression are almost the

FIG. 55. — Primary wing-feather of Heron (less than natural size). The outer web is narrow.

only movements which it can produce."[1] Almost everything beyond the mere up and down motion he attributes to the resistance of the air. It is true that some important movements can be set down wholly or in part to this. Still much is left for the muscles to do.

Before their position and their working can be

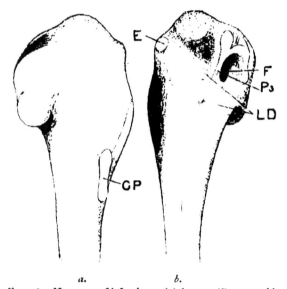

a.   *b.*

FIG. 56.—Humerus of left wing. (*a*) lower ; (*b*) upper side.

E, elevator muscle attaches. The point of attachment varies, in distance from the shoulder and from the præaxial margin. The action remains much the same. F, air foramen ; LD, latissimus dorsi attaches ; GP, great pectoral or depressor ; P3, third pectoral.

understood, some further account must be given of the humerus. Its position, even when at rest, is abnormal ; it has received a twist at the joint which has left it set differently from the humerus of any other animal, so that you must not use the terms "above" and "below," "postaxial" and "præaxial," before carefully finding your bearings. In addition to this it

[1] *Animal Mechanism*, p. 214.

so rotates in the course of the stroke that further
bewilderment is apt to arise. When the wing is
folded, what is really the upper side of the humerus
looks partly upward, but mainly towards the body.
It may be easily recognised by an unmistakable
landmark, the foramen or aperture through which the
bone is aerated (see Fig. 56). In the primitive ancestors of birds, with their forelimbs not yet adjusted
for flight, this would have been on the upper surface,
and postaxial. On what is really the under surface,
but in existing birds looks forward instead of downward when the wing is at rest, there is another landmark. Where the broad expansion at the rear end
of the bone begins to narrow down, there may be seen
a rather long mark on the bone (GP). This is
where the Great Pectoral muscle attaches—on what is
properly the under side near its præaxial edge. In
describing what we may call the geography of the
bone, we must always state what would be the case
if it were set as it is in other animals, and as it is in
the bird itself during the down stroke.

At its near end it is broad, and, according as a
muscle attaches at one margin or the other, can be
made to rotate either way. A pull from below on the
præaxial margin will make it turn its under surface
backward. A pull on the præaxial margin of the
upper side will make it face forwards. And so forth.

The Great Pectoral muscle springs from the lower
part of the keel (supposing the bird is placed breast
downwards), partly also from the sides of the breastbone above the keel and from the ribs where they
join the breastbone. From the breast it passes forward,

fastens firmly to the clavicle all along its length, and then by a very short tendon attaches where I have pointed out the mark of it on the humerus, on its under side and its further or præaxial margin. I have in several species found another less strong attachment, also on the under side of the bone, but near its postaxial margin ; and I cannot help thinking that the bird can make the muscle act mainly on the one or the other at his pleasure. In both cases the wing would be lowered, but it would be rotated differently ; working through its main tendon attached to the præaxial margin of the bone it causes the wing to face to the rear as it descends.

Every one must have noticed that, when the breast of a chicken is carved, the greater part of the meat flakes off clean from a thinner layer that lies below in the angle between the upright keel and the nearly horizontal sheet of bone below. This upper part (the bird now lying upon its back) is the great pectoral that lowers the wing, the part below is the Elevator muscle. The muscular fibres in the Great Pectoral may be easily seen in an uncooked bird running forwards, or, more strictly, forwards and inwards, converging from both sides on a line of tendon in the middle. The *set* of the fibres shows the direction in which they pull. But since the muscle does not arise only from the breastbone, but also from the clavicle, the result of its action is not to draw the wing backwards and downwards, but simply downwards. The forward movement is, as I shall show, due to the action of the air (see p. 213). To turn to the Elevator muscle. Unassisted, it could not raise the wing since it

lies below it. But the humerus turns as on a pivot
at the joint, and if it be pulled inward it will be
raised to an upright position, if only the pull comes
from a point not below the pivot. A tendon, therefore,
must be made to pass through a pulley fixed at a
point high enough, and must attach to the inner side of
bone some little way out from the joint. By such means
a mast may be raised, if it be prevented from slipping
at its base. A pulley on a level with the shoulder-
joint is available. There are two bones, as explained
above, which meet to form the socket, the coracoid
and the scapula or shoulder blade. On their inner
side the top of the clavicle or merrythought meets
them, and the three together form a tunnel of bone.
Through this passes the tendon and fastens on to the
back of the humerus near its præaxial margin.

The upstroke is at first in a backward direction,
mainly owing to the action of the wind due to the bird's
own velocity; such a wind must necessarily drive the
wing backward and at the same time lift it.[1] The movement to rearward, which is often difficult to detect in
photography, is clear in diagrams obtained by Professor
Marey by various methods.[2] Towards the end of the
upstroke the wing is moved forward, till it stands above
the pulley and the pivot, mainly by the action of the
Elevator muscle. The way to see the working of
these muscles is to take a dead bird and cut away the

[1] The third pectoral muscle, springing from the outer and
lower part of the coracoid and from the sternum close to the
ribs, assists—its chief office being to draw the wing backward.
It attaches to the upper side of the humerus, just over the air
foramen.

[2] See p. 221.

Great Depressor and the Elevator from the bone while
leaving their tendons attached to the humerus,
then pull them and watch the result. Much that
otherwise must be obscure then becomes perfectly
clear. Not the least interesting point is the way in
which the Elevator, being attached where it is, raises
the front or præaxial margin of the wing, so that in
attaining its position for a fresh stroke it turns the
edge to the air and meets with little resistance. These
two muscles can also be worked at the same time, the
one antagonising the other ; the Depressor lowering
the wing to the horizontal, while the Elevator holds
the præaxial margin fast, so that the hinder part
cannot be tilted up. A bird sets his wings thus when
he wishes to halt. A movement that looks perfectly
simple may be due to the combined action of a
number of muscles.

The Spreading of the Wing.

It is a strange thing that in these days when it is
boasted that machines can be made to do most things
that a man can do, that sailors should still have to
run up the rigging, be the weather foul or fair, and
straddle across the yards in order to furl or set
the sails. It would not seem to be beyond human
ingenuity to devise machinery by the aid of which
this work should be managed from the deck. Some
progress towards this has, I believe, been made. In
the bird we find such machinery brought to great
perfection. Instead of men we have muscles, and by
the machinery of tendons and ligaments these muscles,

situated on or near the body, are able to spread the
wings and regulate their utmost extremities. It is
all-important that it should be so. All the weighty
organs must be accumulated in the body. To speak
metaphorically, the wings must be made up of very
little besides masts, sails, and cordage.

The great muscles that move the humerus I
have already described ; they spring from the breastbone and neighbouring bones. The muscles that
bend or straighten the arm at the elbow arise from
the top of the coracoid and from the anterior end of
the shoulder-blade respectively. Nearly all their bulk
and weight is near the body. One of them, the
triceps, does a great work ; it straightens the elbow-
joint, whereupon the hand is extended and the great
ligaments get to work and spread the feathers, and
then only small points remain for small muscles to
see to. There are ten muscles springing from the
further end of the humerus. These, of course,
are not large, and most of them extend only to the
wrist or metacarpal bone. Two of them, however,
by the help of tendons move the fingers. Altogether,
to do this work, there are five long muscles springing either from the humerus or the ulna. And
one of these attaches to the much-reduced thumb,
called the bastard wing.[1] There are also no less
than eight very small muscles springing from the
wrist and metacarpal bones, and filling up the space
between the latter. All of these are attached to the
fingers or "thumb," which, actually, engrosses no

[1] See p. 42, where it is discussed what fingers in our hand
correspond to the three in a bird's wing.

P

less than four; the second digit (the first finger as we call it in our own hands) has three, and the third digit only one. But it must be remembered that these two digits are fixed together so that one cannot move without the other. Counting long and short muscles together we have thirteen to move the " thumb " and fingers. Of these the " thumb " has five, one long and four short.

Active and Passive Machinery—Summary.

(1) All the muscles of any size at all arise not further from the body than the far end of the humerus or the near end of the forearm. All the really large muscles arise from the body. The spreading of the wing is much simplified by the fact that the radius, when the elbow-joint is straightened, slides back and extends the hand. The extension of the hand involves the stretching of the elastic ligament, and, consequently, the spreading of the great feathers. The straightening of the arm also spreads the anterior and axillary membranes, thereby greatly increasing the wing area.

(2) The fingers must have a great deal of freedom of movement, since they have so many muscles attaching to them. Similar evidence seems to show that the " thumb " cannot be quite rudimentary. Later on I shall show that it is sometimes used.

(3) Muscles, which, if worked separately, have contrary effects, may work together with good results. Thus if the muscle which bends the wrist be contracted at the same time as the one which puts the hand in a

line with the forearm, the result will be that the hand will be pulled hard against the wrist. This will help the ligaments to resist the very great strain put upon them. The wonder is that, with all its strength, the wrist joint does not succumb.

(4) The air, to a considerable extent, determines the movement of the wing. This will be explained more fully later on.

(5) There are muscles which rotate the great secondary feathers and hold them in the best position to make the wing impervious to air. All the great wing feathers are so shaped that the action of the air upon them assists the muscular machinery.

Such is the wing, at once strong and light; pliable or stiff, according as pliability or stiffness is needed at different parts, or at different times; quickly spread and quickly flexed, capable of the nicest adjustment to suit every phase of flight; worked by machinery, all the weightier part of which is massed upon the body or close to it, and turning on a pivot which stands firm under all pressure.

Weight of the Breast Muscles.

To realise how important are the muscles that lower the wing, it is only necessary to know what proportion their weight bears to that of the whole body. I have weighed those of two Wood-pigeons and two domestic pigeons, and have found in each case that they accounted for either just under or just over one fifth of the total weight. In one of the

Wood-pigeons [1] the three pairs of breast muscles represented three thirteenths of the whole—*i.e.*, a little less than one quarter, a very large proportion, the average, among birds, being less than a fifth. The Elevator is very small compared with the Depressor, often so light that the most delicate scales are required if trustworthy results are to be obtained. The differences in different species are very striking. In the Wood-pigeon I have found the weight of the small muscle to be a little less than one fifth of the greater, in the starling just over one ninth.

Movements of the Wing partly due to the Action of the Air.

The muscle which lowers the wing rotates the humerus, as I have shown, so that the under surface of the wing looks *backward* and downward. And since the whole expanse of feathers lies to rearward of the bones, the action of the air will tend to turn the wing round in the same direction, just as the wind swings a sign-board. When once an upward

[1] These figures do not agree with those given by two German investigators, Legal and Reichel, in the *Jahres-Berichte der Schlesischen Gesellschaft für Vaterlandcultur*, 1879. They give $\frac{1}{3\cdot43}\left(=\frac{100}{343}\right.$ = more nearly $\frac{1}{3}$ than $\frac{1}{4}\right)$ to represent the relative weights of the three pairs of pectoral muscles and of the whole body. This seems impossible, nor is it clear why in the pigeon the breast muscles should weigh so enormously heavier in proportion to the weight of the body than in any other bird. In the case of other species their figures are not so startling, and they may be more trustworthy.

incline from the front to the hinder margin has
been brought about, the resistance of the air will
no longer act vertically, but at right angles to the
plane of the wing. And the force thus acting may
be resolved into two, one raising the wing, the other
urging it forward. When the end of the descent has
been reached, muscular action and the air acting
mainly on the front margin,[1] cause the wing to change
front and face *forward* and downward. The wind
due to the bird's own velocity will act on the oblique
surface, and lift it backward and upward. Thus when
the bird is flying rapidly the air relieves the Elevator
muscle of a great part of its work, and this accounts
for its small size. The velocity due to the action of
the great Depressor muscle comes to the assistance
of the small Elevator. Even when there is no great
speed to create a current of air relatively to the bird,
the descent of the body during the upstroke helps to
lift the wing. In the same way during the downstroke, the work is lightened and the extremity of
the wing appears to travel a much greater distance
than it really does. For the raising of the body
means a relative lowering of the wings, and helps
them home just as the motion of the boat seems to
help the oar through the water.

The Tail.

The tail feathers have their elastic ligament. At
their bases they are firmly held by muscles, and are
arranged like a fan. Some little way out from their

---

[1] See p. 190.

base they are bound together by a strong elastic band, the outer ends of which pass into muscles which arise from the vertebræ of the tail. When these muscles contract, the fan opens, the distance between the quills being increased where the elastic band holds them, their bases meanwhile being held firm. The tail itself can be moved in any direction, having several pairs of muscles attached to the vertebræ and to the pelvis at different levels so that it can be raised or lowered, and also (since one member of a pair of muscles can contract without the other) moved to right or left. It is often important that the tail should form a hollow on its under side. This is ensured by the form of the feathers which is similar to that of the primaries and secondaries in the wing. The outer webs are very narrow in all except the one or two central pairs ; the broad inner webs offer more resistance to the air and are forced upward, each pressing hard against the outer web of the feather next to it on the inner side. The result is that the tail, besides being almost impervious to air, presents a curved surface with the concavity underneath. The Woodpecker uses his strong tail feathers to support him as he clings to a tree ; and consequently one is not surprised to find that in him the muscles which lower the tail are very highly developed.

Rate of Stroke.

There are three ways of estimating this, one of which has been tried, I believe, only in the case of insects. These three ways are—(1) that of unassisted observation—to watch a bird flying and count the strokes per minute; (2) to determine the note made by the vibration of the wings, and from that to calculate the velocity; (3) to apply machinery by which the bird or insect registers each stroke. These three methods may be called, respectively, the method of observation, the acoustic, and the graphic method.

(1) The first can only be employed when the bird is flying slowly, and even then it often happens that two observers do not agree. But it is impossible to bring any machinery to bear upon a bird in a state of liberty, so that the third method gives us the wild wing-beats of some poor wretch, the subject of alarming experimentation. I have repeatedly counted the strokes of Gulls making long flights, and find 120 per minute to be a common rate. Friends whom I have got to count for me have come to conclusions not far different. With birds like the Pigeon, whose stroke is much more rapid, the estimates are far from dependable. The Puffin's wings move so rapidly that you only see a shimmer in the air, and you can no more count the strokes than you can see the individual spokes of a wheel in rapid motion.

(2) The acoustic method depends on the fact that a tuning-fork when its vibrations have a certain frequency gives off a certain note, and in the same way the wings of an insect beating, as they sometimes do, 20,000 times per minute. But the exact tone varies as the insect flies towards or away from us. An engine whistle sounds shriller as the train approaches. In our present investigations there is besides this the insuperable difficulty that the whirring of a bird's wings

is often quite inaudible. Even when we can hear the note it does not tell us much. It depends on the rapidity with which the extremity of the wing moves, not on the number of wing-beats in a second, and so cannot tell us what we want.

(3) We now come to the graphic method, in applying which Professor Marey has shown wonderful skill. A sheet of paper blackened by the smoke of a candle was stretched upon a cylinder, which was made to revolve at a uniform rate. An insect, the frequency of whose wing movements was to be studied, was held by the abdomen in a delicate pair of forceps, and was placed so that one of its wings, at every up or down stroke, brushed against the blackened paper. With birds the method was, necessarily, far more elaborate. On the extremity of the wing an apparatus was placed which at each alternate movement broke or closed an electric circuit. In Professor Marey's book (*Animal Mechanism*, p. 230) the bird may be seen carrying his burden of electric wires and other machinery. As in the case of the insect, a tracing was made on a revolving cylinder.

The results were:

	Revolutions of wing per second.
Sparrow ...	... 13
Wild Duck ...	... 9
Pigeon... ...	... 8
Screech Owl ...	... 5
Buzzard ...	... 3

These results seem quite dependable, and it is much to be regretted that we cannot arrive at conclusions equally certain with regard to less flurried flight. The slowness of a bird's stroke compared with an insect's was most remarkable, a common fly attaining the astounding rapidity of 330 per second, and a bee 190. It must be borne in mind that the extremity of a long wing may move very rapidly, though the number of strokes per minute be few, and that a bird's wing with its long sweep may produce more effect, even when we allow for the greater weight to be supported and propelled, than the insect's can by its many rapid pulsations.

There is the further question of the comparative velocity of the up- and downstrokes. Photography has proved what we should not have anticipated—viz., that the upstroke is the more rapid of the two.[1]

	Duration of upstroke.	Duration of downstroke.
Duck ...	$\frac{3}{60}$ sec.	$\frac{3\frac{2}{3}}{60}$ sec.
Pigeon	$\frac{3}{60}$ sec.	$\frac{4\frac{1}{2}}{60}$ sec.
Buzzard	$\frac{8\frac{1}{2}}{60}$ sec.	$\frac{13}{60}$ sec.

This is accounted for by two facts — (1) that the air offers little resistance to the passage of the rounded upper surface; (2) that when the pace attained is great the air itself lifts the wing and relieves the Elevator muscle of a great part of its work.

[1] See Marey's *Vol des Oiseaux*, p. 101.

Phases of the Stroke. [1]

Instantaneous photography has in many ways surprised the world. Horses no longer trot or gallop as they did. Birds get their wings into the most surprising positions, utterly unlike anything to be seen

FIG. 57 (after Marey).
Gull flying.

in the conventional bird of the artist. Many Gulls have been photographed on the wing by Messrs. Wyles, at Southport; some Storks, the favourite bird in the Fatherland, by Germans; the American Eagle and other birds, by Mr. Muybridge; and Professor

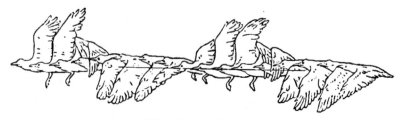

FIG. 58 (after Marey).
Gull flying—50 images per second.

Marey has obtained images of flying Gulls, at the rate of fifty per second, showing the various phases of the up- and down-strokes. The Southport Gulls are

[1] Some of this has been necessarily anticipated. See "Active Machinery," and "Movements of the Wing partly due to the Action of the Air."

FIG. 59.—Gulls on wing (from a photograph by Messrs. Wyles).

winging their way quite unconscious of cameras, and sensitive plates, and fame. On the other hand, Mr. Muybridge's American Eagle, with his somewhat draggled plumes, looks like a scared captive, conscious that the camera is being aimed at him. However, it is only under conditions like these last, that photographs such as those of Professor Marey, showing the position of the wing at every stage, can be obtained.

When the bird is flying with great energy, he raises his wings high till in some cases they touch one another, and this is the cause of the slapping noise that we hear when a Pigeon rises from the ground. The wing next moves forward and downward, its under surface looking backwards and downwards. In its forward movement it meets with little resistance, since it cuts edgeways through the air. When it can strain no further forward and down, it is drawn backward and bent sharply at the wrist-joint, facing during the process forwards and downwards. During the last period of the upstroke there is a further turn, and it moves edgeways forward.[1] This description of the movements of the wing refers to very vigorous flight, such as we most commonly see when the bird is getting up steam. When he has plenty of way on there is no need for him to take these very long and exhausting strokes, unless, like the Duck, he is one of those that seem always to fly with effort. In birds of long flight, the wing does not rise very high or descend very low, and it is flexed very little, if at all, when it is raised. These points can be made out if a Gull is watched when it is flying steadily. In some of

---

[1] Further details under next heading.

Messrs. Wyles's photographs of Gulls, flying horizontally at some height from the sea, there is not a single
one among the large number that has its wings flexed.
(See frontispiece.)

Figures described by different parts of the Wing.

If you take an insect (a Bluebottle, for instance, or a
Drone) and hold it down, the wing tips as they vibrate

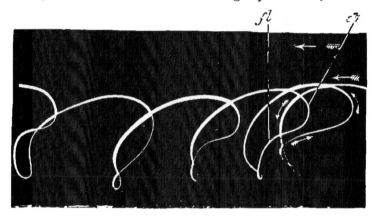

FIG. 60 (after Marey).
Figure described by tip of Crow's wing.[1]
The backward movement near *fl* is largely due to the flexing, the forward movement
near *st* to the straightening of the wing.

will be seen to describe a figure of 8. If the sunlight
be made to fall upon them, it will be all the clearer.
I have tried painting the tips with body white, but
the rapid vibration soon dislodges the paint. It is
much harder to discover the trajectory of a bird's
wing. Professor Pettigrew has strongly insisted that
it is an 8 as in the case of insects, but the lower circle

[1] I have corrected the mistake by which the words "right"
and "left" have been accidentally transposed in Professor
Marey's explanation of the figure.

of the 8 either does not exist, or at any rate is reduced
to very small dimensions. Applying machinery to
the bird's wing, Professor Marey succeeded in tracing
the figure described by the outer end of the humerus.
It is an ellipse with the long axis inclining downwards. The difficulties were found to be great in
obtaining by the aid of similar machinery a tracing
of the course followed by the wing tip. Professor
Marey at length hit upon the following plan. He
fastened a small piece of white paper to the tip of a
crow's wing, and as the bird flew in front of a perfectly
black screen, he took a photograph of this moving
speck of white, while of course no image of the crow
appeared upon the plate. In the figure the long
forward sweep of the downstroke comes out very
clearly ; at last the line curves backward, the wind
of the bird's velocity making the wing retreat : the
muscles arrest this backward movement, and we have
an apparent forward twitch (due perhaps to the onward
momentum which the wing-tip shares with the whole
body), forming the small loop at the bottom. Soon
the wing hunches up at the wrist and for some distance
the tip moves upward and backward (β). It will be
noticed that as the bird moves from right to left with
increasing speed, the tracings alter, and at last the
smaller circle disappears altogether. The figure, in
fact, varies considerably even when the same bird is
experimented on, especially when it begins to get up
speed. When the velocity is at all considerable, no
ellipse is actually formed. It only exists in imagination, like the ellipse which we say the moon forms
in revolving round the earth. The earth itself,

meanwhile, is moving rapidly onward, so that the
line of the moon's course never meets or crosses itself.
When the moon moves backward and circles round
us, its backward movement is only relative to the
earth. In reality it is moving onward, only with less
velocity. To apply this to a bird's wing : suppose
that a pigeon is flying at the rate of thirty miles an
hour—*i.e.* at a fairly easy-going pace if the weather be
good, and with a stroke of 300 per minute. This
gives an advance of $2\frac{1}{15}$ yards per stroke. More than
half of this advance will be made during the downstroke. The downward curve, therefore, will be
altogether out of reach when the time comes for
putting in the upward one to complete the ellipse,
and when a velocity of fifty or more miles an hour
is attained, the ellipse becomes still more theoretical.
But though it is desirable to point this out it hardly
diminishes the interest of what Professor Marey has
proved, that the trajectory of the humerus and of the
wing tip, when the figure is not destroyed by the
rapidity with which the bird travels, is an ellipse
with, in the latter case sometimes, a small loop at
the lower end.

The Bird's Trajectory.

Meanwhile the bird's trajectory is an undulating
one. It rises with every downstroke, and sinks with
every upstroke. Though in the course of the latter
there seems to be in some species a slight momentary
rise, caused by the wind of the bird's velocity catching the wings and his whole surface, yet the main

movement is, as we should expect, downwards. The broadjumper, as he rises and descends, describes in the air a curve not unlike the curves of the bird's trajectory. Many of our small birds—*e.g.* the House-sparrow—may be seen as they fly to take a regular jump upward, and then with outstretched wings glide onward and slightly downward. The centre of gravity of course rises and falls, but not so much as a particular point in the bird—the eye, for instance; for when the bird rises his wings are lowered, and this lowers the

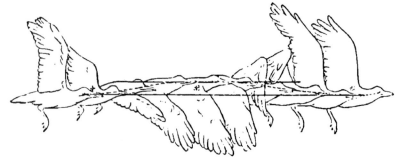

FIG. 61 (after Marey).

The space between the two straight lines shows the limits of the rise and fall of the eye. The cross shows the position, according to calculation, of the centre of gravity at the moments when the wing is highest or lowest.

centre of gravity; it is at a higher point in the bird when he sinks, for at this moment his wings are raised aloft. Thus the centre of gravity moves along in an undulating line, but its oscillations are not so great as those of the eye, since every *rise and fall* of the bird is accompanied by a *fall and rise* of the centre of gravity.

Long Distance Flight.

Long wings are best suited for long distances. With a single short stroke they send the bird far on his way, the further end of the lever moving with great velocity and force. The short wing must beat frequently and with a longer swing. Put the wing of a Swift beside that of a Duck, and compare the two. The cut of them at once shows the flight of each. The Swift's is long and very narrow towards the end, the duck's short for its size, and rounded. The Swift

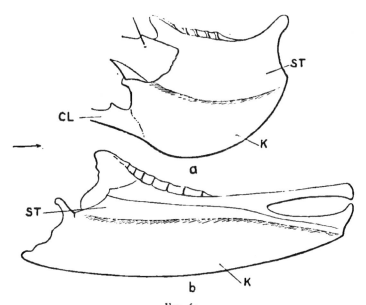

FIG. 62
Breast-bone of (a) Frigate Bird, (b) of Duck, ⅔rds natural size.
CL, clavicle ; CO, coracoid ; K, keel ; ST, sternum proper.

covers, probably, 60 miles in the hour without great effort and without a very rapid stroke : the duck keeps up a good pace, but only by means of strokes that are at once very rapid and very long. If a Gannet be watched as he goes leisurely onwards it will be seen that his wings do not rise much above or descend much below a horizontal line from the

Q

shoulder.   A gull as he travels keeps his wing slightly
bent at the wrist, as photographs show, and probably
also at the elbow, and does not flex them any more
than this for the upstroke : they are merely rotated
(*i.e.* a turn at the shoulder raises the front margin),
and then lifted for the downstroke again (frontispiece).

The birds which take long strokes have long
pectoral muscles arising from long breastbones : those
which take short strokes have the pectorals corre-
spondingly short.   I have above explained the rule
that the amount of contraction possible to a muscle
depends upon its length (see p. 142).   If we bear this
in mind it will be very interesting to set side by side
the skeletons of a Frigate Bird and a duck.   The breastbone of the former is extraordinarily short, but deep,
showing that his typical wingstroke is a very short
but powerful one ; the duck's has a great superiority
in length, but not in depth, suggesting the quick long
strokes of his far more laborious flight.

Some small birds cross wide seas, and we are apt to
think of them as having no special qualification for
such voyages.   Golden-crested Wrens come to us
in flocks from Norway, and sometimes, wearied out,
cluster in flocks on the rigging of fishing smacks.
But the wings are, for such tiny creatures, long and
fine ones.

Upward Flight.

Watch a lark as he is mounting.   He holds his
body inclined steeply upwards, often at an angle of
about 60 degrees with the horizon.   While he is in
this attitude his wings are set so that their under

surfaces face downwards and slightly backwards.
Why, then, if they are adjusted nearly as they are
for horizontal flight, is his progress almost vertically
upward ? The natural action of his wings is to drive
him onward as well as upward. But not much onward
movement can take place, since the air offers too much resistance to the expanse of his breast and tail. His onward velocity is, in part, therefore, converted into upward
velocity ; and thus he is giving a practical illustration
of the working of the parallelogram of forces. He
always faces the wind, and derives, no doubt, great
help from it ; how, I shall explain later on (see p. 239).
Some birds can ascend much more rapidly, *i.e.* at a
much steeper incline than others. The reason of this
is, I believe, that they have greater freedom at the
shoulder joint, so that they can turn their wing further
over, giving it a steeper slope from the front to the
hinder margin. If a bird has but little power of
doing this, when he inclines his body upward so as
to form a large angle with the horizon, his wings will
beat backwards and forwards instead of up and down.
Wishing to test this I examined the wings of a good
many birds, some of them alive, some just after they
were shot. I found that the lark when its wing was
extended could lower its front margin a great deal
without any strain. The same was true, though not
quite to the same extent, of the jackdaw, jay, crow,
chough, magpie, rook, raven, quail, plover, eagle, all of
which, I believe, are capable of ascending at a fairly
steep incline. On the other hand the gannet, herring
gull, blackheaded gull, pelican, cormorant, had none
of them much power of rotating the wing, the cormorant,

I think, least of all. The pelican's flight I do not
know, but the rest ascend by a comparatively gentle
gradient ; some of them even require the help of a
head wind, if the ascent is to be made with reasonable
ease. The cormorant, when he leaves his fishing,
struggles hard before he gets clear of the water,
advancing quickly but ascending slowly, a striking
contrast in every way to the skylark as he mounts
lightly to the upper air.

Downward Flight.

It is a beautiful thing to see a pigeon, with wings
partly flexed, glide downwards through the air, then,
as he nears the ground, suddenly give his body an
upward instead of a downward slope, spread his wings
to stop himself, and, with all the grace of the " Herald
Mercury," alight.

The suddenness of the change from horizontal or
upward to downward flight is very striking. It is often
maintained that it is due to a shifting of the centre of
gravity by the elongation of the neck or of the legs, or
by some of the other little manœuvres known to birds,
which have this object. But the pigeon has no length
of neck or legs to extend. If you watch him change
all at once the incline of his body, you will see no
working of either. The very quickness of the movement shows that it must be due to muscular action,
and it is no doubt the work of the muscle called the
Latissimus Dorsi, which in horizontal flight raises the
hinder quarters by hauling upon the wings and which,
as I have shown, probably helps in the process of
breathing (see p. 89).

A jerk due to the sudden contraction of this muscle would have exactly the effect which we see when the pigeon in a moment gives his body a downward slant from tail to head. Hawks have, of course, exceptional power of swooping suddenly downwards, and I have found in the kestrel an altogether unusual development of this muscle. It has occurred to me that this power may be also in part due to the pliability of the waist in upward and downward directions, which some birds have in a much greater degree than others. The kestrel, swallow, sand-martin, all three of them able in a moment to put their bodies at any incline, have this qualification to a remarkable extent. Ducks, on the other hand, are very stiff at the waist, and they are, comparatively, but poor performers. The gulls and terns, however, are also remarkable for the same stiffness, and this makes me doubt whether pliability of waist is absolutely essential for these sudden up and down movements. At any rate, much nimbleness can exist without it.

The wings, as pointed out above, are partly flexed as the bird descends, since it is the front margin which mainly gives support when he is gliding, and if he were to form an extended front, he would travel more slowly and with a less rapid incline downwards, or in a horizontal or upward direction (see p. 190).

Horizontal Flight and Gliding Flight.

These have already been described (pp. 180, 190, 223).

Flight in Troops.

The formations adopted by birds when flying in troops are very interesting, but unfortunately not much is known of the subject. A wedge shape, the point

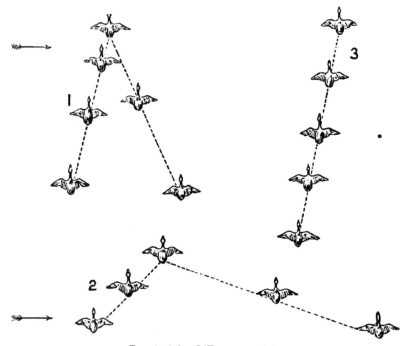

FIG. 63 (after D'Esterno partly).

Ducks in formations for troop-flying.

The arrows in 1 and 2 represent the direction of the wind. In 1 the wash passes between those to leeward; in 2 the leeward line is too far off to feel it. In 3 (wind ahead or aft or none), travelling each along his own line, they escape the wash and so also in V-formation.

leading, is the favourite, certainly among most of the great water birds such as swans, cranes, and pelicans (see Fig. 63). Whatever the formation, the object is not that those in front may break the resistance of the air for the benefit of those behind them. A bicyclist, driving as he does a mass of air before him, gives material assistance to another following close after. A bird's body, on the contrary, is so shaped that it does not meet with much resistance and consequently does not "break" the air to any great extent, and, in addition to this negative result, the action of his wings causes a back current, to which, in fact, his progress onward is due. A bird who finds himself in this back current is probably at least as badly off as a boat in the wash of another boat. In whatever form birds marshal themselves for flight, their aim probably is to save each from the wash of those in front. Even when they are apparently flying in Indian file, as ducks often do, we need not see an exception to the rule. It is by no means certain that their heads point exactly along the line : very probably all are following parallel tracks a short distance apart (see 3, Fig. 63). It is probable that the formation varies according to the direction of the wind relatively to the line of flight. Unfortunately the wind at a great altitude does not always blow from exactly the same point of the compass as the wind below. Another difficulty is that a flock of birds far above us may be flying some in one horizontal plane, others in another, though they appear to us to be in the same. It is very difficult to make trustworthy observations.

Changes *en route* take place frequently. The leader drops behind or there is a general rearrangement, apparently quite orderly, each falling without confusion into his place.

Wind and Flight.

Before going on to describe other varieties of flight, it will be well to make clear, as far as possible, how the wind may help a bird to rise to a higher elevation. Many begin early to gain the skill that is necessary if they are to avail themselves of this assistance. As soon as he has the use of his wings a young gull may be seen for a good part of the day busily practising. And the great proficients in the art— eagles, vultures, storks, and albatrosses—have acquired their skill by experimenting on all varieties of currents. The problem presents far greater difficulties for us. With labour and complicated contrivances we obtain some notion of what wind is, of its force, its currents, its eddies and gusts. By long and painstaking ob- servation the naturalist discovers what curves the bird describes in the air, whether he looks down the wind, or in the teeth of it or across it, and what angle his body forms with the horizon. Mercilessly the mathematician applies his laws showing that the theory of soaring that the naturalist fondly cherishes is built on an absurd assumption, while he himself, without inventing conditions which possibly do not exist, may fail to show how the aerial play of the gyrating vulture is physically possible.

With all these difficulties before us, let us first lay a sound mathematical foundation. However tempting the theory may be, that a Senior Wrangler has one system of mathematics and a Pelican a totally different one, we must not be beguiled by it.

The great principle to be borne in mind is that a bird can be helped to rise by a horizontal wind, only if he have a velocity of his own relatively to it. A man in a balloon that is sailing swiftly with the wind, is not conscious of his motion unless he looks down at the earth and marks his progress by the hills, trees, and houses that he leaves behind. Instead of considering that there is a breeze blowing, we may think of the earth as turning round without carrying its envelope of air with it. And this would have no effect on a balloon and its occupants.

A bird is often compared to a kite, and the simile is a correct or misleading one according to circumstances. If he has velocity of his own and inclines his body upward, the wind due to his own passage through the air will lift him like a kite. His own momentum takes the place of the string, and the force of the current that meets him is resolved into two, one acting upward, and the other horizontally. But supposing that he has no momentum, no velocity of his own, he is a kite without a string and is carried with the wind, not lifted by it.

It is possible that a bird may obtain relative velocity without any effort of his own by the help of irregularities in the wind. There may be currents of different velocity forming strata, or it may come in gusts. It has long been known that the wind near the earth's surface is retarded by friction. With a view to obtaining accurate measurements as to the amount of retardation and of the height to which the speed of the wind continues to increase, some experiments were undertaken by Mr. R. C. Gilson, Mr. J. P. Gilson, and myself.

These were by no means so complete as we had hoped they would be, owing to an accident to our anemometer. This small instrument, which presents sails like those of a windmill to the wind, and, as it turns, registers the length of the stream of air that has acted on it in the allotted time, was all that was required for the lower levels.

The place chosen, New Romney sands on the coast of Kent, has exceptional advantages for such experiments. There are no hills or cliffs to tilt the wind upwards, no trees or other obstacles to make it play tricks, so that it was a horizontal wind without complications that was experimented on.

The following are averages made out from four series of experiments :—

Altitude.	Velocity of the wind per minute.
2 inches	... 515 feet.
1 foot	... $736\frac{1}{2}$,,
2 feet	... 770 ,,
4 feet	... 918 ,,
7 feet 6 inches ...	... 1,021 ,,

As the wind comes in gusts, it is necessary, if the results are to be trustworthy, to make a number of measurements and strike averages. The figures show that the rate of increase diminishes as you ascend, the difference in velocity at two inches from the ground and one foot being very great. The following are the averages from only two series :—

Altitude.	Velocity of the wind per minute.
7 feet 6 inches	... 1,375 feet.
9 feet 6 inches	... $1,457\frac{1}{2}$,,

The plan for measuring the velocity of the wind at

higher altitudes was to run the anemometer up the string of a kite by means of another string passed through a pulley ; as soon as it had reached the right altitude a third string, passed between the vanes and hanging loose, was to be pulled out, thus allowing the instrument to work. The altitude was to be measured by means of a sextant. Alternate hurricanes and calms put obstacles in the way of kite flying, and finally the anemometer struck work and refused to register. But results that are far from valueless were obtained by attaching the kite to a spring balance which measured the pull at different heights.

Altitude measured by sextant.			Pull of kite.
420 feet ...	...	...	25 lbs.
357 feet ...	...	...	19 lbs.
350 feet ...	...	...	24 lbs.
204 feet ...	...	...	18 lbs.
126 feet ...	...	...	15—20 lbs.
60 feet ...	...	...	14—19 lbs.
42 feet ...	...	...	11—20 lbs.

There is the question whether the greater length of string carried as the kite mounted higher may not have to some extent modified the results. Probably, however, the error due to this cause was but slight. At low levels, from 126 feet downwards, the jerking of the kite made an accurate measurement of the pull very difficult. But the series suggests, though it does not prove, that there is a steady though diminishing increase up to 420 feet. The pull at 357 feet measured during a temporary lull is the only false note in the scale.

As a supplement to these kite-experiments, I tried the plan of letting go a number of small balloons, inflated with hydrogen gas in different degrees, and allowing them to race : those which were more distended, rising to a height of 500 feet or more, quite outpaced the smaller ones floating below them. But, as far as I could judge, small differences of elevation at the higher levels did not much affect the velocity.

Since making these experiments, I have found that far more elaborate ones, with kite-wire suspended anemometers, had already been recorded. They showed that the velocity of the wind increased up to a height of nearly 1,100 feet above the ground, but that the rate of increase there was very slight, the difference being only forty-four feet per minute between the velocities at altitudes of 795 feet and 1,095, and eighty-five between 549 and 795.[1]

It seems probable, then, that the wind increases in velocity up to a certain altitude, but that above that there is no appreciable increase. This being so, we must look for some other irregularity of which a bird soaring over a level plain can make use when he has passed this limit. It is within every one's experience that wind often comes in gusts. But we not unfrequently speak of a steady breeze, meaning one which is almost or entirely free from such fitfulness. Our experiments with an anemometer at New Romney went to show that a steady wind, in the strict sense of the term, does not exist. We had to expose the instrument for not less than a minute at a time, make a series of experiments, and strike averages, in order to obtain dependable figures. Professor Langley has by means of a delicate anemometer made more thorough

[1] *Nature*, April 22, 1886.

investigations, and his results show that the actual
variation is far greater than would ever have been
thought likely.[1]   When he measured the velocity at
intervals of seven to seventeen seconds at an altitude of
fifty-three feet, it varied from ten to twenty-five miles
per hour, and the inertia of the anemometer may, as he
says, have reduced the apparent variability. The greater
the velocity of the wind, the greater was the fluctua-
tion.   On one occasion he found that a wind blowing
forty miles an hour would almost in an instant drop to
a calm.   His anemometer once stopped dead for one
second in a high wind.   Another trial, when the
velocity was measured every second, showed that a
wind of twenty-three miles an hour may in ten seconds
rise to thirty-three miles, within ten seconds fall
again to twenty-three, then in another thirty seconds
rise to thirty-six.   As to the cause or the nature of
the apparent gusts it is difficult to speak positively.
It is impossible that the onward movement of a large
volume of air in motion can be suddenly checked.
Possibly the irregularity may be due to eddies, the
anemometer during an apparent lull being really within
the centre or the back current of an eddy, whereas
during what seems a sudden gust it is in the eddy's
onward sweep. But, whatever the explanation, the
inequality certainly exists, ready for a bird who has
the skill to make use of.

But is the wind blowing over the level plain horizontal ?   No one would imagine that it is otherwise,

[1] *American Journal of Science*, January 1894: " Internal
Work of the Wind," by Professor S. P. Langley. [Since
published separately.]

when no exceptional cause intervenes, had not Herr
Lilienthal tried to prove, by means of a vane working
vertically up and down, that its normal direction is
upward, at an incline of 3°—4° to the horizon.[1] If
this is really the nature of wind when not interfered
with by hills or any irregularities and when there
is no updraught from a sun-heated surface, there will
soon be no air left in which Herr Lilienthal, who
is ambitious to be a modern Dædalus, may try his
wings. If a vane under these conditions were to point
upwards, it would be more reasonable to regard the
fact as an indication of the eccentricity of all vertical
vanes, or of that particular one. While at New
Romney I had one made for me having for its larger
arm a piece of thin deal one foot long by six inches
broad, exactly balanced by a lump of lead attached to
the shorter arm. It is true that so small a deviation
as 3°—4° would be hard to detect, but this instrument
indicated, as far as I could judge, that a wind blowing
over a level expanse is perfectly horizontal. Experiments on the direction of the wind on, or on
either side of, a small barrier had more interest for
me. While standing on a bank only two feet high,
its tripod lifting it four feet above the bank, the vane
pointed decidedly upwards. Five yards to leeward of
a bank eight feet high it indicated that the wind blew
downwards, making a large angle with the horizon;
there was but rarely an upward gust. Ten yards from
the bank the direction was still mainly downward, but
with not unfrequent upward movements. At twenty

[1] *Der Vogelflug als Grundlage der Fliegekunst*, by Otto
Lilienthal. (Berlin, 1889.)

and thirty yards' distance the wind came in wild gusts, as often upward as downward. Twelve yards to windward of a bank only rising eight feet above the level the vane was not quite steady, but on the whole horizontal. At a distance of six yards there were occasional upward swings; at four yards' distance there was a decided upward tendency, and this though the bank itself presented only a very gentle incline. These facts go far to explain the soaring of birds over hill-tops or cliffs.

Rising with the help of the Wind.

One way to catch Condors is " to place a carcass on a level piece of ground within an enclosure of sticks with an opening, and, when the condors are gorged, to gallop up on horseback to the entrance and thus enclose them ; for when the bird has not space to run, it cannot give its body sufficient momentum to rise from the ground." [1] A Cormorant, wishing to lift himself from the water, faces the wind, and flaps along the surface for some distance and at considerable speed, before he is able to mount upward. The Red-throated Diver is said to be so powerless to begin his flight without a head wind to help him that if you sail down upon him *with the wind* he must either fly towards you or remain upon the water, the third alternative of diving often not occurring to his mind. I have never seen a Lark rise facing any way but head to the wind. In fact, all birds seem to derive great assistance from this.

---

[1] Darwin's *Journal of Researches*, chap. ix. p. 133 (Minerva Library).

I long thought perfectly true what some writers on flight still maintain, that a uniform horizontal wind would lift the bird if he faced it, as it lifts a kite. But a fact that ought to have been obvious has now been pointed out to me—viz., that the bird, a moment after he has left the ground, becomes part of the moving current, so that it will make no difference as far as his upward progress is concerned whether he fly with it or against it. There might as well be not breeze enough to shake an aspen leaf. You may imagine him flying in a globe filled with air, the globe itself moving with the current. The fact that the globe is moving will not affect the bird's flight.

Mr. R. C. Gilson first showed me how it is that a bird wishing to rise derives advantage from facing the wind. He is perpetually passing from a slower into a faster current. Thus at every stage he has his own inertia, which is equivalent to momentum, to help him. When he first jumps from the ground, if we divide the wind in theory into separate layers, he has at his service the whole velocity of the lowest layer. As he passes out of this he is helped by the difference in velocity between layers Nos. 1 and 2. As he ascends higher, the rate of increase in the wind's speed diminishing, he will be helped less, but, as I have shown, he will not be left entirely to his own unaided efforts, at any rate until he has passed an altitude of 1,000 feet.

Onward Flight and Air Currents.

When at the seaside it is blowing with a violence that must startle an anemometer familiar only with sheltered places inland, it is a beautiful sight to see a

Gull flying at right angles to it without moving his wings. A diagram will make clear the method.

He descends swiftly at a gentle incline, making an angle with the wind that, but for leeway, would be a right angle, then suddenly turns and faces the wind, rising by a short steep ascent to his former level, after which he begins the process over again. He descends from the more rapid current into the slower, and so has the advantage of his relative velocity, after which he again ascends, and profits by his passage from the slower to the swifter. The upper current lends him pace, the

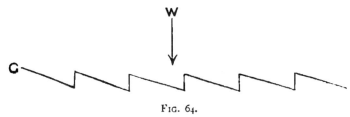

FIG. 64.

W shows the direction of the wind ; *G* the line of the Gull's flight.

lower we may look upon as a floor off which he rebounds like a ball. As he ascends into the more quickly moving air, he has, belonging as he does now to the slower current below, an inertia which makes the wind act upon him as upon a kite. A glance at the line of his course will show how he keeps making good his leeway as he goes. The Albatross, those who have been lucky enough to see him say, has brought this mode of progression to perfection, working onward by the hour without a motion of his wings. A Gull is often reduced to putting in a stroke or two, though I have seen them cover a considerable distance without once resorting to this. It is said that some birds make head directly against the wind in something the same way, half flexing the wings for a rapid descent down a gentle incline, then spreading them for a steep ascent. Their course is a perfectly straight one head to the breeze, only rising and falling.[1]

During the terrific blizzard that fell upon our east coast in January 1894, I saw gulls making their way against the wind by flying as low as possible along the sand by the seaside, appreciating the fact that even a blizzard is comparatively mild near to the earth's surface.

Soaring.

When Eagles, Falcons, and Buzzards were common in our islands, the phenomenon of soaring was much more familiar than it is now. The popularity of hawking brought it to everybody's notice. Sportsmen or their gamekeepers are now making everything in the shape of a bird of prey, beyond a Kestrel or a Sparrow Hawk, a rare sight. But, happily, an opportunity still occasionally comes to us to see a bird soaring in grand style, a Buzzard among the hills of Westmoreland or over Cornish cliffs, or a Raven over some rocky headland on our coast. But the grandest soarers of all are not natives of Britain. They may be seen in many lands, but nowhere better than over a great plain in Upper Assam. There they have been watched through a telescope by Mr. S. E. Peal, who has well described their circling flight in *Nature*.[2]

[1] See Marey, *Vol des Oiseaux*, p. 18.
[2] See *Nature* for November 4, 1880; September 26, 1889; May 21, 1891.

The skilled performers are Pelicans, Vultures, Storks, and, perhaps the finest of all, the Adjutant Birds. Under different circumstances the last-named may be seen at the Zoological Gardens, looking lethargic and far from athletic, their length of leg more apparent than their mighty spread of wing. They rise the first 100—200 feet by their wings, and then, apparently without the faintest suspicion of a wing-beat, sweep round in spirals, or what is more properly called a helix, gaining ten to twenty feet, it is estimated, with each gyration, the wing and tail being rigidly extended and the primary feathers separated. During the first part of each turn of the helix they are flying with the wind, their direction being slightly downward ; at the end of the descent they sweep round and face the wind, which carries them upward. When the curve described is towards the left, the right wing points upward and the left downward, but the two wings always form one rigid rod, and only move with the body (see p. 250).

In this way they attain an elevation of one or two miles, and so restful does this upward circling appear that Mr. Peal is of opinion that they go aloft to doze. There is always a wind at the time, generally from the N.E. or S.W., blowing steadily at a rate of five to ten miles an hour, and since the plain presents a dead level of 200 miles by 60, the direction of the current can hardly be upward. When there is no wind there is no soaring. It is remarkable that there is always a considerable loss of leeway. This description agrees in all essential points with that given by other observers.

Birds, like all matter living or dead, are subject to physical laws. We must, therefore, not relegate soaring to the realm of miracle, but try to find some solution of the problem.

There are three explanations possible, all of which may be true, each of them being applicable to particular circumstances.

(1) There may be upward currents. We have already condemned as fantastic Lilienthal's notion that the general tendency of the wind is upward. But, as I have shown, in particular places it undoubtedly is so. A Raven or a Vulture soaring over a hilltop is probably making use of alternating upward and downward currents, or else, if the streams of air in that particular spot flow steadily, sweeping from a downward into an upward one. This means of soaring is, it cannot be doubted, put at his disposal through the diversion of the wind when it comes in contact with a high ridge. If the results I have described could be produced by a bank only a few feet high, what great irregularities, what tremendous up and down blasts, may be caused by such a barrier as a hill of only moderate height! Gulls are very quick in finding out such currents, and enjoy playing in them. When the wind is blowing hard against a cliff and is diverted upward, they will fly again and again to its base and let themselves be carried to the top. Or they will float and circle high above a cliff, profiting no doubt by the upward slant of the breeze. They will often follow a steamer with wings perfectly motionless, and the explanation of this, probably, is that the passage of the vessel through the air causes

an upward current. I have tried to detect such a
current by means of small scraps of paper let fly from
the stern of a steamer. They showed that immediately
behind the vessel the air rushes violently downward
to fill the vacuum left as she moves onward. But
the rebound of this current from the water was by no
means so marked as I should have expected, though
there were unmistakable signs of a certain amount
of updraught.

It cannot be denied that when beneath a tropical
or sub-tropical sun a plain is heated in various degrees
at different places, according to the nature of the
surface, there are upward movements of air, and it has
been held by some writers that the up-currents thus
formed are sufficient to render soaring possible. It
is urged in support of this view that birds soar chiefly
during the great heat of the day, and more in summer
than in winter, and it is certainly remarkable that to
see soaring at its best you have to go far south. But
before we can believe in the adequacy of these up-
currents we want further evidence. The fact, too,
that soaring does not begin till 100—200 feet up
seems to me to tell against this view.[1]

(2) Increase of the wind's velocity with altitude will
explain much, but the principle must be cautiously
applied. If this progressive increase extended to
altitudes of a mile or two, the grandest feats of soaring
birds might easily be explained, as Lord Rayleigh and
others have shown.[2] The Adjutant wheeling upward
would be only doing on a grand scale what Gulls may

[1] See *Nature*, October 1st, 1891.
[2] See *Nature*, May, 1883, May 9, 1889.

be seen doing when they advance at right angles to the wind without moving their wings. Descending with all the velocity of the upper current, he would rebound from the slower one below, and the inertia due to this undercurrent would make him rise like a kite when he re-entered the more rapid stream at a higher level. But, as I have shown, it is very improbable that there is a regular progressive increase in the velocity of the wind at high altitudes. We know, too, that it comes in gusts, and this would bring it about that the bird, if he depended on the arrangement of the air in strata of increasing velocity, would, when the breeze happened to strengthen inopportunely, find himself in a slower instead of a more rapid current.

Whatever the difficulties that meet us when we try to explain by this principle the phenomenon of soaring, it is certain that near the surface of land or sea the increase of velocity with altitude is rapid enough and constant enough to assist a bird in rising or in making progress at right angles to the wind.

(3) I believe myself that the irregularity of the wind may supply the explanation of soaring. The wind is a "chartered libertine," and, even when steadiest, blows, as Professor Langley has shown, with great fitfulness. A bird, when soaring, if this explanation be sound, will face a strengthening breeze : when it begins to slacken will turn and go with it, until conscious it is freshening again, when once more he will sweep round and face it, his aim being always to feel the wind blowing in his face, sure evidence that he has momentum that will lift him. To do

this he would have to be perpetually feeling the
pulse of the wind, and, moreover, soaring would
be a much less regular progress upward than it
is supposed to be. Some turns of the helix would
be failures. There would be a loss instead
of a gain of elevation, or nothing more than a
maintenance of level would be achieved. But when
we watch a bird circling at a great height, what can
we tell of his progress during a particular minute?
We only know that his general tendency is upward.
Gulls make many only partially successful turns when
they soar, and it is possible that similar failures in
a nobler performer like the Adjutant may remain
undetected.

Supposing the irregularity of the wind to be due to
eddies, the bird may still be able to avail himself of
it, turning to account the difference in velocity of the
outer and inner rings of the whirl. This supposes that
the eddy is of a convenient size. It may be either so
large or so small as to be useless to him. The complications of the problem, when we introduce into it
the question of eddies, are almost insurmountable.
In the present state of our knowledge we can only
say that there are great irregularities of velocity, to
whatever cause they may be due, and that it is highly
probable that a bird in soaring turns them to account.
We are apt to speak of soaring as being effected
without any muscular effort. But it is by muscles
that the wings are held fixed and immovable, and the
strain must be considerable. Apparently, however,
there is hardly any limit to the time during which a
bird can continue an exertion of this kind. No such

thing as an ache or cramp disturbs him. The wing-muscles are as unwearying as the leg-muscles that are stretched when he sits upon his perch.

Steering.

A modern writer boldly asserts that birds "neither do nor can use their tails as rudders." This shows how rash it is to dictate to nature what she may do or may not. I have already shown (p. 214) that the necessary muscles are present for moving the tail upward or downward, and for lowering one side relatively to the other. And a little observation with the naked eye, or, better, with a field-glass, will show that numbers of birds actually do pull down the left side of the tail when they wish to steer to the left, and *via versa*. Rooks make great use of the tail in steering, the whole expanded fan of feathers being sloped so as to make quite a different angle with the horizon from that made by a line passing through the two wing-tips. In Jackdaws it is almost equally conspicuous. If, from below, you watch a Lark as he rises, you can easily see that he keeps his head to the wind by the perpetual play of his tail. The Swallow, House-martin, Sand-martin, and Swift guide themselves largely by the tail, as one might expect from its great development. The divided tail seems always to be much used as a rudder, though the loss of the single long feather from one side makes no apparent difference to a Swallow. Perhaps the domestic Pigeon shows tail-steering more conspicuously than any other bird ; he trusts much to it, and he is easy to observe.

How, then, did the idea originate that the tail was not employed as a rudder ? It was owing, I believe, to the fact that a bird who has lost his tail still manages to direct his course without great difficulty. A Rook whom one of the many tussles that go on in a rookery has left tailless is not a ship without a helm. He can steer, but, as far as I have observed, he cannot rest between the strokes of his wings. The tail is a valuable parachute, and, bereft of that, he must not loiter. His loss, too, reduces his power of stopping suddenly. Moreover, steering is not necessarily perfect steering, and I have no doubt that a tailless swallow misses many gnats which he might otherwise have caught.

Two things are quite clear, then : (1) the tail is a rudder ; (2) there is some other means of steering. I think I have seen gulls when flying fast adopt another method which is in its nature the same— let down a foot on the side towards which they wish to go. More often they kick vigorously when they make a sudden turn, or when they are about to settle, working the feet together, and not alternately as they do in swimming. Clearly, steering by means of the feet must be limited to web-footed birds.

There is another plan very different from those we have mentioned. If he wishes to steer to the left, the bird flings himself on his left side, his left wing pointing downward and his right upward. The onward course of the fore part of his body is retarded by his outspread wings, the hinder part moves more quickly, and this causes him to describe a curve. So far, it is simple enough, but when we come to inquire how the change of balance is effected the difficulty begins. We might naturally suppose that one wing beats harder than the other; in the turn to the left the right wing would work with greater energy, so as to throw the body on to its left side. That being so, it is puzzling at first, when we see the turn made, to find that the right wing which should give the harder stroke is held aloft while the left wing is lowered. This, however, is not an insuperable difficulty. Each wing makes the same angle with the body, so that a line connecting the tips would either pass through the shoulder-joints or be parallel to a line passing through them. It is only the rolling over of the body on to its side that causes them to point upward and downward respectively. This being the position in which we see the wings as the bird wheels, can the right have struck harder than the left in order to effect the turn? Possibly it may have. In ordinary flight, as we have seen, the body at once rises in response to the beat of the two wings together, and thus they are brought home to their lower limit, without the stroke having to be pulled through. The right wing, then, if it gave the stronger beat, might instantaneously raise the body on the right side and produce the desired result, the change of balance; when, very possibly, all we should see might be the bird sailing on with the right wing pointing upward and the left downward. Still there would be an instant at which the wings would form unequal angles with the body, and what evidence of it can we obtain? If a Gull be watched as he slowly wheels, there seems to be absolutely no inequality of angle; when a rapid turn

is made, the whole operation is like a flash, and
your opportunity has gone before it has come. If the
inequality were great, photographs would of course
supply irrefragable evidence ; but for or against such
a minute difference as the one in question their
testimony is not worth much. In this dearth of
evidence we can only say that, when other animals
have freedom of movement, it would be strange that
birds should have their wings tied to one another, and
that nothing but an unequal stroke can account for
the rapidity with which a Swallow dashes from right
to left. But, though I lean to this view, I believe that
a bird has other means of altering its balance for
steering purposes, which are very likely the sole
means employed in the slower turns and co-operate
in effecting the most rapid. I have already mentioned
that a bird's back is at this point by no means the
rigid rod that it is said to be. The waist is capable of
considerable movement not only up and down but
from side to side. I give what measurements I have
to show the amount of pliability, regretting that the
evidence is so meagre.

	Angle formed by backbone bending sideways at waist.
Kestrel	$141\frac{1}{2}°$
Swallow... ... .:	$150°$
Common Tern	$155°$
Kestrel (another specimen)	$156°$
Domestic Duck	$165°$

A black-headed Gull and a Sand-martin both showed
great flexibility, but I have no measurements. From the
figures it appears that a Kestrel, the first specimen
measured, had a. more flexible waist than any of the

others. The Swallow, like the Kestrel a first-rate
steerer, comes second. The Duck, who turns in a long
curve and with labour, has the stiffest waist of all. It
seems probable that a bird alters his balance in order to
change direction much as a skater does. Supposing
that he is curving to the right on the outside edge
on the right foot, the skater turns to the inside
edge (on the same foot), and curves to the
left by swinging the weight of his shoulders across.
And this is done by contracting the muscles at the
waist which lower the left shoulder. A bird may well
change balance in a similar way, swinging his hind-
quarters to right or left according to the direction
in which he wishes to go, and beneath the feathers
the process may not be visible to us. Certainly
the head is often turned at the moment of wheeling,
apparently to help the movement. Occasionally, however, like a good skater who despises conspicuous helps
to a change of equilibrium, such as a swing of the leg,
a Gull may be seen looking to the right while he slowly
turns to the left. It is these slow turns, when there is
almost certainly no beat of the wings, and during which
the head is occasionally turned the other way, that
make me think a bird alters his balance by a bend at
the waist as a skater does. In the more rapid turns
there may well be a momentary unequal beat of the
wings that defies detection.

Stopping. Use of the Bastard Wing.

When a Pigeon in mid-flight wishes suddenly to stop
he alters the inclination of his body, which has been
nearly horizontal, and, relaxing the muscles that had

held it in position, lets it hang almost vertically down-wards. The wings are held extended, with just a slight bend at the wrist, facing forwards, and so putting the break on as strongly as possible. The tail forms the largest fan it can spread to. For stopping it is perhaps more important than for steering. If the Pigeon be watched from underneath, another very curious point may be made out. It will be seen that the bastard wings are called into play to add to the spread of canvas. They are often spoken of as quite rudimentary, or as useful only in strengthening the wing, though how they can act in this way is difficult to see. One ornithologist imagines that in making a turn a bird extends one bastard wing and revolves round it as on a pivot! I had long wondered what their use could be or how so many muscles could be wasted on a mere rudiment, when I saw a Pigeon, when checking his speed in order to settle, lift the bastard wing so that daylight was visible between it and the long feathers, this petty appendage jutting out, and impudently spoiling the beautiful line of the front margin of the wing from shoulder to tip. If you stand at the entrance to the British Museum (the Antiquarian Department at Bloomsbury) this curious phenomenon may easily be seen, as the Pigeons which are usually feeding in large numbers on the gravel in front fly up and settle overhead on the pediment. In two specimens of Kestrel Hawks which I have examined, the extension of the wing necessarily extended the bastard wing, the tendon within the anterior membrane attaching not only to the metacarp but also to the thumb. The purpose of this is not clear, nor have I noticed anything of the kind in other birds.

In Mr. Muybridge's [1] photographs of a Cockatoo on the wing, both bastard wings may be seen to be slightly raised, for what purpose it is hard to say. In the Pigeon too they project during a vigorous stroke, but I have seen no other bird use them either for stopping or striking.

FIG 65.—Drawn from a photograph by Ottomar Anschutz, showing bastard wing extended during downstroke.

The Centre of Gravity.

In the bird the centre of gravity falls at a point low down in the body: the heavier organs are accumulated there, the lighter ones up above. Below are the great breastbone and the ponderous muscles of flight (the

[1] See Mr. Muybridge's *Animal Locomotion,* to be seen at the Brit sh Museum.

pair that lower the wings sometimes weighing one fifth of the whole weight of the body), and the entrails. High up, just under the backbone, come the lungs with their spacious air-sacks. This arrangement is no doubt advantageous. Imagine a flying-machine with wings springing from a point many yards above the engine which supplied the motive power. It would have a constant tendency to right itself if it capsized. In the same way the bird is helped in balancing by the fact that his centre of gravity is low down, but to a much less extent, since the point lies only a little below the wings when expanded horizontally. The lower the weight lies, the greater the space through which it must be raised before a capsize can take place. And owing to the way the wings work, it must lie, as I hope to show soon, mainly behind the shoulders. But the power of recovering balance at any moment by making the appropriate movements is quite as important as the exact position of the centre of gravity. A bicyclist never ceases to make the necessary adjustments, though he may be unconscious of the fact. And if a lark be carefully watched from below as he rises he can be seen to be perpetually moving his tail to left or right, thus maintaining his balance and at the same time keeping his head to the wind. If there is a dead calm, he trusts more to movements of his head. Moreover, a bird uses, I believe, his power of bending to right or left at the waist and so shifting his centre of gravity. To recover equilibrium, he might give a harder stroke with one wing or the other, but it is not certain that the wings ever beat unequally. When at the end of the stroke they are mainly beneath the level of the body, this last means of balancing is out of the question, and the bird must trust to head, waist, or tail.

The question at what point between the head and tail the centre of gravity lies is a very important one. Probably if we divide the keel into three equal divisions it will fall in the middle one, in a vertical line passing a little behind the point at which the second rib joins the trunk. It is impossible to decide exactly. It has been supposed that birds can at pleasure shift the centre of gravity backwards and forwards. To some extent no doubt they can, but their power of doing so has been much exaggerated. Any bird, but especially the long-necked ones, can move the centre of gravity forward by extending the neck to its full length. But owing to the lightness of the skull this has not so much effect as might be thought, except perhaps with large-headed birds like ducks. Then again a long-legged bird as he flies may move it in a backward direction by trailing his legs full length behind him. Many of them do habitually carry their necks or legs stretched out during flight—their necks, possibly, in order to shift the centre of gravity. The filling of the air-sacks will have little effect, since they extend before and behind the important point. The movement of the wings forward or backward will, no doubt, carry the centre of gravity to some extent with it. These small changes, however, do not help us to understand how the bird is able during flight to maintain a horizontal position, for the main weight still lies behind the points where the wings attach.

Of the many means that have been suggested for

shifting the centre of gravity, none are, I believe, except in quite exceptional birds, efficacious, and I doubt whether any bird makes much use of them. The problem, then, remains : when the body is suspended from the wings and the centre of gravity lies at a point farther back, how is a nearly horizontal position maintained? Hold up a bird, that has just been shot, by the wings, and the hinder part of the body will drop till the incline from the tail to the head (with the partial exception explained on p. 227) is a very steep one. This it is, no doubt, that has caused ornithologists to look for some means by which the bird could at pleasure move the centre of gravity forwards. The true explanation is that during horizontal flight the body is maintained in its position, with only a slight upward incline, not by balance, but by muscular effort. If you watch a Pigeon's movements and see how instantaneously, without a motion of head or legs, he changes the inclination of his body, you can hardly doubt that it is the work of muscles.[1] The muscle called the Latissimus Dorsi, which I have described in connection with respiration, arises from the verte-bræ and attaches to the humerus (L. D. fig. 56). During the downstroke it contracts, hauls upon the wings, and thus raises the hinder quarters. The enormous strength of the Great Pectorals prevents all possibility of the wings yielding when thus pulled by the Latissimus. The body must rise, since the wings will not give. And, thus, indirectly, in addition to their other work, the Great Pectorals help to bring the body to the horizontal. When the wing rotates beyond a

[1] See Bronn's *Thier-Reich*, vol. "Aves," p. 229.

certain point, its lower face looking backward, the effect
will be the same, without the help of the Latissimus.
During the upstroke the hind-quarters drop no more
than the rest of the body. The centre of gravity
is always behind the shoulder; in fact, when the
hinder part of the body is raised, it retreats still further.
It ought not to fall in a vertical line between the points
of the wings' attachments any more than a skater's
centre of gravity, when he describes a curve, ought to
be directly over his skate. The action of the wings,
nicely regulated by the Latissimus, is to raise the
hinder and lower the anterior part of the body, and, if
the bird were balanced horizontally between them,
would send him heels over head. The fact that the
main weight is behind prevents this, and enables him
to choose his course.

If an animal uses for progression at one time his
fore limbs only, at another his hind limbs, the centre of
gravity question cannot fail to be interesting, as equilibrium must be maintained under two different sets of
circumstances. How well the point is situated for
flight, I have shown. In standing or walking, the
thigh-joint is a long way behind the main bulk of
the body, and the long toes are necessary to give
support at the required point. The horizontal or
nearly horizontal carriage of the body calls into play
muscles which, passing from the posterior end of
the pelvis to the thigh-bone, pull the hind-quarters
downward, and so raise the head and shoulders. The
more upright the bird, the farther back the centre of
gravity, and the less the pressure upon the toes.
When standing, a bird is in the position of a man who

leans forward, bending at the hips, with the result that the fore part of the foot bears all the weight, and the heel tends to rise. This is not a comfortable position to maintain long. But the stiffness of the bird's back, due to the fusion of vertebræ, no doubt, makes the attitude an easy one for him.[1]

Force Exerted in Flight.

Borelli, a man of science of the seventeenth century, calculated that a bird in flying employs a force that exceeds ten thousand times his own weight.[2] This astounding conclusion he arrived at by trying to estimate the disadvantage at which most animal levers work, the power being applied close to the fulcrum while the weight is at the end of a long arm. By the same methods he calculated that the force exerted by a man in jumping exceeds three thousand times his own weight. Obviously he has much overshot the mark, but it is very difficult to devise any plan by which correct results may be obtained. Professor Marey has attempted to settle the question of a bird's muscular power by experiment.[3] A Buzzard was hooded, and so plunged into "a sort of hypnotism." The Great Pectoral muscle was laid bare, the elbow-joint was disarticulated, and all of the wing that lies beyond was removed. A cord was fixed to the

[1] That the centre of gravity must of necessity be where it is, was first shown me by Mr. R. C. Gilson.

[2] Borelli, *De Motu Animalium*, p. 191: "Potentia musculorum alas flectentium plus quam decies millies superat pondus avis volantis."

[3] *Animal Mechanism*, p. 214.

extremity of the humerus, and at the end of the cord
was placed a scalepan into which small shot was
poured. The muscle was then stimulated by electric
currents, and shot was added till the contraction of the
muscle was exactly counteracted. The weight raised
was just over 6⅓ lbs. Troy. But in the lever the
power was much nearer to the fulcrum than the weight,
and, when this was allowed for, the effort was calculated to be equal to just over 33¾ lbs. Troy. What is
the value of this experiment? Does the muscle under
the electric stimulus work up to its full power? This is
very doubtful. Myself I cannot help altogether dis-
trusting the results. But the muscles of mammals
have been treated in the same way, and it seems that
they can develop at least equal energy.

Experiments might be made with Homer Pigeons
which would throw much light upon the question.
They might be weighed in delicate scales both before
and after a long flight, when the loss of weight would
help us to estimate the amount of energy put forth,
though it must be owned that to eliminate all causes
of error would be extremely difficult. Similar experiments have often been made with men, their weights
being accurately taken immediately before and after a
race, or hard exercise of some kind. The comparison
of the loss of weight by man and birds in covering
equal distances would have great interest. It is much
to be regretted, therefore, that owners of Homer
Pigeons have as yet made no experiments that might
supply the necessary facts. The mere opinion that
the loss of weight is slight is of no value.

But, however much we may wish for definite evidence,

there are facts at our disposal which are full of meaning, and which in a rough and ready way settle the
question. (1) Birds have large appetites and rapid
digestions, a great proof of vigour. (2) In proportion
to their size they give off from their lungs more carbonic acid than other animals, and this means greater
destruction of tissue, which implies a greater expenditure of energy. (3) Their temperature is exceptionally
high, irrefragable evidence of the rate at which they
live. (4) They are capable of as great rapidity of
movement as mammals, and they tire less soon.
This points to superior quality of muscles.

Proportion of Wing Area to Weight in Large and Small Birds.

This is a more difficult question than it might on
first thoughts appear to be. One elementary cause
of error may be disposed of at once : the doubling of
the size of the bird will not mean the doubling of the
length and breadth of the wings, for in that case the
wing area would be quadrupled.[1] This will explain
the following figures : the comparative wing areas of
a Herring Gull and a Great Tit are represented by
541 : 31, *i.e.*, the Gull's expanse of wing is rather more
than eighteen times that of the Tit, whereas the length
is less than six times as much.[2] It is the areas, then,
and not the lengths or breadths, that we must compare,

[1] See fig. 29.
[2] I take the areas from Pieter Harting, quoted by Marey
(*Animal Mechanism*, p. 224), and the lengths from Howard
Saunders's *Manual of British Birds*. The results are too broad
to be affected by differences in different specimens.

and we should expect that unless some new factor should come in and upset the calculation, the areas would vary as the weight of the winged animal, whether bird or insect. That this is not the rule is shown by the following examples.[1]

	Wing area per kilogram.
Dragon-fly	44,032 sq. inches.
Swallow	1,544½ ,,
Vulture	260 ,,
Australian Crane	139 ,,

Thus the Australian Crane has in proportion to its weight only a little more than half the wing area of a Vulture, rather less than $\frac{1}{11}$ of that of the Swallow and not quite $\frac{1}{316}$ of that of a Dragon-fly ![2]

How are we to account for these facts? Before

[1] These figures are those of M. de Lucy, quoted by Professor Pettigrew, *Animal Locomotion*; also by Professor Marey, *Animal Mechanism*, p. 222. I have not referred to M. de Lucy's work, but the quotations agree.

[2] The following figures from L. P. Mouillard's *L'Empire de l'air* are interesting. They give in grammes the weight supported by one square metre of surface, the whole undersurface of the body as well as that of the wings being included. The small birds, as a rule, have far more surface for their weight, though the cock Kestrel heads the list and is an exception difficult to account for. Most startling is the small amount of surface that the Goose, Turkey, and Duck have to support them.

	Grammes supported by 1 sq. metre of surface.		Grammes supported by 1 sq. metre of surface.
Kestrel (cock) ...	1,968	Golden Plover ...	3,565
House Sparrow ...	2,066	Kestrel (hen)	3,773
Swift	2,073	Bustard	6,410
Turtle Dove	2,133	Goose	8,333
Kite	2,226	Turkey...	9,345
Starling	2,932	Duck (*Anas Clypeata*)	
Raven	3,012	,, hen	9,750
Stork	3,536	,, drake	11,050

giving what I consider to be the explanation, I shall first try to show that what is accepted as the solution of the problem by some noted ornithologists in reality leaves it just where it was.

If you take two cubes, a side of one of which is twice the length of a side of the other, the larger one is in bulk eight times the smaller, but its surface area is only four times as great (see figure 29, p. 113). This will hold of other figures of three dimensions. Magnify a bird till it is eight times its former size: yet you will only have multiplied the surface area by four. This is no doubt a true principle in geometry, and it might be applied to the present case if symmetry were the only thing under consideration. We should then be doing right if we took the proportion of bulk (not area) of wing to bulk of body, and it would turn out that the build of big birds and small is not very different.[1] But the present question is really one of dynamics. The problem which nature has to solve when she increases a bird's size is : " If the weight of the bird be multiplied by so many, how much will the area of the supporting surfaces have to be increased ? " In other words, how much must be added to the wing area, in order that the bird may be able to fly ? And the answer is (except for modifying circumstances which I shall pass on to soon), that if the weight be doubled the supporting surfaces must also be doubled.

There is an undeniable interest in the fact that when we compare birds' bodies and wings (the legs are

---

[1] Those who wish to apply this principle should take the cube root of the bird's weight and the square root of the wing area.

often long beyond all justification) we find a certain
proportion maintained with no great deviation, that
when their bulk has been trebled their wing surface has
not at the same time been trebled, in defiance of the
laws of symmetry and geometry. But, looked upon
as flying-machines, why do small birds require larger
wings, in proportion to their bulk, than big birds?

Since, allowing for his greater weight, the big bird
has less wing to support him than the small bird, we
must see what advantages he has that enable him to
do with less. To begin with, if we compare the sustaining powers of two wings of different lengths, we shall
find that the superior power of the long one is altogether
out of proportion to its superiority in length. Suppose
the shorter one to be one foot, the longer two feet,
long. Then if the two are worked by muscles of
equally rapid contraction, the extremity of the latter will
move with a velocity that is far more than double that
attained by the extremity of the former. And since
the resistance of the air increases nearly as the square
of the velocity, it is clear that to judge even by the
comparative velocities of the extremities is to under-
estimate by a great deal the superiority of the longer
wing. Secondly, it has been found by experiment
that the air passes lightly off the margins of a plane
surface which moves through it, and so does not offer
much resistance to them.[1] The loss is proportionately
greater with small planes than with large ones, since
for each square inch of area they have more margin.
The resistance of the air in the case of a square plane
having an area of two square feet, moving in a direction

[1] Marey, *Vol des Oiseaux*, p. 214.

vertical to its surface and at a certain pace,
would be more than double what it would be
in the case of a plane one foot square under similar
circumstances. Hence small birds get less support
from the air than large ones. It is true that, as
explained above (see p. 190), the front part of the
wing does most of the work during its lightning-like
downward movement, and therefore we find that
the wings of most of the best flyers have narrow
extremities. But during flight the bird's whole under
surface forms a parachute, and a gain in area means a
disproportionate gain in supporting power, even when
we make allowance for the principle just mentioned.
Moreover, a short wing necessitates a quick stroke,
and much power is lost by the small bird in constantly
raising the wing for a fresh effort. A few less
important advantages must also be mentioned. The
great flyers, even when we take into consideration
their greater size, have larger and stronger bones than
the best flyers among small birds, and the absence of
marrow has prevented an increase in weight that
might have been set against the increase in strength.
In large birds the coracoids, if we take the average,
are directed more outwards than in small birds, a
gain in strength without any drawbacks. It is
probable that in proportion to their total bulk they
require less flight muscle than small birds that
resemble them in other respects. Some interesting
measurements which go to prove this have been made
by Legal and Reichel. In the case of the Pigeon, as
I have shown (see p. 212), their figures do not agree
with the facts, but in most cases they are, probably,

more dependable. These two investigators found that in expenditure on flight muscle a big bird is more economical than a small one of the same family, a big Tern than a small Tern, a big Gull than a small Gull. Even when birds of different families are compared, the rule generally holds. The Eagle and other birds of strong flight have, for their size, lighter muscles than small birds. The heavy-flying Geese are an exception. Incalculable factors complicate the problem, but, clearly, many big birds can save in muscle and devote more vital energy to other organs.[1]

Helmholtz undertook to show that a big flying bird is an impossibility, since as the supporting power increases the weight increases more rapidly.[2] This runs quite counter to the figures just quoted. Even if his calculation is right in the abstract, it ignores some important facts that ought to make us hesitate before we apply his conclusion to birds as they are. It ignores the fact that the work done by a large wing surpasses the work of a small wing by far more than the superiority in area. It disregards what, if not established fact, is yet not far from it, viz., that pterodactyls, with wings measuring 25 feet from tip to tip, were able to fly. It is now still further

---

[1] In three Terns, the comparative weights of which are represented by the figures 53, 116, 174, the total weights were $5\frac{19}{25}$, $6\frac{33}{50}$, $7\frac{63}{100}$ times the weight of the breast-muscles in the respective specimens. See *Jahresbericht der Schlesischen Gesellschaft für Vaterland-Cultur.* Breslau, 1879.

[2] The calculation was as follows : If the linear dimensions increase as 1 : 4, then bulk and consequent weight (and presumably strength) will increase as $1 : 4^3$, that is, as 1 : 64, but the sustaining force must increase as $1 : 4\frac{1}{2}$, that is, as 1 : 128.

damaged by the fact that Mr. Maxim's flying machine, weighing 3½ tons (a very heavy bird !), has actually risen from the ground. It is true that all the giant fossil birds that have been discovered seem to have been allies of the Ostrich and incapable of flight. Since, however, the geological record is not only imperfect but has, much of it, still to be read, we cannot say that giant flying birds never existed. Supposing that they once existed, they may have died out for reasons not connected with flight. Many large mammals and reptiles have become extinct, the smaller having some advantage in the race of life.

When we come to compare the actual achievements of big and small birds, it will be found that the honours are divided. The small can rise with greater ease, the line of ascent being far nearer to the vertical. This may in many cases be due to the greater stiffness of the shoulder-joint in large birds, which prevents the wing turning its under surface backward, as it must turn for ascent up a steep incline (see above on upward flight). But in one of the big birds that I have examined, the Eagle,[1] this stiffness is not found. If we concede that small birds rise with less effort, on the other hand, the big are, I believe, even allowing for their greater bulk, better weight-carriers. An Eagle will carry a young lamb; for a House Sparrow a very small piece of bread is a heavy burden.

In long-distance flight the two classes are about equally matched.

Small birds never soar, and it is generally supposed

---

[1] It can rise with greater ease, I think, than many big sea-birds that are stiff at the shoulder.

that their weight is insufficient to give them momentum.
This may be the true explanation. When we speak
of a soaring bird as a kite, the momentum is the
string, and the small bird with a spread of wing, for
him, so large, may be like a kite whose string is too
weak to hold it. Those who maintain the superiority of
the small to the big, would perhaps say that they do
not get the wind to help them, because they have no
need of its help.

Velocity.

Many and various are the methods by which
attempts have been made to measure the velocity of
birds' flight. Audubon found rice in the crops of
Pigeons which, judging by its condition, he estimated
had been eaten six hours before. This rice they could
only have obtained in Carolina, which was 300—400
miles distant. These data give at the lowest estimate
a velocity of fifty miles per hour. The Frigate Bird
is often seen flying over mid-ocean, and it is said that
he never travels at night, and never sleeps upon the
sea. Hence, a very rough calculation of the pace of
his flight may be made.

Such methods, however ingenious and interesting,
are most unsatisfying. We want indisputable
measurements, and it is only in the case of one or
two species that they are obtainable. The racing of
Homing Pigeons is a popular amusement in England,
Belgium, and other countries, and "times" are
accurately taken. In 1892 a pigeon, according to
the published record, accomplished a flight of 114
miles at a rate of eighty miles per hour. This is so

much in excess, not only of anything achieved in any other race during that year, but of the velocity of any of the birds competing in the same race, that I cannot help hesitating to accept it as trustworthy. The next best record for the year was seventy-one miles per hour in an eighty-two mile race.[1] Even when the conditions are most favourable, when there is a tail-wind blowing—*i.e.*, a wind carrying the birds towards their destination—sixty miles an hour is a very exceptional pace in a race of 100 miles and over. When the weather is all that could be wished, fifty miles per hour or slightly more is a velocity more often recorded. In 1883 the average velocity of the winning birds in eighteen of the races of the United Counties Flying Club was thirty-six miles per hour, the fastest having maintained a rate of fifty-five miles for a distance of 208.

In France, the experiment has been made of employing Swallows in place of Homing Pigeons. The idea is a very ancient one, for Pliny tells us that a certain Roman knight who wished to let his friends at Volaterræ in Tuscany know who had won the chariot races used to take with him to Rome—a distance of 130 miles—some Swallows which he let loose after dyeing them the colour of the winner.[2] Of the experiments in France I have not been able to obtain any account at first hand. One flight is reported to have been a very grand one, far surpassing anything credited to a Homing Pigeon. A Swallow was taken from Roubaix to Paris, a distance of 258

[1] See Burgess's *Homing Pigeon Fanciers' Annual* for 1892.
[2] Pliny, *Natural History*, x. 34

kilometres, or 160 English miles, and in ninety minutes
from the time of its liberation at Paris it was back
again. It had maintained an average pace of 106
miles per hour![1] This may appear startling, but the
figures may possibly be correct. It must be remembered that the Swallow is better built for rapid flight
than the Pigeon. Of the velocity attained by the
Swift, who in his flight is very like the Swallow,
though probably more than his match, many people
have arrived at a much higher estimate.

A few years ago some experiments of indisputable
accuracy were made in a range constructed for experi-
mental shooting. Two " screens " formed of very
fine threads were put up at a distance of forty yards
from one another. These screens were connected
with electrical apparatus, by means of which the time
occupied by the bird in traversing the forty yards was
registered. The highest speed attained by any of the
twelve Pigeons experimented on was at the rate of
33·8 miles per hour, the lowest at the rate of 26·1.
This is much lower than we should have expected,
considering that the " screens " were placed at the
farther end of the gallery in order to allow the birds
to get up pace. The velocity of four Pigeons was
measured in the open on a calm day by persons
stationed at a certain distance from one another, who
marked carefully the moment at which the birds came
opposite to them and registered it with a stop watch.

[1] See an article quoted from the *Globe* in the *Zoologist* for
1889, p. 397. In the *Homing News* for September 13, 1889, is
an account, apparently, of the same flight, the distance being
given as 250 kilometres.

The fastest travelled at the rate of 27·9 miles per hour. Pheasants were experimented on in the same way in the range and in the open : in the former case the greatest velocity was 33·8, in the latter 36·1 miles per hour.[1]

These experiments, made in a gallery where the air was perfectly still, or in the open, when there was little or no wind, lead us to conclusions very different from those which we draw from the records of the races of Homing Pigeons. All the best of these records are, as I have said, obtained on very favourable days, when there is a tail-wind blowing, the velocity of which has to be added to that due to the bird's own exertions. But the difference seems to be too great to be accounted for in this way, even if we make no allowance for the fact that the Pigeon expends time and strength in circling to a height before starting for home, and for the probability that his course is not an absolute bee-line. It is possible that it is easier to attain great pace in rarefied air at a great height ; at an altitude of 6,000 feet, the density of the air, as may be seen by referring to a mountaineer's aneroid barometer, is only four fifths of what it is at the sea-level. It is true that such air will afford the bird less support, and that, therefore, the minimum pace that is necessary, if he is to maintain his level when gliding, is greater than in the denser air near the earth. But supposing that he can support himself, he will advance with greater rapidity since he will meet with less resistance. We

---

[1] See Charles Lancaster's *Illustrated Treatise on the Art of Shooting*, p. 175. Sir R. Payne-Gallwey (*Letters to Young Shooters*, p. 152) mentions similar experiments made by himself by aid of stop watches.

have somehow to account for what seems to be a well-established fact—viz., that the American Golden Plover as it travels southward in autumn accomplishes over 1,700 miles in one flight. Even if we assume an average rate of sixty miles per hour, the birds would be over twenty-eight hours on the wing, and this is a long time to be without food.

Further experiments on the velocity of the flight of birds of different species under varying conditions are much to be desired.

A pace of over 30 miles per hour is maintained by race-horses over a short course. Ladas' time over the Derby course, $1\frac{1}{2}$ miles, gives him a velocity of $32\frac{1}{2}$.

A Note on Flying Machines.

It is difficult in writing of flight to leave unmentioned the subject of flying machines. At the same time, an elaborate account of them would be out of place here. Not many years back it was supposed that only in balloons was aerial navigation possible for men, and the problem that was for ever being debated was, How is it possible to steer a balloon? With a vehicle that travels with the air and has no velocity of its own, steering is practically an impossibility. Since this has been realised, attention has been diverted from balloons to flying-machines, which are, necessarily, heavier than the surrounding air, since, if they are to do as they are intended to do, they must develop in themselves energy sufficient to lift them from the ground, and drive them forward, when required, in the teeth of the wind. Naturally, the first idea has been that the propelling force must act by means of wings. Quite recently Herr Lilienthal has tried to navigate the air with an equipment resembling a bird's. But though his wings have enabled him, starting from an elevation, to sail over 800 yards before sinking to earth—a truly wonderful feat of pluck and skill— it is improbable that any one could ever succeed by the help of such appliances in rising and main- taining himself in the air ; and nothing short of this can be called flight. Mr. Maxim has advanced a great deal further. He has seen that we ought not, in trying to rival a bird, to imitate it slavishly, as the first sewing-machine is said to have imitated the hand-sewn stitch, and he has, therefore, employed screws for the propulsion of his flying-machine. In animal mechanism, where the different parts cannot be separated, screws are, of course, out of the question. In man-made machinery a screw is better than a lever. It has no idle intervals, whereas a wing during the upstroke would be no better than a parachute. Besides this, it is doubtful whether machinery would not be too clumsy to effect all the turns that a wing must make even in straight-ahead flight. As soon as Mr. Maxim's machine was allowed to run along its line of rails at a rate of thirty-six miles per hour, it rose in the air, and but for contrivances designed to restrain it from mounting more than a very little, there is no knowing what heights it might have reached. This great aeroplane, weighing 8,000 lbs., imitates a sea-bird rising from the water : it presents to the air a surface inclined slightly upward, and this inclined surface causes it to rise when it travels fast. But

T

important questions of balance have yet to be decided. Moreover, it cannot as yet leave the earth without iron rails on which to get up pace. Wherever it might alight, it would remain helpless as a stranded ship. But the man who has got so far towards solving the problem of flight may well get further.

Conclusion.

This ends my account of flight. Much, I hope, has been made clear, but much remains that is inexplicable. Mathematicians will, no doubt, some day arrive at a formula of flight that will claim to be a complete solution of the problem. Nevertheless birds will still excite the wonder of men. Even those who can quote the formula at a moment's notice will, when they look at a Swift doing his sixty miles an hour for mere play, or if they happen to see a soaring Adjutant, relapse for a moment into blank astonishment, the mental state of the Pacific islander when a steamship first invades his lonely seas and claims a place in his philosophy. It will always be difficult to forget for long together, that, however much is learnt on such a subject as flight, a great deal more remains to be learnt.

SOME OF THE LITERATURE OF THE SUBJECT.

Marey's *Vol des Oiseaux*.
Marey's *Animal Mechanism* (International Sci. Series).
Alix's *Appareil Locomoteur des Oiseaux*.
The article on " Flight " in Newton's *Dictionary of Birds*.
Pettigrew's *Animal Locomotion* (International Sci. Series).
Books and papers referred to in the footnotes in the course of this chapter.

CHAPTER VIII

THE BIRD WITHIN THE EGG

IN writing of birds, as of other subjects, it is logical to begin *ab ovo*. This system, however methodical and German it may be, I have deliberately avoided, since in practice it is unwise to begin with what is least intelligible. Now that the reader understands the circulation of the blood, he will more easily understand some important points in the development of the embryo. If the pages that describe the circulation are not fresh in his memory, he is recommended to look them up before reading this chapter.

If a sitting hen be watched upon her nest, she may sometimes be seen to raise herself a little, and stir the eggs with her feet. Many people have imagined that the sole object was to turn them over. This may be an advantage, since the eggs require damping, and, by this means, each side in turn is moistened by the ground.[1] No turning is required to ensure that the embryo which lies just

[1] Eggs that are much exposed to damp in the nest have a waterproof layer.

within the thin membrane that envelopes the yolk is
sometimes at least next to the breast. Break a hole
about half an inch square in the side of a hen's egg,
and on the yolk will be seen a round, whitish spot.
If now the hole be walled up with sticking plaster so
that the white will not run out, and, the egg having
been turned over, another similar hole be made on the
other side, the whitish spot will again be seen. The
yolk has rolled over, as it always does when the egg
is turned. The white spot is the place where the
embryo lies, and it is always at the top, close to the
body of the bird. If the eggs under a sitting hen
are marked and examined the day after, the main
object with which she moves them will soon become
apparent. It will be found that she has shifted the
outside ones to the middle, and the middle ones to
the outside, so that all may have a turn at the warmest
place and consequently hatch about the same time.
For several days I marked the eggs in two nests, in
which they lay in a circle with three in the middle.
As a rule only two of these three (for no system
works perfectly) had been replaced by others from the
outer ring.

Now for the cause of the yolk's rolling over when
the egg is turned. When you break a raw egg, you
can hardly help seeing two twisted cords, of an
opaque white, which at their ends spread out and lose
themselves in the albumen. It has been supposed,
and in some recent books on natural history it is
still maintained, that these cords are the machinery
by which the revolution is brought about. But since
they only float in the albumen, it is difficult to see

how they can help towards it. They have a use, for they. act as buffers and save the yolk from violent concussion when the egg is shaken. The turning is due simply to the fact that the yolk is lighter on that side on which the embryo lies. If you examine a hard-boiled egg, you will see that the yolk is not uniform in colour ; most of it is yellow, the rest is whitish yellow, the two being different not only in colour, but in microscopic structure. The white yolk,

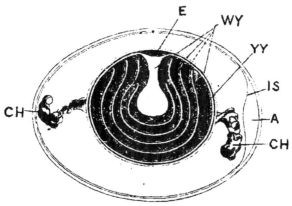

FIG. 66.—Egg, after Foster and Balfour. A, air-chamber between two layers of shell-membrane ; CH, chalazæ ; E, embryo ; IS, internal shell membrane ; WY, white yolk ; VY, yellow yolk.

as it is called, lies under the round white spot, and, swelling out like a flask, descends to the centre of the sphere. When the egg is turned, the yolk becomes top-heavy, and therefore rolls over. As yet this is only a rough description. Besides the flask-shaped mass of white yolk, there are four very thin layers dividing the yellow into five.

There is another feature that belongs only to an egg that is not perfectly fresh—the chamber at the large end. This· appears after a time, even if the egg is put under a hen, and gradually increases in size as the white shrinks by evaporation.

To follow in detail the kaleidoscopic development of the embryo from day to day, till at last by the help of the "egg-tooth" at the end of his beak he pecks his way out, is quite beyond the scope of this chapter. I merely wish to make clear one or two of the most interesting points. To the right understanding of these, some preliminary remarks are necessary. It is generally held that the embryo goes through in a short space of time many of the various stages by which in the course of ages the species has become what it is. Thus the progenitors of the butterfly were wingless crawling creatures, and the change from the caterpillar to the perfect insect is a brief abstract of the history of long ages of slow development. In the same way when we find in the embryos of reptiles, birds, and mammals organs that are the same in nature and origin as the gills of fishes, we infer that these three classes of animals were once water-breathers. The heart and the blood-vessels, as they advance step by step to the perfected form that we find in the mature bird, show us clearly that if we trace upward the avian and reptilian pedigrees we shall come at length to a point at which they meet, and that if we proceed further, we shall find the line joining another, where the common ancestors of birds and reptiles drew apart from the more primitive types that continued to make their home in the water, the progenitors of the fish of the present geological period.

This being so, it is well beforehand to get some

idea how the blood of a fish circulates. The heart is
a very imperfect one, and mixes the pure and impure
blood. It has one ventricle and one auricle. From
the former the blood is driven through a great artery
to the gills, and from them is gathered into another
great artery which branches and distributes it all over
the body. Thus, as a necessary consequence of the
absence of lungs, there is only one circulation.
The blood on leaving the heart is purified in the gills
and does not return to the heart before doing its work
in the body and limbs. Every one is familiar with
the gills of fishes. On the right and on the left sides
are arches of gristle which spring from the top of the
back part of the mouth and stand out, like bent bows,
on either side. Their frames of gristle or cartilage
are covered with delicate red fringes through which
the blood flows, separated only by a thin membrane
from the water which contains the oxygen it stands
in need of. In principle, therefore, they are the same
as lungs. The great artery, the aorta, which brings
the blood from the heart sends off branches to each
of the gills. Thus there are aortic arches as well as
gill arches (G, fig. 67).

To return now to the chick. On the third day of
incubation, there are clear signs of arches such as I
have described. There are four clefts on each side,
and each cleft has a fold on its front border. The
fourth cleft has a fold both before and behind, and
thus there are five folds and four clefts. These folds
and clefts are homologous to the gill arches and clefts
in fishes. It is true they are now functionless. The
chick breathes throughout the twenty-one days of

incubation, but not through its gill arches, nor through
the lungs, which are not for some time connected with

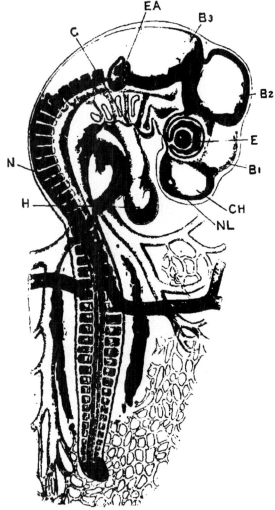

FIG. 67.—(After Duval.) Embryo of sixty-eight hours. B1, forebrain, to become
optic lobes ; B2, mid brain ; B3, hind brain, to divide into cerebellum and medulla
oblongata ; CH, cerebral hemispheres ; E, eye ; EA, internal ear ; G, gill arches, with
clefts between ; H, heart ; N, notochord, to pass into backbone ; NL, nasal pit.

the heart, and do not set to work till respiration begins
with the hatching of the bird. The system of breath-

ing is peculiar to the embryo, and is carried on by means of a wide extension of blood-vessels, rendered possible by its protected situation within the shell.   The round spot, called the blastoderm, at the top of the egg, grows all round its circumference, and, its edges at length meeting, it becomes a bag, with various pockets, which envelopes all the yolk.   Out of the folds of the blasto-

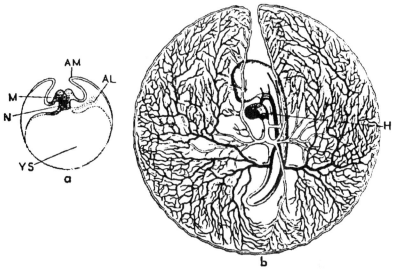

FIG. 68.—(*a*) after Gadow.   Transverse section through embryo during third day ; AL, allantois : later it spreads out and lies, full of blood-vessels, close under the shell ; AM, amnion, a fold formed from embryo and enveloping it ; M, spinal marrow ; N, notochord, to pass into backbone ; YS, yolk-sack.   (*b*) Diagram of the circulation of the yolk-sack at the end of the third day of incubation.   The veins are marked in outline, and the arteries in black.   H, heart (after Foster and Balfour).

derm the chick is formed ; it lies like a crease in the walls of the bag, and sends out its blood-vessels into two of the pockets, one called the yolk-sack, the other the allantois, which forms a branch of the alimentary canal.   The first few days the work is done mainly in the yolk-sack ; later on the allantois plays the more prominent part.   The shell, of course,

is porous, and allows of the passage of gases out
and in.

All the pairs of arches except three, the first, second,
and third, become obliterated in the mature bird. The
first pair become the lower jaw: branches sent out
from them form the upper
jaw. The hyoid bone, which
lies at the bottom of the
mouth and helps to support
the tongue, represents the
second and third pairs. The
first cleft, the only one which
does not get obliterated, becomes connected with the organ of hearing, and forms the
eustachian tubes.[1] The branches of the aortic artery form
pairs of arches corresponding
to the folds visible on the
surface. The first pair of
aortic arches lies within the
first fold, the second pair in
the second, and so on. There
are five folds and five pairs of
aortic arches within them. At

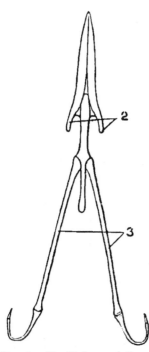

Fig. 69.—Hyoid bone of Crow.
2, second arch ; 3, third arch.
The jaws are the first.

a very early stage there is another pair between
No. 4 and that just spoken of as No. 5, which must,
therefore, rank as No. 6 (Fig. 71). On the fourth
day the first two pairs also disappear, leaving
only three, and we must carefully trace the history
of these three and their connection with the heart.

[1] See p. 134.

By the end of the fifth day the ventricle of the heart has divided into right and left chambers. On the seventh day the artery leading from it follows suit and divides into right and left branches, which are quite separate. And of these two arteries, that from the right chamber connects with the sixth pair of arches, while that from the left connects with the third and fourth. Meanwhile the lungs have come into existence, being in their origin pouches formed in the gullet. The sixth pair of arches open a connection

a   b

FIG. 70.—(After Foster and Balfour.) Diagrams illustrating arterial circulation (*a*) on third day—the first three pairs of arches, Nos. 4 and 6 not yet formed, No. 5 not represented ; (*b*) on the fifth or sixth day. The first, second, and fifth pairs have been obliterated.

with them, and here we have the final arrangement, the artery from the right side of the heart leading to these arches, and, so, onward to the lungs. Meanwhile the third pair of arches has been growing weaker, and the fourth stronger. Finally, only one of the fourth pair is left, that on the right side ; it is the great aorta, which may be seen curving to the right, one of the three single survivors out of five pairs, the other two being the pulmonary arteries, which lead to the left and right lungs and represent the sixth pair. Occa-

sionally the left arch, opposite to the aorta, may be
seen in a rudimentary form.   I have once seen it in a
chicken.   In mammals it is the left arch, instead of the
right, of the fourth pair that survives, and forms a
most important distinction between them and birds.
Reptiles generally have only the fourth pair of arches
surviving, but in many lizards both the third and fourth

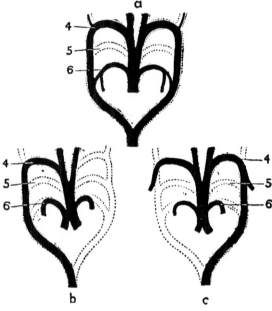

Fig. 71.—Diagrams—after Boas—illustrating (*a*) lizard's heart ; (*b*) bird's heart ;
(*c*) human heart, viewed from the front ; 6, 5, 4, the 6th, 5th, and 4th pairs of aortic
arches.

are found.   For a time the bird is, judged by his
heart, a reptile.   The crocodile's heart, which in several
points comes near to that of birds, may be called a
noble failure.   It has four chambers instead of, like
most reptilian hearts, only three.   But it has two aortas
instead of one.   Of these, one springs from the left
ventricle and carries pure blood ; the other from the

right ventricle and carries impure.   Outside the heart
the two arteries cross and there is a small passage
from one to the other, so that the pure and impure
blood are mixed.   The fourth pair of arches have
become separate except at this one point ; but what
should have followed, has not—viz. the reduction of
the right aorta to a rudimentary state.   Otherwise
the crocodile might have become a warm-blooded and
altogether finer beast.

SOME OF THE LITERATURE OF THE SUBJECT.

(1) Foster and Balfour's *Elements of Embryology.*

(2) The article on " Embryology " in Newton's *Dictionary of Birds.*

(3) Bronn's *Thier-Reich*, vol. "Aves." [Dr. Gadow is the author of both 2 and 3.]

(4) Duval's *Atlas D'embryologie.*

CHAPTER IX

YOUTH, MATURITY, AND AGE

THE lives of most young birds are fairly familiar to most of us. Young chickens, not long after they are hatched, run after their mother, picking up what she tells them to eat, and listening to her warning cry. Young ducks soon take to the water, and the method of their bringing-up may be easily seen. Young Blackbirds stay long in the nest and wait open-mouthed to be fed. All this is an old story. There is one bird, the Hoatzin, the bird of British Guiana already mentioned, whose infant life and infant powers it is difficult to describe without exciting incredulity in the mind of the reader. But the interest does not end with the strangeness of the bird and its ways. As we watch him we may feel sure that we are learning much of the build and of the habits of many ancient birds that have made room for more highly developed types.

The Hoatzin is more nearly related to the Fowls than to any other birds. But he diverges from them so far that he is regarded as the sole representative of a distinct group. All his near kindred have passed away, and he stands solitary, a living fossil, the only survivor of a number of families that have either disappeared, too primitive to hold their own, or have advanced to a higher organisation.

Apparently about as large as a rather under-sized Pheasant, the Hoatzin is really considerably smaller ; his long tail, his large wings, and his crest suggest a larger bulk of body than he really possesses. He and his kind are born from eggs that are usually smaller than a hen's, but which vary much in size. His breast-bone has a very slight development of keel, and that only in its hinder part, and the clavicles, from the point where they meet, send back a long bone which looks remarkably like a reptilian interclavicle. Among the trees and bushes that form a jungle-growth along the banks of the Berbice and often overhang its waters, Hoatzins are plentiful. When a boat passes they will generally remain concealed among the leaves. They seldom fly, their large wings having but weak muscles to move them. The longest observed flight was no longer than forty yards, and that with a considerable descent, from a high growth on one bank to a lower one on the other. Mere jumps or the very shortest flights are more usual when the crack of a gun disturbs them. The food consists, as far as is known, entirely of leaves : they are crushed in the crop, which is formed of thick walls of muscles with outstanding ridges. The nest is formed of a few sticks intertwisted. When the birds'-nester comes, cutting a way for his boat through the bushes, or wading thigh-deep through the mud, the old bird makes off upon the wing. The nestling, unless very recently hatched, crawls off on all fours, making much use of not only his enormous feet, but of the great claws that grow at the ends of the two first digits of his hand. If you try to pull him from the nest by the legs, he holds fast by means of these wing-claws and his beak. Often a young bird may be found clawing his way onward some distance from the nest. If he tumbles into the water he proves to be a born swimmer and diver. All this is so astonishing that some people are inclined to hesitate before they accept it as true. But the paper by Mr. J. J. Quelch, from which I derive this account of the bird's habits, is based upon patient and careful observation. Nor does the Hoatzin, so far as his infant mode of life is concerned, stand absolutely alone. The young Ionornis, a Florida bird, has been seen to climb out of his nest by means of his wing-claws,[1] and besides this the anatomy of the young Hoatzin bears witness to his habits. The wing-digits are enormously developed. I have already mentioned that the embryo has a distinct rudiment of a fourth. More remarkable is the great length of its first. Though No. 2 is of wonderful dimensions, yet No. 1 is more than half its length. And each of these two carries at its end a very big claw. Contrast with them the digits of a Swift's wing ; there we find the first hardly more than a quarter of the length of the second, and there is no sign of a claw on either.[2] In the

---

[1] Shufeldt, *Ibis*, vol. ii., 1890.

[2] The hand of the embryo Hoatzin is here compared with that of an adult Swift. The hand of an embryo Swift would probably present a very great, though not so great, a contrast.

nestling Hoatzin the hand is longer than the forearm ;
gradually it grows shorter, while the other parts of the
wing lengthen, till, in the fledged bird, the forearm
surpasses it (Fig. 72 *a*, *b*). The feathers, too, adapt
themselves to changing circumstances ; in the nestling the growth of the two outermost primaries is
completely arrested, so that the use of the claws
may not be impeded ; when it is fledged and can
fly, they begin again to grow and attain their full

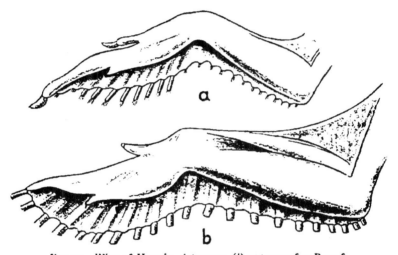

Fig. 72.—Wing of Hoatzin—(*a*) young, (*b*) mature—after Pycraft.

length.   With maturity, too, the claw on digit No. 1
grows small, while that on No. 2 is lost altogether.
The pause made by the growing quills was first
noticed by Mr. Pycraft, and he has further pointed
out that in the common chick we have traces of a
similar development.   There too we find the hand of
the young bird longer, though only by a little, than
the forearm ; the second digit has a claw only in the
embryo stage ; the first is much reduced, but retains

U

its claw. But the most wonderful point of all is that the three outermost primaries have their growth arrested while the others advance in length ; later on they grow to their full size. This can be well seen in the series of young chickens in the hall at the South Kensington Museum. And so the chicken, a thoroughly modernized relative of the archaic Hoatzin, still retains this queer trace of its ancient life.

The anatomy and habits of Hoatzin may help us to understand what may have been the manner of life of Archæopteryx. Mr. Pycraft suggests that it used its claws mainly during its infancy. May it not also have had recourse to them when moulting ? A poor flyer at best, and its leg-muscles possibly weak, it might well, when bereft of some of its big feathers, or, through an imperfect system of moulting, bereft of all at once, appreciate fully the value of wing-claws, to help it to climb out of the reach of reptile enemies.

We will now pass on to a comparatively commonplace subject. As a rule a young bird differs in plumage from a mature one. The cock bird as he grows up often puts on fine plumes unknown to his youth. If there is a difference in brightness between the old birds and the young, it is always the latter which are characterised by the more sober dress. But beyond this it is impossible to find a rule that will apply to all. When the cock is more conspicuous than the hen, the young usually resemble the mother. The young cock Blackbird, however, is easy to distinguish in the nest by his darker tint. In the Painted Snipes and the few other species in which the female bird is more gaudy than the male, it is the latter that the young birds resemble. If the two sexes are alike when mature, the young birds may, as with the Robins, have a distinct plumage of their own ; or, as with the Kingfisher and Jay and many sober-hued birds, young and old may be alike. Still the resemblance is often not exact. When, as in the case of the Dunlin, both sexes put on a distinct and richer dress in spring, it is the old birds in their winter garb that the young resemble.

The age at which maturity is attained varies much in different species. Our small birds are ready to nest the first spring after their birth. In some cases there is no difference of plumage ; the young swallows arrive later than the old ones, but when they have arrived they are indistinguishable. Gulls, however, do not appear in quite mature plumage till their third or fourth year, or even their fifth—*i.e.*, till the moult at the end of their fifth summer. The young Lesser Black-backed Gull keeps his first plumage till the summer following. Then comes a moult, after which we find him still brown but paler than in his first year. At the end of his third summer his colour becomes an ashen gray, and the tail is in some specimens white, in others mottled. None of the primary wing-feathers, or, at any rate, only one of them, has a white spot or "mirror." The moult after his fourth summer brings him to the plumage of his maturity—back and wings black, breast white, head white with dusky streaks that will pass away and leave pure white in spring. A Gannet, which may be described as grown up, has not a single black feather except the primaries ; all the rest of him is white .except the fine cream-coloured head and neck. The young bird is blackish, speckled with white, and at each moult some of the incorrect feathers are weeded out. These changes, it is believed, give a rapid recapitulation of the history of the Gannets. At one time they had throughout their lives these blackish feathers ; in the course of generations they attained to their present spotless white. It is probably not till the fifth autumn that the plumage reaches the perfection of maturity, and the next spring the bird makes his first nest. In the photograph at South Kensington of Gannets sitting on their eggs, there is apparently not one whose plumage shows any sign of immaturity. The youth of a Golden Eagle lasts ten years, or even longer. The rate of mortality is great among young birds, and but few Golden Eagles, probably, survive to build a nest and rear young. And this leads us on to the subject of the age attained by birds, for there is no doubt that there is a connection between this and the age of maturity. There is a good deal of evidence that Eagles and their allies live to a great age—to 100 years and more ; and even if particular cases are doubtful, yet on the principle that a number of weak sticks make a strong faggot, I think we may accept it. Suppose that an Eagle lives to only sixty years, and becomes mature at ten, then a pair will produce 100 eggs in the fifty years, the number laid being usually two, and of the hundred birds hatched only two will live to grow up. This calculation, which I quote from Professor Weissmann, even if only roughly correct, is valuable as bringing together three facts which must be viewed in connection—(1) the great length of an eagle's natural life ; (2) his late attainment of maturity ; (3) the high death-rate among the young. The ages to which birds may attain are as a rule but vaguely known. Our small singing birds sometimes live to be ten years old ; a Magpie has lived twenty years in captivity, Parrots upwards of 100. Humboldt's story of a Parrot, whose words the Indians said could not be understood because it spoke the language of an extinct tribe, is an amusing myth sprung from an old belief. Some idea of the age attained by Guillemots, Razorbills, and Puffins may be formed from the fact that they lay only one egg, and, though the young are exposed to great dangers, yet the numbers of the species do not diminish. Even if they sometimes have two nests in the year, yet unless their span of life were a fairly long one they could not keep up their numbers. Ravens have lived nearly 200 years in captivity, and a White-headed Vulture captured in 1706 is believed to have died at the Zoological Gardens at Vienna in 1824.

LITERATURE BEARING ON THE SUBJECT.

Darwin's *Descent of Man* (see vol. ii., p. 187, and onwards).

Weissmann's *Essays on Heredity* (see p. 11 and onwards).

Professor W. K. Parker on the "Morphology of Opisthocomus Cristatus," *Transactions of the Zoological Society*, vol. xiii., part 2.

Mr. J. J. Quelch on the "Habits of the Hoatzin," *Ibis*, vol. ii., 1890, p. 327.

Mr. W. P. Pycraft on "The Wing of Archæopteryx," *Nat. Science*, Nov. 1894.

(I am also indebted to Mr. C. M. Adamson's *Some more Scraps about Birds*, printed for private circulation.)

CHAPTER X

BIRD POPULATION

BRITISH ornithologists have good reason to be depressed, and to wish that they had lived in the days of their grandfathers. One bird after another passes away exterminated by sportsmen, collectors, drainage, or increase of population. The Bittern when he comes to us is shot before he can nest ; the Great Bustard only occasionally strays here ; the Golden Eagle is only to be seen in remote mountainous parts of our islands, and the Bearded Tit lingers on in but two or three counties. And the evil seems likely to increase. Nothing, I believe, but the establishment of protected districts, on a larger scale than has hitherto been accomplished by private persons, can check it. Parliament may perhaps some day grant charters to societies of naturalists allowing them to maintain such oases, and punish as a thief any one who steals eggs or birds from the sacred precincts.

The question of diminution of species is, however, quite different from the question of diminution of population. There are probably as many birds, when all told, in the British Isles as there were in the last century. Cultivation supplies them with abundance of food almost everywhere, and if you wish to find the greatest possible number of birds' nest in a day, there is no better place to search than a garden. There are far more small birds there than in a big forest, or an open moor. In a day's walk in Sutherlandshire you may see nothing but some Grouse, a Raven or so, a Buzzard, and perhaps an Eagle. A rickyard simply swarms with birds. The preservation of game has led also to a preservation of Warblers. They are saved from birds'-nesters, and Hawks are kept down. Now that Scotch firs and larches are common trees, we have more Golden-crested Wrens. With the spread of plantations the Robin and the Blackbird have extended their range further north. The Missel Thrush is now found as far north as Caithness, and though unknown in Ireland before 1800 is now common there, even as far west as Connemara. In Scotland Chaffinches are on the increase, and in many parts Starlings, never seen some forty years back, are now familiar birds. The Peewit, whose nests grow rarer and rarer in England, breeds in greater numbers than formerly in the north of Scotland. The conditions, in short, have changed, and under the new conditions some kinds thrive and multiply, others dwindle and vanish. But new species do not come to us, except in very rare cases, to replace those that pass away, the tendency of civilization being to reduce more and more the amount of variety upon the earth. There is one bird, the House-sparrow, who is always at home amid the bustle of human life, and who, if England were to become one big city, would out-do Sir Boyle Roche's famous bird and be, not in two, but in all places at once.   Happily he is not the only bird which takes to town life.   In Germany there is the Stork, and in London we have the Domestic Pigeon, the descendant of the Rock-dove, at Westminster, at the National Gallery, at the British Museum, at Liverpool Street Station, and many other places. And in Regent's Park in January I have heard the Thrush and the Robin singing in a thick and choking London fog.   There are a great many birds that will live happily and without fear amid the noise of human life, or in a comparatively quiet town-garden or park, where, however much they may be looked at, they are free from actual molestation.   Even the Wood-pigeon is now a Londoner.

BOOKS ON THE SUBJECT.

Facts bearing on this question will be found in almost all books on the natural history of birds.   See Mr. Hudson's *Birds in a Village.*

CHAPTER XI

Nature of Colours

WHILE others were discussing for what purpose the brilliant colours of birds existed and what part they played in the life of the species thus adorned, some German investigators with characteristic thoroughness set to work to discover the nature of the colours themselves. They found that the colours in birds' feathers might be divided into two classes. There were first those which appeared the same from any point of view ; secondly, those which changed as the bird, or as the person who watched it, moved. To these classes have been given the names of objective and subjective colours. The first class had to be subdivided into two—viz., those which were due to pigment alone, and those which were due partly to the pigment and partly to the feather's structure.

Thus we have—(I.) objective colours, (1) due to pigment ; (2) due to pigment, plus structure ; (II.) subjective colours.

(I.) *Objective Colours.*

Colours due to pigment alone may be: (*a*) black; (*b*) brown; (*c*) red; (*d*) yellow or greenish-yellow; (*c*) very rarely green; in fact, only in the feathers of the Touracou.

White pigment has been found in the pineal eye of the Lamprey and in one butterfly.[1] But it does not, as far as is known, exist elsewhere in nature. Black, brown, and red are always due to pigment alone, yellow sometimes. These are occasionally modified by another layer of pigment overlying them.

Blue and violet belong to the second division of objective colours; pigment and structure combine to produce them. Take any blue feather and hold it up to the light, so that the rays pass through it. It is no longer blue, but a dull black or gray. Hammer it, and all the blue vanishes. Green, except in the one case mentioned, is also a pigment-structural colour. Hammer a green feather from a Parrot, and it becomes yellow, the colour of its pigment.

No blue pigment has been found; that which a blue feather contains is black-brown to yellow. The colour which it presents to the eye is due to the structure of the horny feather coating which encases the pigment. It has been found that under a thin outer sheath, there are a number of small polygonal cones; from the surfaces of these cones project extremely fine ridges, and it is believed that to these

---

[1] See Beddard, *Animal Coloration*, p. 4.

ridges, with the very narrowest interstices between them, the colour is due. No doubt they somehow break up the light rays, but how they act in combination with the underlying pigment I am unable to explain. Violet and green feathers have no cones like these, but long thin ridges lying close together have been found, so that in them too the cause of the colours is the same.

The underlying pigment in the case of the green feathers is yellow. There is one structural colour which seems to be produced without the help of

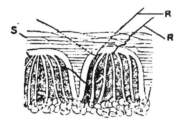

FIG. 73.—(After Gadow). Cone with fine ridges, found in blue feathers. s, thin surface layer overlying cone ; R, R, rays of light.

pigment, or possibly the pigment has not been discovered. However this may be, the resulting colour, yellow, is found in the feathers of the Pitta or "Ant Thrush."

(II.) *Subjective Colours.*

Take a feather which has a metallic lustre. The Bronze-winged Pigeon's will do fairly well ; Humming Birds, I think, supply the best. Hold it horizontally on a level with the eye, and look along it from either end or across it, and it looks simply black ; but look down upon it, and move it to and fro, and it will show some of the colours of the spectrum following one another in their right order. Beginning with bronze-red it will change to golden green, to green, and thus, in some cases, on to blue and violet. There is no brown or gray, but only the colours of the spectrum; another fact that makes it probable that they are prismatic. The light when it falls on the feather is broken up by a number of prisms in the same way as drops of rain break up the light and form a rainbow.

" In the spring a livelier Iris changes on the burnished dove."

These colours, then, are properly called iridescent.

But it never happens that all the colours of the spectrum are visible. Of this various explanations have been suggested, for instance, that two prisms overlap, and that the complementary colours produce white light. Iridescent colours are seen also in reptiles. The reticulated Python at the Zoological Gardens shows wonderful changes when the sun falls upon it.

White stands by itself. It is due to the rays of light being broken an infinite number of times and reflected. It requires no pigment. To this breaking of the rays is due the whiteness of powdered glass and of snow.

The lustre of feathers as distinguished from colour is due to the reflection of the light from the polished surfaces.

Variety of Colours in the same Bird.

This variety is often most striking. The Beautiful Grass Finch (*Poephila mirabilis*) displays blue, yellow, green, and red. There is a kind of Parrot, the Red-sided Eclectus from New Guinea, which has a black beak; a thin ring of blue skin round the eyes; the head, the under side of the neck, and the upper part of the breast a rich dark red; a half ring of indigo blue on the back of the neck; the lower part of the breast also indigo blue; the wing coverts and the back claret colour, and the tail scarlet. There is none of the limitation of colours which we find in flowers. It is rarely that we find among flowers a species, a genus, or even an order in which red, blue, and yellow are represented. A blue rose has not yet been invented. All the many butter-cups are yellow or white. In the multitudinous British compositæ, red is unknown and blue is rare. In the order which is more remarkable than any other for elaborate specialisation, the orchids, there is, among all the British representatives, no decided blue or yellow. Thus we find individual birds which show more variety of colours than many orders of flowers. Two well-known genera, the anemones and the hyacinths, have blues, yellows, and reds, and this makes them quite remarkable. Besides the splendour of feathers birds often have grand combs and wattles, which latter are appendages on the throat. This will bring the Turkey-cock to any one's mind. Tetrao Cupido, a kind of Capercailzie, has an orange-coloured sack on each side of its neck. The Umbrella Bird has a kind of fleshy dewlap thickly covered with scale-like blue feathers. The Cassowary carries a blue horny elevation at the top of his head.

Patterns.

On first thoughts the patterns in which we find the colours distributed on the surfaces of birds and butterflies seem to show an infinite variety. But on investigation it proves not nearly so great. There is one law which always operates in wild animals, the law of bilateral symmetry—*i.e.*, the right and left sides are always coloured very nearly alike. In birds, the head is often of one colour, the breast of another, and so forth ; but this can hardly be called a pattern. As a rule the patterns are varieties of lines or spots, and this is true, not only of birds, but of other classes of animals ; among mammals, for instance, of the deer and the great carnivora. The ocellus, or peacock eye, is a spot in its most perfect development ; the centre is surrounded by one or more rings of different colours or of different shades. The delicate shading is more beautiful in the ocelli of the Argus Pheasant than in those of the Peacock, though the colours are not so brilliant. And in this bird one and the same feather shows how the ocellus grows out of a line through the transition stage of a vague ellipse. As we look at it, the work of Nature's "'prentice hand" and mature skill seem presented to us at once, suggesting the gradual stages by which the species has developed its magnificence. There was a time when Argus

Pheasants had no ocelli. Slowly, in thousands of generations, they have attained to their present beauty, and the record of the process is written on their feathers.

To show how similar patterns run through nature, a writer in the *Spectator*[1] points out that the peacock eye is found not only in the Peacock, the Peacock Butterfly, the Eyed Hawkmoth, and other allied insects, but also in a small fish (Guppy's Cyprinodon) and in a kind of Iris. The fish in question, recently to be seen at the insect house at the Zoological Gardens, is very minute, hardly more than an inch long, but the males are adorned with several unmistakable and very beautiful "eyes." Thus we have the same form of decoration in birds, insects, fish, and flowers.

Perhaps the beauty of birds is not due mainly either to their brilliant colours, or to the patterns in which they are arranged. Some sober-coloured birds are far more beautiful than some of the most gaudy. The lines of the figure have often a grace almost unequalled in Nature. Take for instances, the Crane's neck, the gentle curve where it joins the body, or the lines of the Gull's expanded wings as he floats in the air. Colour and fine symmetry are, of course, often combined, but the less gaudy birds seem to have the advantage in figure, unless it is that over-brilliancy of colour distracts the attention from other charms. And even in the dullest the eye is always bright. A wild bird must be in a bad way if he has a lacklustre look.

[1] June 3rd, 1893.

Protective Coloration.

On one point every one is in agreement—viz., that many birds are protectively coloured. They escape the hungry eyes of birds of prey, reptiles, and other enemies, from the fact that they are of the same colour as their surroundings. The birds of the Sahara are most of them sandy-coloured. Pallas's Sand-grouse, a native of desert tracts north of the Himalayas, must be familiar to most people. The sober browns and grays of our common birds are well suited to their life in woods which half the year are leafless, whereas the evergreen tropical forests afford concealment for more conspicuous plumage. The Ptarmigan drops his dark summer dress for one of a pure white that may make him almost invisible on the winter snows. The Canary Islands have two very remarkable instances of this adaptation to surroundings. There is a Chaffinch (*Fringilla teydea*) that lives among the pine trees on the high slopes beneath the peak of Teneriffe, and to harmonise with the glaucous hue of the pine trees, he has become a beautiful blue-gray. There is no doubt that this bird is a descendant of European Chaffinches. Teneriffe is a volcanic island, thrown up from the bottom of the ocean, and it has only upon it such animals as have found their way over sea, though these have often been curiously modified. The Trumpeter Bullfinch is of a uniform bright salmon colour, but on the ochre-coloured rocks of the nearly desert island of Hiero he is extremely difficult to see. In the Natural History

Museum at South Kensington there are some admirable illustrations of protective coloration.

Sexual Coloration, Song, Antics, Combats.

Where there is a difference between the two sexes it is almost always the cock-bird that is the more brilliant of the two. The vocal powers also of the hens are very limited. The superior endowments of the males are accompanied by two allied characteristics, the love of displaying their fine colours and voices, and great pugnacity. The Peacock spreads out his splendid sea of eyes, and there can hardly be a doubt that during the display he is filled with pride and vanity. Sometimes he will back against a wall; whether to hide the less brilliant back view, or to escape from the wind is not clear. The Turkey-cock puffs himself out, spreads his tail, and drags his wing-tips on the ground, no doubt with a view to effect. The Barndoor-cock looks often the personification of pride. Many of our small birds are constantly singing, and there is no doubt that love of display, emulation, and excitement are among the motives that actuate them. Bird fanciers match birds against each other to see which will sing the longest, and a really keen one will sometimes sing till he drops dead. Where Nightingales are common they often seem to be singing against each other. Bird-catchers attract Cock Chaffinches by exposing a stuffed bird to view while a first-rate singer carols in a cage out of sight. To decide for certain what the motive in a bird's mind may be, is, no doubt, impossible. Even to know what is in the mind of

X

another man with whom we are familiar is a difficult problem ; we are each of us so isolated from every one else. When it comes to reading the thoughts of a bird, we must expect sometimes to arrive at very wrong results. Poets in ancient times invariably represented the Nightingale as a melancholy bird who poured forth a dirge. They read their own thoughts into the bird's song, like a German commentator who reads profundities into the simplest line of Shakespeare. And then the legend of Philomela made permanent a notion which otherwise might have given place to a more natural one. In this case the modern view can hardly be wrong, that, though no doubt there is a strong admixture of other motives, the Nightingale sings to give vent to his exuberant spirits. There are some birds whose song, if it expresses anything at all, expresses the wildest jubilation. Such is the song of the Lark. The Robin, it is true, seems even in spring time to put into his note something of the melancholy of autumn. But what seems melancholy to us need not be so to him. The hideous cry of the Peacock is, no doubt, charming to himself and, very possibly, to the Pea-hen.

Society has on many birds an exhilarating influence : Rooks when they come home for the night fly round and round, making a babel of cawing, before they settle down to rest. Mr. Hudson[1] describes several great flocks of Crested Screamers singing alternately —a splendid and orderly concert. Wild birds have superabundant health and spirits from the simple fact that illness nearly always means for them speedy

[1] *Naturalist in La Plata*, p. 227.

death. In fact, happiness is the general rule in the animal world, and chronic melancholy is unknown.

In all these displays of plumage and song, in every exhibition of high spirits, it is the cock-birds who play the leading part. The nesting season is the time of jollity and hilarity, in whatever way expressed. It is in springtime that there take place among some species those elaborate performances that go by the name of love antics; in spring, too, the cock-birds engage in their most desperate fights. Colour-display, singing, antics, and fighting are all allied phenomena; and all are manifested at the time of pairing and nesting.

In many species there are special preparations. The cock-birds have a partial moult, after which they don far gayer plumes than they have worn during the winter. The Linnets, Red-polls, Dunlins, Golden Plovers, Gulls, brighten up their old dresses or adorn themselves with new. Ducks and their kin get ready over-early; the male Teal, having been since July as dull as the hen-bird, in October blossoms out in the black, chestnut, green, buff, and white which he wears in spring. The Ruff puts on a noble breastplate. Even the Cormorant appears with a white patch on each thigh that breaks the monotony of his attire. So different in many birds is the spring plumage from that of the rest of the year that when you shoot a specimen in autumn or winter it is often quite unlike the pictures in the books which, as a rule, give the birds at their best. In many cases, however, for instance in that of the Peacocks and Pheasants, the grand plumes are worn throughout the year.

When the birds have arrayed themselves for spring, there is heard that outburst of song that gives to an English wood or shrubbery a charm that is said to be often wanting in a tropical forest. In England, however, we have not the performances that are made up of music, partly vocal, partly instrumental, and dancing that is sometimes sedate and sometimes madly wild. The best account of these is given in Mr. Hudson's *Naturalist in La Plata*, a book which should be read by all who wish to enter into the lives of animals. I give a few instances from other sources. In the *Nineteenth Century*,[1] speaking of the dances of a kind of grouse Mr. John Worth writes : " One of the cocks lowers his head, spreads out his wings nearly horizontally, and his tail perpendicularly, distends his air-sacs[2] and erects his feathers, then rushes across the floor, taking the shortest of steps, but stamping his feet so hard and so rapidly, that the sound is like that of the kettle-drum ; and at the same time he utters a kind of bubbling crow, which seems to rise from his air-sacs, beats the air with his wings, and vibrates his tail so that he produces a loud rustling noise, and thus becomes a really astonishing spectacle. Soon after he commences, all the cocks join in, rattling, stamping, drumming, crowing, and dancing furiously ; louder and louder the noise, faster and faster the dance becomes, until at last they madly whirl about, leaping over each other in their excitement." The Australian Bower

---

[1] April, 1893.

[2] *I.e.*, the coloured sacks on his neck. The " floor " is the spot where the birds meet for these performances.

Birds are equally wonderful. A number of these combine to erect a bower, which they decorate with shells, feathers, and anything that commends itself as ornamental, the cock-birds doing most of, but not all, the work. In these bowers go on antics of a much more gentle and sedate kind than those just described. It is much to be regretted that the Bower Birds at the Zoological Gardens seem recently to have had no spirit for architecture or for elaborate sports. Among our English birds, as I have said, antics on a grand scale are unknown, perhaps because they have a richness and variety of song sufficient to express any

FIG. 74.—Snipe's outer tail-feather (after Darwin).

emotion. But we have occasional instances of instrumental music in our domestic and wild birds. The Peacock rattles his quills. The "drumming" noise made by the Snipe, as he descends with wild speed from the sky, is now known to be caused partly by the curiously curved outer tail-feathers. If one of these is held in the hand and waved rapidly through the air, the "drumming" is actually heard. The wings probably assist.[1]

Fighting is very often combined with antics, notably by the Blackcock and Capercailzie.

In some cases the fighting itself seems merely to be of an antic character, the males sparring with little

[1] See Darwin's *Descent of Man*, vol. ii., p. 64.

danger to each other before the females. The Ruffs, who, unhappily, no longer breed in England, supply the best instance of this. They have regular places at which they assemble, known to fowlers by the grass being trampled down. Here day after day they congregate and go through their fantastic performance.

Fighting pure and simple unaccompanied by antics is common. Humming-birds are said to fight desperately. The males of the Common Waterhen have great battles, standing nearly upright in the water, and fighting with their feet. Robins are great fighters. The males of gallinaceous birds are often very pugnacious and in their spurs they have a formidable weapon. The courage and ferocity of the Gamecock is proverbial. As a rule it is among polygamous species that we find the combats most desperate and the antics most elaborate.

Theories to explain these Phenomena.

Darwin was first in the field with a definite theory, to which he gave the name of Sexual Selection. The cock-birds fought and the hen-birds were the prizes. There is no doubt that this theory rests on a foundation of fact. Selection by battle goes on in many classes of animals, notably among deer and cattle. But an explanation of the brilliant plumage was more difficult to find. The theory which we owe to him is very ingenious and plausible, but the evidence on which it rests is insufficient. The female bird, he maintained, selected the handsomest male bird, or the best singer, or the one that performed the most striking antics. Those who were selected left descendants behind, and thus grand plumage and voice became more and more developed. He found support for his view in the habits of those species in which the hen is more brightly coloured and larger than the cock-bird. With them it is the hen-birds who fight among one another ; the males sit upon the eggs and care for the young. Among these birds is the Indian Turnix Taigoor, the females of which are kept, like Gamecocks, by the natives for fighting. The cock-birds, it is said, undertake the whole duties of incubation and nursing, the hens absenting themselves and collecting in flocks as soon as they have laid. The Painted Snipe, another Indian bird, is an instance of the same thing. Ostriches and their allies have similar habits. The cock-birds are responsible for incubation and the care of the young. But the female is, at any rate not in all the allied families, the statelier bird. The male Cassowary is larger and more brightly coloured about the head than his partner, and the cock Ostrich is larger than the hen-bird whose eggs he hatches.

Darwin saw in the Indian Turnix and Painted Snipe a confirmation of his theory. The brilliant colours were due to selection. But here it was the brilliant hen-bird that was selected by the male. One of his strongest arguments was the fact that the splendid plumes were often a serious inconvenience and even a danger to the bird which carried them. Instead of natural selection lopping off these cumbersome appendages, female taste stepped in and preserved what, according to the great law of the survival of the fittest, ought to have passed out of existence. The portentous feathers carried by the Argus Pheasant render him nearly incapable of flight: he keeps to the jungle and trusts to his running power. The comb and gills of a Gamecock put him at a great disadvantage with an antagonist who has had them trimmed off. The Bird of Paradise with his forest of plumes, and the Lyre Bird with his far-spreading burden of beauty, seem very ill-fitted for the struggle of life. Of Peacocks a good authority writes: "Peafowl run very fast, but the old cocks, burdened with tails six feet in length, are poor flyers; and I have frequently seen my men run them down during the hot hours of the day by forcing them to take two or three long flights in succession, in places where they could be driven from one detached piece of jungle to another."[1] The question, then, was to prove (1) that the cock-birds largely outnumbered the hens so that some would necessarily remain without mates; (2) that the hen-bird actually did exert a choice. The evidence on the first point is still insufficient. Dr. Guillemard mentions in the *Cruise of the Marchesa*, that his collection of birds included 584 males, 285 females, and 111 of undetermined sex. This seems to show a large preponderance of males. But the male is the more conspicuous, and therefore is more likely to be shot. The question, however, is not so important as it might appear, since a large number of the species in which the cock-bird has the grander plumage are polygamous, and in them the number of males is obviously excessive. Even in the case of monogamous species Darwin was able to argue

[1] Hume and Marshall's *Game Birds of India*, vol. i., p. 88.

plausibly that the selected males would pair earlier, and thus have time for a second or third brood. It must be owned that the evidence of female preference is deficient. Sometimes when the Peacock is making the most of himself, the Peahen looks the other way. Sometimes he shows off to men, or even, it is said, to pigs. Most of the instances of a hen-bird falling in love with a particular cock-bird seem to show caprice rather than a regulated taste for the beautiful. A male Blackbird and a Thrush pair together. Out of a flock of twenty-three Canada Geese one pairs with a solitary Bernicle Gander. A male Wigeon, living with others of the same species, has been known to pair with a Pintail Duck. We have also the damaging fact that some Pigeons dyed with magenta were not much noticed by the others. But there is some really valuable evidence from Audubon's *Ornithological Biography* that in the United States hen Woodpeckers, Red-winged Starlings, and Nightjars actually do make a choice among several suitors. Again, persons who have had great experience of Canaries maintain that a hen-bird will choose out the best singer. But, when it is all added up, the direct evidence does not amount to much; and there is adverse evidence such as this, that the cock of the farmyard, who has beaten his rivals in battle, does not lose caste though all his plumes are draggled. The arguments often brought against this theory are not necessarily fatal—(1) that it presupposes a highly cultivated æsthetic taste in the hen-birds; (2) that selection by battle and by female preference cannot go on at the same time; (3) that some birds sing at all times of the year. It is not

required the hen should admire each particular
ocellus, or the delicate pencilling of each feather, but
only the grandeur of the whole display, since the
theory assumes not that her admiration is the cause
of the fine plumes, but only the cause of their not
being weeded out by Natural Selection. The constancy of the colours, and the markings of the feathers
as one generation succeeds another, is no doubt a
difficulty, since one kind of brilliancy might be as
pleasing to the hen-bird as another. But the patterns,
as I have said, are simple, and much may be explained
by what is called correlated development, of which
a good instance, illustrating our present subject, is
given by Darwin. In all breeds the males have the
elongated feathers called hackles on the neck and
loins. In cases where both sexes have a topknot,
that of the cock-bird alone consists of hackle-shaped
feathers. Thus there is in the cock-birds a tendency,
due to causes as yet unknown, to produce hackle-
shaped feathers in certain parts of the body. We
need not then assume that in these species female
taste demands hackles in one place and not another.
With regard to the second objection, it may well be
imagined that where grand plumage and pugnacity
are combined the hen-birds admire the splendour of
feathers as the natural accompaniment or corollary
of warlike prowess. The third objection was well
met by Darwin. That the Robin sings nearly the
whole year round does not prove that the power of
song was not originally developed to charm the hen.
Animals take a delight in the exercise of their powers.
A Gull, for instance, delights in its evolutions in the

air, though its power of flight is due solely to the fact
that it could not live without it ; and the horribly
cruel instinct that leads a cat to play with a mouse
before killing it may be, perhaps, accounted for in
the same way.

Dr. Wallace seeks to explain the facts by an
entirely different theory.   But before entering into
this, it is necessary to clear the ground a little.   In-
organic things—*e.g.* gold—have brilliant colours.   Mere
brightness of colour, therefore, requires no theory to
explain it.   In animals the pigments are probably
waste products derived from their food, and if not
employed for this purpose would be of no service
at all.   It is easy, then, to account for the bright
colours of many deep sea animals, where there is no
light except from the occasional phosphorescent lamps
borne by some of the fishes.   Even the bright colours
of a butterfly may be no tax upon its strength, for,
very probably, they can be as easily produced in the
animal system as a dull neutral tint.   The difficulty
consists partly in the constancy of the colours and
patterns, but, chiefly, in the long plumes, the annual
production of which must tax the bird's strength, and
which are a source of danger to it.   The moulting
season brings with it an increased rate of mortality
among the birds at the Zoological Gardens.   How
the Argus Pheasant is over-burdened by its plumes, I
have already shown.

With regard to the constancy of colours Dr. Wallace
has pointed out that much may be explained on the
principle of protective coloration.   The hen-bird is
exposed to greater danger than the cock-bird, since

she sits upon the nest. We might expect, then, that
she would be more soberly coloured than her partner.
And this is what we do find, with the remarkable
exception which so admirably supports Dr. Wallace's
theory, that among birds which nest in holes, so that
the hen as she sits is concealed, the bright colours
are very frequently common to both sexes. This is
the case *e.g.* with the Kingfisher. The hen Woodpecker is brilliantly coloured, though less so than the
cock. The conspicuously coloured Pigeons sit exposed
upon the nest ; but Natural Selection only requires
that a species should have some means of maintaining
itself. The particular means which we find in operation is due to unknown causes. Thus the Pigeon's
great power of flight, and the ease with which he finds
food, may render protective coloration unnecessary
to him.

There is good reason, then, why in most cases the
hen should be dull-coloured. But this affords no
explanation of the enormous plumes of the Peacock,
the Argus Pheasant, the Lyre Bird, and the Bird of
Paradise.

Dr. Wallace's views on this subject I will give
in his own words : " The fact that they (long plumes)
have been developed to such an extent in a few
species is an indication of such perfect adaptation to
the conditions of existence, such complete success in
the battle for life, that there is in the adult male, at
all events, a surplus of strength, vitality, and growth
power which is able to expend itself in this way without injury." [1] This is very strange as coming from the

---

[1] *Darwinism*, p. 293.

greatest living champion of the theory of Natural Selection through the struggle for existence. Elsewhere, Dr. Wallace speaks of this struggle as unceasing. As with artificial selection, every advantageous variation is selected, every disadvantageous one is weeded out. In Domestic Pigeons—*e.g.*, in the Dragons and the Pouters—peculiarities have been artificially produced which are not well suited to wild birds. If such breeds of Pigeons are not kept up by constant selection on the part of the breeder, they will soon tend to return to the characters of the wild Rock-dove from which they have sprung. If highly-bred horses are allowed to run wild they gradually lose many of the points which were produced by artificial selection. But the Peacock and the Argus Pheasant, whose plumes render them ill-fitted for wild life, are, according to Dr. Wallace's theory, so full of vigour and vitality that Natural Selection ceases in their case to operate. These birds, it seems, having won their laurels, are not compelled any longer to enter the lists, and are at liberty to expend their vigour on finery which, however beautiful to us, must be pernicious to them. Of the dancing and antics, however, the theory gives a satisfactory explanation, and perhaps even of the elaborate vocal performances of the Thrushes and Nightingales. These do not, as a rule, endanger the birds in question, or draw largely upon their vitality. Health and high spirits are the result of the working of Natural Selection.

Dr. Wallace's view has been developed by Professor Geddes. In nearly all species of animals, the males are the more vigorous; in them most variations are

produced, and if the sexes show a difference in adornment, it is almost always the male that is more
brightly coloured. In many butterflies, and in some
fishes and crustaceans, there are such differences.
Among sea-urchins and starfish there is thought to be
in some cases a superiority in point of colour in the
male over the female.[1] It is very important, if we
are to come to a right conclusion upon this question,
that all the facts should be considered, and one of the
most important facts is this which Professor Geddes has
emphasized, that in many of the lower animals, and as
a rule among the higher, we find the male possessing
some superior adornment. Here we have an undoubted
tendency, however we may seek to account for it.
But to explain the Peacock's enormous plumes we
require something further. We want to know why
the regulating law of the Survival of the Fittest has
not reduced their growth. If we ask why a Peacock
is encumbered by a train that may easily lose him
his life, it is no answer to be told that in a certain
species of crustacean (*Squilla stylifera* for instance)
the male is rather more brilliantly coloured than the
female.

Mr. Stolzmann has, I believe, supplied the clue to
this puzzle. According to him it is advantageous to
the species that the number of cock-birds should be
kept down, and their grand plumage helps towards
this end. This is an extension of Dr. Wallace's view
that it is the female which mainly needs protection.
Mr. Stolzmann maintains that the cock-bird in many
species not only needs no protection, but that it is

[1] See Beddard's *Animal Coloration*, p. 255.

desirable that he should fall a victim to a bird or beast of prey. He takes as proved, what I have said still requires proof, that the cock-birds largely outnumber the hen-birds. But even if this is not so there must in the polygamous species (which are chiefly in question, for in them the male is most the slave of his plumes) be an excess of male birds. Where this excess exists, the hen-bird, when she is sitting, will be liable to be disturbed by cock-birds which have not found a mate. Certainly, many game-preservers maintain that you get more young pheasants, if you keep down the numbers of the old cocks. Thus the gorgeous plumes and the desperate fights of the pairing season have for their object the reduction of the number of males.

It may well be thought that there is something of an over-statement here. It might have been safer to formulate it thus, that since the males are largely in excess, Natural Selection ceases in their case to work. They run riot in plumage, because they are of little importance to the species, and it is only for the preservation of the species that Natural Selection cares. If a cock-bird's loud song attracts his enemies and so causes his death, there are plenty more to take his place. In the same way, the drones of the beehive, of which there is a monstrous superfluity, are liable to be easily caught, and have no sting to defend themselves with. However great the death-rate among them, the life of the hive goes on and the species continues. Natural Selection does not kill them, but lets them die.

> Thou shalt not kill ; but need'st not strive
> Officiously to keep alive.

Summary.

Coloration can be in many cases explained as protective. Dr. Wallace's theory of exuberant vitality goes a long way to account for bright colours, song, and love antics. Patterns are in the main simple, and depend on laws of growth not yet understood : to one of these laws the name of correlated variation has been given. The grand plumes are explained by Mr. Stolzmann's theory that the males are largely in excess, and that, therefore, Natural Selection in their case does not act, or even tends to make them less adapted for the struggle of life.

SOME OF THE AUTHORITIES ON THE SUBJECT.

Gadow : " The Colour of Feathers affected by Structure," *Proc. Zool. Society*, 1882.

Gadow : Article on Colour in Newton's *Dictionary of Birds.*

Gadow : Bronn's *Thier-Reich*, vol. " Aves."

Darwin : *Descent of Man*, vol. ii.

Wallace : *Darwinism.*

Beddard : *Animal Coloration.*

Geddes and Thompson : *Evolution of Sex.*

Stolzmann : *Proc. Zool. Society*, 1885, p. 421.

Hudson : *Naturalist in La Plata.*

See also references given in footnotes in the course of this chapter.

CHAPTER XII

COLORATION OF EGGS

THE eggs of reptiles are white, and the reptilian origin of birds would lead us to the conclusion that the eggs of primitive birds were like them. But the eggs of existing birds present a great variety of colours, though it is seldom that very bright tints are found, and the question is how these colours are to be accounted for. There can hardly be a doubt that the coloration is in some cases protective, but we must be careful not to extend this explanation too far. Dr. Wallace has pointed out that a very large proportion of the eggs that are white or light-coloured enough to be conspicuous are found in domed nests or nests built in holes, so that they cannot be seen. For instance, Kingfishers and Puffins nest in holes in the ground; Woodpeckers, Hoopoes, and Owls in holes in trees; Wrens and the Willow-warblers build domed nests. Ducks and Grebes lay their pale eggs in open nests, but they have the habit of covering them up: these exceptions are, therefore, a very first-rate illustration of the principle. There

Y

are other exceptions which require a different explanation. Swans, Herons, Pelicans, Cormorants, and Storks lay whitish eggs, and leave them exposed ; but they are strong birds and can protect themselves from enemies, the more easily if, like the Herons, they nest in colonies. On the other hand, the Plover and the Snipe, who have open nests upon the ground, and who could not beat off enemies, lay eggs so like the surroundings that it requires a very good eye to see them. Blue eggs, such as the Hedge-sparrow's, Dr. Wallace maintains, are not at all conspicuous among green foliage.

I shall now mention some of the difficulties that we encounter if we try to press the theory. Pigeons lay white eggs, and, whatever may be said about their being concealed among the leaves, they are often most conspicuous. The Short-eared Owl leaves its eggs on a tump of grass or heather, and they are white like the eggs of other Owls which nest in holes. The case of the Barn-door Fowl counts for nothing.

The eggs of Gulls are protectively coloured, and as the birds nest in crowds together, they probably need no protection. The same may be said of Rooks' eggs. Moreover the rookery would be visible enough to any egg-seeking enemy, and it is hardly likely the eggs would be saved by any dulness of colouring. The eggs of Hawks and Eagles are not conspicuous, and no enemy is likely to invade their nests. The Redstart's blue eggs are laid in holes, where, according to the theory, we might expect them to be white. Moreover we often find among birds that are nearly related, a suspicious family likeness, regardless of the

fact that different species have different nesting
habits. The eggs of the Raven, Crow, Rook, and
Jackdaw are by no means unlike in colour. The
Gulls are nearly allied to the Plovers, Curlews, Ruffs,
Sand-pipers, and Avocets ; and this fact, probably,
supplies the explanation of the supposed protective
colouring in the case of Gulls' eggs, which require
no protection. In the same way we can account for
the white eggs of the Short-eared Owl. Occasionally
we find a species whose eggs are differently coloured
from those of its allies, without there being any
difference of nesting habit to explain it. The Little
Bittern, for instance, lays eggs of a dull white, while
those of other Bitterns are of a brownish olive colour.
It seems, in fact, that Natural Selection does not
work either universally or very promptly upon the
colours of eggs. If the Wood Pigeon's eggs were of
an inconspicuous tint, it might be a slight gain to the
species. But the birds are so vigorous, so strong on
the wing, and so able to find food, that a slight imperfection such as the whiteness of their eggs does not
materially reduce their numbers. The large number
of eggs laid by the common chicken may allow for
the destruction of a good many nests, so that concealment can be dispensed with. And it must also
be borne in mind that when a bird lays only one or
two eggs, sitting begins soon, so that there is more
need for the concealment of the birds than the eggs.
Though it may seem a paradox to say so, it is sometimes because the eggs are many and sometimes
because they are few that protective colouring is
unnecessary. .

Natural Selection does not bring about absolutely perfect adaptation, but only so far moulds a species to the conditions of life as to enable it to live and thrive. White eggs without protective colouring may be only a slight source of danger and, so, continue, just as we often find an organ continuing in a useless rudimentary state, not eliminated in the struggle for existence, because, if useless, it is also almost harmless. It must not be supposed that the production of colour puts a great strain upon the system. It is merely a waste product of the body, which otherwise would be made no use of. The pigments are very similar to those of the bile, though they are not exactly identical.

Natural Selection has no doubt in many cases turned colours to account. It is impossible to deny that they are in some cases protective. But imagine the case of a species which at one time needed protective colouring for its eggs, and which afterwards changed its nesting habits, or was relieved of the presence of some enemy that preyed upon its eggs, so that the protection became unnecessary; then it is highly probable that the old tint and markings would continue because of their harmlessness, though they had ceased to be beneficial. This may be the reason of the protective coloration of the eggs of Gulls; it explains, too, the want of it in the case of the eggs of the Short-eared Owl. The old style of egg common to the family has been maintained because, though in this species some colour might be a slight advantage, the question has not become a burning one.

If Natural Selection is so slow to act upon them, how is it that the colours of eggs are as constant as

they are ? Guillemots seem never to lay two eggs
that are similarly coloured. The ground colour
varies from blue through many stages to white, and
the flail-like marks vary much or are omitted
altogether. Out of thirty Guillemots' eggs it is often
impossible to pick out two that are really alike.
How is it that we do not find in other eggs a similar
tendency to variation ? To answer this question is
difficult, but perhaps not so difficult as it might at
first appear. Eggs have either a plain wash of colour,
or else a ground colour marked with spots or dashes.
All the markings, it is believed, are originally circular,
but as the egg moves down the oviduct, they become
smeared or lengthened out. Sometimes they take
a spiral form—for instance, in some birds of prey—and
this would seem to show that the egg rotates as it
moves forward. Thus there is nothing that can
properly be called a pattern to account for, and, as
the pigment is simply a waste product used up, its
constancy does not perhaps require a very profound
explanation. There is really more variation in the
eggs of many species than one is apt to think. But
in a small egg the change in the shape of spots and
blotches does not attract attention as it does on a
larger egg, such as the Guillemot's, where they too are
on a large scale. In that, the most striking example
of variation, the remarkable phenomenon is the range
of the ground colour from what is almost a deep blue
to white, and this can be paralleled. With birds that
lay only two eggs it often happens that nearly all the
colouring matter is deposited on one only, sometimes
on the first, and sometimes on the second of the two,

I shall speak of the variations in Cuckoo's eggs in the chapter on Instinct and Reason.

SOME AUTHORITIES ON THE SUBJECT.

Wallace : *Darwinism* and *Contributions to the Theory of Natural Selection*.

Newton : Article on " Eggs" in *Dictionary of Birds*.

CHAPTER XIII

INSTINCT AND REASON

IF a frog's spinal cord be divided at the neck and a drop of strong acid be placed on his thigh he will bend his leg and rub it off with his foot. The brain can give him no help, for the connection has been severed. Only some lower nerve centre is called into play, and there is no consciousness. It is such action that we call reflex. If we accidentally touch hot embers, then suddenly draw back, the action of drawing back is as reflex as the frog's movement of his leg. So far all is easy. But no one can approach the subject of instinct and reason without feeling that it is an extremely difficult one. An instinctive action is different from a merely reflex one in this, that it originates with the brain, and is probably accompanied by consciousness, though there is no conscious working towards an object in view. When a hungry Blackbird sees a worm he at once proceeds to eat it without going through a process of reasoning. But he is probably conscious, all the while, what he is doing. It is, therefore, an instinctive and not a reflex action. Next let us look for some examples of reasoning power or intelligence in birds. If they learn by experience that men in their neighbourhood do not shoot on Sunday, and if, in consequence, they are much less cautious on that day than on week-days, they are showing intelligence. In the same way Pheasants learn by experience to distinguish a rifle from a shot-gun. The former has no terrors for them, and they will feed quietly while the bullets pass over them. I have seen the same complete indifference to the noise of rifle-shooting in the Great Spotted Woodpecker. To learn wisdom by individual experience is of the very essence of reason. Without intelligence or reasoning power of a kind, a Redpoll could hardly learn to pull up his bucket of water when he is thirsty. Probably he does not consciously connect the means and the end. He is like the man who puts a penny in the slot and takes his piece of chocolate without any knowledge of the machinery, the working of which has given him what he wanted. He connects the penny and the chocolate, but does not know by what process the one produces the other.

There is no doubt that some actions are purely instinctive, but it is comparatively seldom that a " little dose " of reason is absent. Intelligence often modifies instinct. A caterpillar who weaves a small web of silk from which to suspend his chrysalis will, if he finds himself in a box with a muslin lid, economise in silk and hang his chrysalis from the muslin. A bird will modify the form of his nest to suit changed circumstances. Instinct is in fact plastic. A particular action may be partly instinctive and partly intelligent. Professor Lloyd Morgan has contributed a good deal to the understanding of the question.[1] He took some eggs from under a sitting hen and put them in an incubator, and when the chicks emerged from the eggs, he experimented on them. They pecked at almost everything, no doubt by instinct. But they had to learn to peck straight, and to learn to judge distance, so as to know whether a piece of food was within range of their beaks. Experience taught them that burning cigarette-ends were not good for food. When pieces of dark crimson worsted-wool were first substituted for the worms they had so much enjoyed, they were swallowed greedily, but afterwards they were viewed with much distrust and generally rejected. All his life long a bird is learning. An old Heron is far more knowing than a young one. The young Curlew has to learn much from his seniors and by experience before he attains to the proper Curlew standard of wariness. On the other hand, the Cuckoo is to a great extent able to dispense with experience and instruction. For it can hardly be supposed that an old bird takes a young bird in hand and teaches her what to do with her egg, or that the young bird goes through a process of learning to find a nest and entrust her egg to a foster-mother. Birds which are hatched from the egg by the sun, must be born with some ready-made knowledge of the world. Even teaching and experience can only awaken powers that are born in the bird. We often find him at the

---

[1] See his article in the *Fortnightly Review* for August, 1893.

end of his tether. In South America there is a little
bird (*Furnarius cunicularius*) which makes its nest
in a horizontal burrow in the ground, said to be often
nearly six feet long. These birds have been known
to burrow again and again into a mud wall with a
view to nesting there, and were no doubt surprised
when they came to daylight on the other side.
Yet they had flown over the wall, and had had many
opportunities of seeing its small thickness before
they set to work.[1] In the same way with a stupid
persistence one of Mrs. Brightwen's pet starlings
continued to search for grubs in every corner of the
drawing-room. The intelligence, however, comes
oftener to our notice than the stupidity.

Song.

Daines Barrington took three Linnets, when quite
young, from the nest, and put them with different
foster-mothers, selecting three with easily recognis-
able notes—the Skylark, the Woodlark, and Titlark or
Meadow Pipit—and each, he maintained, learnt and
adhered to the song which it heard in the days of its
early youth. The Linnet educated by the Titlark was
afterwards put with other Linnets, but it never unlearnt
the Titlark song. Daines Barrington was one of the
correspondents of Gilbert White, of Selborne, and
these experiments were made in the latter half of
the last century. More recent investigators have
not, as a rule, been led to the same conclusion. Mr.

[1] See Darwin's *Journal of Researches* (Minerva Library
edition), p. 69.

A. G. Butler[1] took a Skylark from the nest which
"sang its own wild song, but introduced into it the
song of the Persian Bulbul." "Chaffinches," he says,
"unless absolutely isolated, readily pick up the wild
song, but if kept in the same room with Canaries, their
song is lengthened (and thus improved), though not
altered in character." A Missel Thrush which he
reared sang only two notes. A Blackbird sang the
first line of "Villikins and his Dinah, and another
the first line of a Psalm tune." A Cock Starling
"sang a jumble of sounds mixed with the guttural
call-note of the Missel Thrush." In fact a bird, if
isolated, sings his own song, if any; as a rule the
power that is in him requires awakening. If he
hears one of his own species carolling, he is very
soon able to imitate it.[2] If he hears only other birds,
he no doubt learns to imitate them, but the process is
a comparatively long one, and often the foreign notes
are only an addition to his own proper song, which
can still be clearly made out. Many of the tame
Thrushes in bird-fanciers' shops have been taken
early from the nest, and they sing the Thrush's
song. Sometimes they may have heard no bird
sing, in which case their music must be due to pure
instinct, or they may have heard the songs of many
birds and singled out that of their own species. The
Cuckoo is not taught by his sire. If instinct does
not teach him, how does he know the one cry amid

---

[1] "The Songs of Birds reared from the Nest" in the *Zoologist*
for 1892, p. 30.

[2] Romanes (*Mental Evolution in Animals*, p. 227) says,
"The singing of birds is certainly instinctive."

all the chorus of the woods that he is to pick out and imitate? Mr. Witchell, who has written much upon the subject, holds that all birds learn their songs from their parents or from other birds. Every one of them, according to him, is a mimic, and is constantly imitating others. We are thus reduced to hopeless confusion. In an elaborate song we have to pick out the bird's ancestral music from all the superadded variations. This is easy with a caged bird, because we can learn his proper song from his kinsmen in the woods. But if there is no limit to imitation among wild birds, chaos must result, and it would be far more difficult to learn the distinctive song of each species than it is. Confronted with the fact that nearly related birds living widely separated often have a similar song, Mr. Witchell is able still to cling to his theory. But if birds have to learn their notes by imitation, surely the American Ferruginous Thrush would by this time have picked up a different song from our common Thrush; the Shore Lark of America would not sing like our Skylark, and the American Snipe would have a different cry from ours.[1] It is a remarkable fact that many birds that are good mimics have little song of their own. This is the case with Parrots, Jays, Jackdaws, Starlings, and Bullfinches. It would seem as if it were an advantage to the mimic to have no old family music for the acquired song to drive out or modify, and this tells strongly against the notion that singing

[1] See " Bird Song and its Scientific Teaching," by C. A. Witchell, in the *Proc. Cotteswold Naturalists' Field Club*, vol. x., part iii., p. 238.

is taught by each pair to their offspring. But
it must be owned that there are exceptions. The
White-banded Mocking-bird of Patagonia not only
imitates every other bird, but has a glorious song of
his own that surpasses all that he mimics.

I have already mentioned the remarkable fact that
some birds that have little or no song in the wild
state have highly developed song-muscles which they
can turn to account when subjected to instruction
in captivity. The Bullfinch, is perhaps, the most
remarkable example of this. His finely equipped
organ of voice suggests that Bullfinches were once
great songsters, but that they have lost the art of
singing. If this is so, the theory that song is instinctive is not affected, since it is quite possible that in a
musical species individuals might be born who had
no impulse to sing ; and if the species did not suffer
through this, there is no reason why the song should
not have become obsolete, while the organ of voice,
being so small as to draw but slightly on the bird's
vital energy, might remain.

The conclusions, then, that we come to are—(1) That
song is instinctive. (2) That in many birds it requires
to be awakened : they must hear their parents sing,
but they pick up the song so quickly that to speak of
their learning it by instruction is absurd. (3) That
when a good singer learns another bird's song his own is
generally traceable still. The several songs of Daines
Barrington's Linnets may have been Linnets' songs
with variations.

Nest-building.

Nest-building is generally held to be entirely the work of instinct. But Dr. Wallace has tried to show that this too is an acquired accomplishment.[1] He was at first inclined to believe that the young birds when still in the nest learnt the principles of architecture. This is as if an infant in arms on seeing a steam-engine should at once understand how it is made. Giving up this theory he suggests other possibilities—that, when they first have to build they see another pair at work and so learn, or that a young bird always pairs with an old one. These views will hardly bear examination. If we wish to get at the true explanation, we must realise that instinct is plastic and can be modified by reason. Birds frequently, as Dr. Wallace says, show, when they are building their nests, that they are not mere machines. They adapt themselves to new situations. The Swallow and the House-Martin have availed themselves of barns and houses. The Palm Swift in Jamaica till 1854 always built in palms. But in Spanish Town when two cocoanut palms were blown down, they drove out the Swallows from the Piazza of the House of Assembly and built between the angles formed by the beams and joists. In America the Tailor-bird now uses thread and worsted for its nest instead of wool and horsehair, and wool and horsehair may originally have been substitutes for vegetable fibres and grasses. In Calcutta an unconven-

[1] See Dr. Wallace's *Contributions to the Theory of Natural Selection*, p. 211.

tional Crow once made its nest of soda-water bottle wires, which it picked up in a backyard. In districts liable to floods, Moorhens often build in trees. In New Zealand the "Paradise Ducks," which usually build on the ground near rivers, have been known when disturbed to build on the tops of high trees, and to bring down their young on their backs to the water. But all this does not show that birds have not an instinctive knowledge how to build. It only shows that their instinct can be modified by reason and experience.

Many nests are works of very great skill. In England we have the Long-tailed Tit's nest, wonderful for its neatness and its beauty. Some of the commonest nests, such as the Chaffinch's, are works of art. The Magpie's, if not beautiful, is a formidable fortress. Among foreign birds there are marvellous builders, such as the Tailor, Weaver, and Oven birds. For fine architecture the feet must have a power of grasp. No web-footed bird builds a really clever nest. But a long fine beak is not, as Dr. Wallace maintains, necessary. Of the four commonest Tits, the Long-tailed is by far the best builder, and his beak is remarkably short, much shorter than that of the other three. The Chaffinch, too, has a short bill and makes a good nest. Some birds—*e.g.*, Ducks—have beaks that could never turn out very good work ; but, speaking generally, skill is more important than a beak of a particular form. And to say that a bird learns how to build a nest from the casual sight of another pair at work is almost as much as to say that she already knows how to do it. The power must be inborn, only requiring to be awakened, or, as Professor Morgan says, requiring "only the touch of the trigger to fire off the complicated train of activities, the ability to perform which is innate." The Razor-bill affords a good illustration ; he is a born diver, and yet cries plaintively when his mother coaxes him to take the first plunge. The principle will become clear if we imagine an attempt to teach a bird to build anything but its own particular nest, to imitate the Bower Bird, for instance, and construct an elaborate arbour, or an attempt to teach the Chaffinch to build a domed nest like the Long-tailed Tit's, or a House-Sparrow or a Wood-pigeon to build a neat nest of any kind. If it were ever successful it would at any rate require much time, whereas just a hint, if even that is required, is enough to set a bird off building as its parents have built before it. Any one who has taught boys must have noticed what is not very dissimilar. A boy—some *rara avis*—will perhaps master Euclid as if geometry were born in him. In classics much teaching, and much work on his part may produce very little result. In short, all faculties are innate, and, supposing them to exist, the only question is, whether it requires any teaching or practice, and if so, how much, to awaken them.

Birds have, compared with man, very few and very limited powers, and they differ from us, besides, in this, that it requires comparatively very little stimulus to bring their faculties into full working order. A few suggestions from an older bird on a particular subject, and a younger one at once advances the greater part of the way towards the furthest point to which his

tether will allow him to go. But within his narrow
limits he still continues to gain by experience. It is
generally said that one bird builds a nest just as
another of the same species does, hence intelligence
cannot come into play at all. It is probable, though,
that there are differences which escape our notice ; at
any rate, as I have shown, individuals are capable of
adapting themselves to new circumstances, and some
authorities hold that a bird's first nest is decidedly
inferior to her later ones.

We conclude, then, that nest building is instinctive
but that intelligence to some extent works upon and modifies the instinct. It is no argument
against this that birds in captivity often build a very
poor nest or are incapable of building one at all.
Among domesticated animals instincts are apt to go
wrong. There is a breed of hens that never sit upon
their eggs. Among the lowest class in our big towns
unnatural conditions of life not unfrequently lead to
the decay of an instinct on which the continuance of
the race depends, the affection of mother for child, an
instinct which is never deficient in savage races.

The Cuckoo Instinct.

The habits of the Cuckoo are so marvellous that if
we were to come fresh to the subject, we should be lost
in astonishment at them. But, as Lucretius says,
even the sun ceases in time to be an object of wonder.
The Cuckoo lays many eggs, and we can hardly be
wrong in seeing a connection between this fact and
the parasitic habit. They are laid, some ornithologists

Z

believe, at intervals of several days, so that if she were herself to undertake the incubation, she would have to leave one for some time unsat upon, or else have eggs and young in the nest together at the same time. A German naturalist, Karl Eimer, gives a rather different account ; the Cuckoo lays two eggs in a clutch ; that is, if she made a nest herself, she would lay only two eggs in it. And as she generally migrates before August, she would not, if she herself nested, get many young ones reared in the course of the summer. In favour of the former view it may be urged that the American Cuckoo, who almost always builds a nest for herself, does have young birds and eggs in process of hatching in the nest at the same time. In any case we must look to the bird's great laying powers for the explanation of the cuckoo instinct. The egg of the Cuckoo is wonderfully small considering the size of the bird. It is less than an inch long, and $\frac{3}{4}$ inch broad. A Hedge Sparrow's egg is about $\frac{1}{2}$ inch long and a little more than $\frac{1}{2}$ inch broad. Thus there is no very great difference in bulk. But the Cuckoo is 12 inches long and the Hedge Sparrow only $5\frac{1}{2}$, a monstrous disparity even when we allow for the length of the Cuckoo's tail. The diminutive size of the interloper's egg no doubt deceives the foster mother, and is necessary if it is to hatch as early as those of the rightful owner. Moreover, if it were not so small, how would the bird after laying it be able to take it in her beak and deposit it in the nest where it is to be left ? The egg sometimes varies, approaching in colour those in the particular nest chosen, so that it is bluish when laid in a Hedge

Sparrow's nest. Many suggestions have been made to account for this fact, the best, perhaps, being that there are varieties of Cuckoo, each of which has its favourite nest for laying in. When hatched, the young Cuckoo has not a vestige of down, and is perfectly blind. His back from the shoulder blades downward is very broad, and has a depression across the middle which fills up after the twelfth day of life. This remarkable form of back is very useful to the still blind young bird. Using it as a shovel, he ousts the other fledglings or an unhatched egg from the nest sometimes before he has completed his second day, when his victims may be picked up round the nest. When once you have seen this blind young demon with his shovel-like back to help him in his murderous career, you can never forget him. The foster-mother devotes all her energy to the murderer of her young. Only one egg (rarely two) is laid in each nest, so that the young bird may get plenty of food.

The instinct of the Cuckoo and all the accompanying modifications have been brought to perfection—the diminutive size of the egg, only one egg (or at most two) in each nest, and laid, moreover, before incubation has begun, the occasional approximation of the egg in point of colour to that of the foster-mother chosen, the hollow back, and the self-asserting disposition of the young bird. It is only in the system of migration that we find imperfection. The old birds, most of them, leave by August ; the young ones sometimes remain as late as October, and have to find their way to Africa, even to South Africa, alone.

The cuckoo or parasitic habit is not limited to one

Z 2

order of birds ; it is found in various stages of development in the different species of the American Molothrus,
a bird allied to our Starlings. One South American
species (*M. bonariensis*) always lay their eggs in other
birds' nests, and never sit upon them themselves, but
the number of eggs laid in one nest is so great that it
is impossible all can be hatched. They sometimes lay
in old forsaken nests, or in a nest of the year where incubation has already begun, or before the building is
finished, so that their eggs are covered by the thick
lining and never hatch. Many are dropped upon the
ground. The parents, too, will often peck holes in
numbers of their own eggs. Sometimes several
together set to work to build a nest for themselves,
but it is clumsily constructed, and, as far as is known,
is never made use of. Another species (*Molothrus
rufoaxillaris*) is also parasitic and apparently not so
foolish as the last mentioned, though not so accomplished a parasite as the Cuckoo. Another South
American species (*Molothrus badius*) is probably never
parasitic. But they sometimes go to the length of
seizing another bird's nest and building their own
upon the top of it. All these interesting facts we
owe to Mr. Hudson, who has carefully observed the
two South American birds that have the cuckoo
habit.

In North America there is a Molothrus which never
lays more than one egg in one nest.

In this genus, then, we see the instinct in its various
stages of development. *Molothrus badius* is a pirate
and not a parasite. *M. bonariensis* is foolishly prodi-
gal of its eggs. *M. rufoaxillaris* shows a greater

spirit of economy. The North American species lays only one egg in one nest. Our Cuckoo in the perfection of the adaptation of its structure and habits seems to surpass them all.

Piracy.

The White-headed Eagle watches the Osprey, and, when the latter has secured a fish, pursues and threatens him till he drops his prey, which, making a swoop downward, he catches as it falls. The Robber Tern lives wholly by the plunder of other birds. The British Avifauna boasts four pirates, two that breed here, besides two that visit us. All these are Skua Gulls, and by far the commonest is the Arctic or Richardson's Skua, intermediate in size between a Kittiwake and a Herring Gull. The Great Skua, which breeds in two islands of the Shetland group and nowhere else in the British Isles, is a much larger bird. When a Gull or a Tern has secured a fish, the Arctic Skua will pursue him with a velocity that makes escape impossible. When he has overtaken the fugitive, he flies over and under him with a menacing air. It is evident that he will brook no refusal, and his victim drops the fish or allows it to be taken from his beak, sometimes crying plaintively the while. Whether the Skua ever finds it necessary to resort to actual violence, I do not know. As far as I have been able to see, threats are sufficient, but the whole scene passes with such rapidity that it is difficult to make out the details of the action. It is certainly probable that he uses his beak with effect, since he is known to prey on wounded birds. He will condescend, too, to pick up worms and molluscs, but I do not know that he ever catches fish for himself. The Great Skua I have never seen upon the warpath. Besides robbing Gulls of their fish, he is known to attack and eat Kittiwakes and even Gulls of larger size.

When it is migrating southward, the Arctic Skua may often be seen upon our coasts. But it is worth while going to Shetland to see both kinds in their breeding haunts. A great part of the day is devoted to gyrations in the air, the smaller bird often accompanying its movements with its peculiarly rasping twangy note, the greater one croaking less harshly. The Great Skua is a bird of majestic flight, ascending high, when there is an upward wind off the cliffs, in easy spirals without a motion of the wings. Though both birds have a grim look and though they live by plundering the weak, a gull who has not just caught a fish shows no fear, at any rate of the Arctic Skua. There is no panic when he appears, as there is among small birds in the presence of a Hawk.

Nesting Habits of the Rhea.

The nesting habits of this bird are so remarkable that it is difficult to pass them over. The hen lays a great number of eggs, so that if she were to leave them till she herself could sit upon them, many would become addled. Several, therefore, lay in one nest, and when a good many have accumulated, a cock bird comes and undertakes the incubation, and not only that, but cares for the young when they are hatched.

XIII INSTINCT AND REASON 343

But the system has not been brought to perfection, for a number of eggs are dropped anywhere about the country. It is believed that Ostriches, too, make a nest that is common to several hen birds.[1] Certainly the cock bird sits on the eggs and tends the young, and this is also true of the Emeu and the Cassowary. The New Zealand Apteryx, however, lays only one egg and sits upon it herself.[2]

The Death-feigning Instinct.

The death-feigning or wound-feigning instinct is very well developed in some birds. The Canadian Ruffed Grouse rises with a loud whirr, then tumbles in front of the pursuing dog, who never thinks of the young and goes after the mother whom he imagines wounded. If the Willow Ptarmigan be approached she crouches to the ground among her brood, and if she sees that she cannot escape notice, she rolls and tumbles along as though mortally injured.[3] The Spotted Tinnamou, or common Partridge of the Pampas, when captured, after a few violent struggles to escape, drops his head, gasps two or three times, and to all appearance dies.[4] The Corncrake is very good at the art. He has sometimes been put in a sportsman's pocket, apparently quite dead, and when his

[1] See Darwin's *Journal of Researches*, chap. v.

[2] See a paper by Mr. P. L. Sclater, F.R.S., in the *Proceedings of the Zoological Society*, June 9th, 1863.

[3] See an article by Mr. John Worth in the *Nineteenth Century*, April 1893.

[4] See Hudson's *Naturalist in La Plata*, p. 204.

chance has come, has run away and escaped.[1]   Mr.
Hudson in his *Birds in a Village* tells of a Reed
Bunting, which, in alarm for the safety of its young in
the nest, flew out on his approach, " but only to drop
to the ground, to beat the turf with its wings, then to
lie gasping for breath, then to flutter on a little further,
until at last it rose up and flew to a bush."   A good
naturalist has just been describing to me very similar
behaviour on the part of a Whitethroat.   The Opossum
and the Fox excel in the art of "shamming dead."
Among beetles and spiders the instinct is more commonly found than among mammals or birds.

We must not put this behaviour down entirely to
good acting.   The animal is actually afraid, often
even paralysed by fear.   In time it recovers itself, and
seizes any opportunity of escape that offers.   But the
natural stunning effects of fear have been turned to
account, and the temporary paralysis caused originally
by a violent shock to the nerves has by long ages of
natural selection been developed and improved so that
now we may look upon it as due to a valuable protective instinct, though helped in most, if not in all,
cases, by actual alarm.   It is very remarkable that
this instinct should be found in creatures so remotely
connected as Spiders, Beetles, Birds, and Mammals, and
among birds in species belonging to widely separated
families, *e.g.* in the Reed Bunting and the Canadian
Ruffed Grouse.

----

[1] See Romanes' *Mental Evolution in Animals*, p. 305.

Origin of Instincts.

It is natural to think of instincts as habits that have been handed down from generation to generation till at last they have become petrified. It is impossible, in spite of the dearth of direct evidence, to deny that acquired habits may be transmitted, but it is not difficult to show that instincts sometimes have a quite different origin. In a beehive it is the worker bees alone that make the hexagonal cells, shaping them with almost mathematical exactness, and fitting them together in a way that involves the least possible expenditure of wax. These workers are undeveloped females and leave no descendants, the eggs from which the young bees are born being all laid by the queen bee, whose sole duty is to lay eggs and who never helps in the work of cell-building. Any habit, then, that is formed by the workers cannot possibly be handed down to the next generation. We must, therefore, look elsewhere for the origin of the instincts of the hive bee. The explanation which Darwin gave was the very simple one that communities of bees which had these three classes, the drones or males, the queens, and the neuter females or workers, throve greatly and multiplied rapidly, whereas in hives in which all the females were both egg-layers and workers, the population gradually dwindled, so that at last the race became extinct. This idea might seem far-fetched had not gardeners produced a similar result with stocks. These flowers are generally double and produce no seed, but among them there is occasionally a single-flowered plant. The seed from this produces plants, most of which bear double, but a few of them single flowers. The barren double flowers correspond to the neuter bees or workers, the single ones to the queen.

Some of the Literature of the Subject.

The chapter on " Instinct " in Darwin's *Origin of Species.*

Romanes' *Mental Evolution in Animals* and *Animal Intelligence.*

Wallace's *Contributions to the Theory of Natural Selection.*

Sclater and Hudson's *Argentine Ornithology* (on " Parasitic Birds.")

Various books and papers to which references have been given in the course of this chapter ; see footnotes.

CHAPTER XIV

MIGRATION

FOR ages past the mysterious going and coming of birds has excited the notice and wonder of mankind. The familiar proverb "One Swallow does not make a summer" is quoted by Aristotle. The noisy march of the Trojans is compared by Homer to the clamorous flight of a flock of Cranes migrating southward. "The Trojans marched with clamour and with shouting like unto birds, even as when there goeth up before heaven a clamour of cranes which flee from the coming of winter and sudden rain, and fly with clamour towards the streams of ocean."[1] In a book of still more ancient date, the Book of Job, we read of the southward flight of the Hawk.[2] Till comparatively recent times, however, men were content to let the mystery remain a mystery. Gilbert White of Selborne puzzled and puzzled over the problem of migration. He knew that most of the Swallows flew far southward for the winter, but he could not entirely

[1] *Iliad*, iii. l. 2, Lang, Leaf, and Myers' translation
[2] Chap. xxxix. 26.

rid himself of the then popular notion, that they
hibernated in holes, or mud or water. Even now some
people are credulous enough to hold this belief, though
the fresh evidence adduced diminishes to the vanishing
point when subjected to investigation, and the evidence from past times is valueless, since it is as
strong for the hibernation of Swallows in water,
which is clearly impossible, as it is for their hibernation in holes. But Gilbert White's book should be
studied as the work of a man who took care to see
with his own eyes what he chronicled, instead of
repeating the myths that are handed down from writer
to writer. And his remarks on migration are a first-
rate landmark that shows how our knowledge of the
subject has advanced. Even now, however, there is
an atmosphere of mystery about it, which can only be
dissipated, if it ever is, by the co-operation of hosts of
patient investigators. When the necessary facts have
been thus accumulated, keen penetration will be
necessary in dealing with them if the meaning is to
be discerned. The progress already made is, indeed,
very great. Modern facilities of travel have helped
forward our knowledge. The nesting places of all
the British migrants except one, the Curlew Sandpiper,
have been found, thanks chiefly to the energy of
English ornithologists. Our summer visitors have
been seen and recognised in their South African winter
resorts by English travellers. But when we think of
bird migration, the mind more naturally turns to
Heligoland than to any other one spot upon the
globe. There, in his tiny rock island, hardly over a
hundred acres in extent, Herr Gätke has been busy for

fifty years watching the mighty stream of migrants
that passes to and fro. All the Heligolanders have
helped him, bringing every specimen they could obtain
that was rare enough to be worth looking at. And
every one in the island turns out for the *battue*, with
a far too slaughterous zeal, when the flocks of migrants
descend upon it. Sometimes such clouds of birds
appear that they cover every square foot of ground
upon the island. The most striking of the recorded
flights took place in October 1882, when for three
successive nights there were thick masses of migrating
Goldcrests, beating thick as snowflakes against the
lighthouse. But these represented only a small fraction of their numbers, for the front of the advancing
host extended from the Shetlands to Guernsey, and
probably even further south. Living thus on his islet,
the ways of migrants as familiar to him as the beat of
the waves, Herr Gätke has been able to give a
life and interest to his book that no writer on the
subject who has gained his knowledge only by reading,
or who has caught only occasional glimpses of the
great movement, can possibly rival. And though he
has seen so much, he has never failed to realise the fact
that what he has seen is much less than what has
passed beyond his ken, or been only dimly descried,
that the birds which have flown over Heligoland, often
far too high for the reach of the human eye, are far
more numerous than those which stress of weather, or
whatever circumstance, has led to settle on the island.
Unfortunately Herr Gätke's work has not been trans-
lated into English, but it should be read by every
lover of birds who is tolerably familiar with German,

The occasional occurrence of a rather wild theory does not much detract from the merit of the book.

In 1880 the British Association appointed a committee to investigate the migration of birds, and with the help of the keepers of lighthouses, against which the migrants often dash themselves, the committee have accumulated a vast body of facts, some of which have already been published. But the work of analysing the facts has not yet been completed. When it is, our knowledge of the subject will, probably, be much advanced. Even then it must be very defective, if only for this reason, that nearly all the observations are made in the northern hemisphere. Observers are wanted in North and South Africa, and owing to the absence, or the great paucity, of them, it is probable that there will long be a great blank in our knowledge of migration.

Ordinary people, who have no special opportunities, who do not live in Heligoland, or Malta, or the Bermudas, or keep a lighthouse, and who cannot travel to particularly favoured spots, can yet see a good deal of migrant birds. They can watch for the coming of the Swallow, the Nightingale, the Cuckoo, the Chiffchaff, and a host of others in spring. When the woods have long been almost silent save for the song of the Thrush and the Robin, there comes a chorus of voices resounding on all sides and most of the singers are migratory birds. It is difficult to see their coming, for it is usually at night. You get up in the morning and you find the Swallow comfortably catching the flies of his northern home and the Blackcap proclaiming his arrival in his favourite covert. In autumn the Swallows will collect together and suddenly vanish, leaving behind them one or two of their number, who may or may not find their way to the far south where their winter should be passed. Even the caged bird, if a migrant, catches the fever and frets impatiently in his prison. It is said that a Brent Goose confined in a yard and longing for his arctic haunts, has been known in spring to migrate from the southern to the northern side of his narrow confines. Winter brings with it the Snipe, the Woodcock, the Fieldfare, Redwing, and many others that come from the north to spend the cold season in our comparatively genial clime. All this is evidence, if we only think of it, of the most marvellous facts. That a Chiffchaff, whose daily occupation for months has been to pick grubs from the trees, and who has never left his favourite wood, should suddenly, some evening, be seized with an uncontrollable impulse to start for North Africa, is surely matter for wonder. Still more astounding is it that the young birds, with defective strength and no experience, should start on the great pilgrimage alone instead of waiting for the old birds to guide them. And in spring, too, when you see the first swallow, it is a startling thought that the small bird whom you see practising his short swallow-flights, perhaps only some ten days before, started on his north-ward voyage from Natal.

It is one and the same migration of which we catch a glimpse when we see these visitors to our shores, whether it be summer or winter. All alike travel northward in spring and southward in autumn. But the British Isles form part of the northern region for some species, of the southern region for others. There is also an east and west migration of which I shall speak soon.

It is vain to search the animal kingdom for other migrations on so great a scale as those of birds. The movements of fish afford the nearest parallel, for they occur annually at regular seasons and are connected with reproduction. At a certain season every year the salmon betakes him to his river, and the herring and the mackerel move towards the coast. These, though far less wonderful than the regularly recurring movements of birds, are true migrations. But when the monkeys in the Himalayas ascend to a height of 10,000 feet or more in summer, or when the lemmings in Norway, at long and irregular intervals, sweep like a great flood towards the sea, they do not, in the strict sense, migrate.

The Distances Covered.

The Sanderling nests in Iceland or on the shores of the Arctic Ocean, and in winter it has been seen as far south as Cape Colony. The nestlings of the Knot have been found in Grinnell Land in lat. 82° 33' N, and the bird is known to winter as far south as Australia and New Zealand. The Turnstone is a great traveller, nesting in Greenland or the coasts of Scandinavia, and wintering in Australia, New Zealand, South America, or Africa. The distances travelled amount sometimes to over 7,000 miles.[1] The diminutive size of a bird is no evidence at all that he is

[1] Mr. Seebohm puts the longest at 10,000 miles.

incapable of flying great distances. Indeed there is little, if any, foundation for the old idea that the big birds carried the small, though it is imaginable that a tired Goldcrest might alight upon a Goose's back as he does upon a ship. The Sanderling, a frequenter of our sandy shores in autumn, is only eight inches in length. The Knot, a common bird on the estuaries and mud-flats of our east coast, measures ten inches. The Turnstone, which may be seen feeding among the seaweed in May, on its way north, and in August or September on its way south, is only a little larger than the Sanderling. The Nightingale is not so great a traveller, but he is known to go as far south as Abyssinia. The Blackcap often nests as far north as lat. 66° in Scandinavia, and winters down in Abyssinia or Gambia.

In the great north and south migration it will be seen that some birds merely rest upon our shores as they pass from one of their residences to the other. The Little Stint, besides the three just mentioned, the Sanderling, the Knot, and the Turnstone, is one of those which use the British Isles merely as a hostelry. The Whimbrel, often known as the Maybird, because of its punctual appearance in that month, might almost be put in the same class. But though its travels are never ended till it has passed Great Britain and Ireland, its nest may sometimes be found in the Orkneys or Shetlands.

The East and West Migration.

There is not only a migration from north to south, but from the far east of Asia to the west of Europe. Richard's Pipit, a bird which occasionally reaches England, nests on the steppes of Eastern Turkestan and east of Lake Baikal. In winter considerable numbers are found in the south of France and in Spain. The Little Bunting's summer quarters are in Russia and never further west than Lake Onega, whence its range extends eastward to the Pacific coast. In the south-east of France it occurs almost every autumn. Five years ago more than thirty specimens had been obtained in Heligoland. The Royston Crows, that breed in the far east of Siberia, migrate westward in winter. Many come to the east coast of England, but, before they have crossed our island, turn southward and, probably, make for France. Migrants from the east on reaching the west coast of France or Spain turn southwards and steer for Africa. There is no corresponding migration from west to east; no birds from western Europe go to Russia or China for the winter. In the cold season they seek a more genial clime, and a bird in Siberia can find this equally by flying west or south.

The Return Route.

The route for the journey home is not always the same as for the journey out. According to Herr Gätke, those that in autumn travel from the east westwards, touching often at Heligoland, and afterwards bend their course to the south, in spring, having a more definite object before them, take the shortest route home to their nesting-place, so that they do not pass Heligoland. In the autumn journey they travel along two sides of a triangle, first to the west, then to the south ; in the spring they steer north-east, direct to their homes. But this change of route seems to be a more common and better established phenomenon in the New World than in the Old. To take one instance, the American Golden Plovers in spring fly northward through the States ; in autumn a great host fly southward over sea, past the Bermudas, while a weaker band, most of them young birds in immature plumage, journey overland by the route by which they or their parents came. On August 31st, in the island of St. Croix, Professor Newton found that all the Golden Plover had some traces of breeding plumage, a sure sign that the young birds had gone homeward by a different road. In this case, the autumn journey from Nova Scotia or further north to South America seems to be the more rapid. This is certainly exceptional, and I do not know that any satisfactory explanation has been suggested. It may be that in spring it is easier to find food upon the mainland, in autumn upon the West India islands, where they pause to rest after their long flight over sea.

Return to the Same Spot.

Every one who has been a birds'-nester knows how year after year a particular nest appears in a particular spot. Gilbert White wondered at the annual return of the same number of Swifts each year (exactly eight pairs) to Selborne. And now it has been put beyond a doubt that many migrants return to their old nesting-place. When a Nightingale in Abyssinia is seized with the migratory impulse, his heart is filled, not with a vague yearning for the north, but with a yearning for one familiar spot.

The Time Occupied in Migration.

The flight in spring is generally, as I have said, more rapid than in autumn. In spring the birds have a definite purpose before them. They wish to set about their nest building, and they grudge every hour of delay. In autumn they pause and loiter in Central and even in Northern Germany. It is difficult to estimate the exact time occupied by the spring flight, but some evidence is obtainable. That particular form of Bluethroat that has a red spot in the centre of the blue, winters in Egypt, often in the regions of the Upper Nile. It occurs frequently in Heligoland, whereas in Germany only the form that has a white spot is found. Since, then, according to the evidence, Heligoland is the first place at which it stops as it travels to its breeding stations in Northern Scandinavia and Russia, it would seem that it covers the whole distance from Egypt to Heligoland—over 1,500 miles—in a single flight. This is very difficult to believe, and to follow Herr Gätke when he maintains that the flight is accomplished in a single night is still more difficult. As evidence, he mentions the interesting

fact that the Bluethroat always arrives at dawn and
not during the dark at the lighthouses. But though
this may show that its flight has been a long one, it
tells us nothing definite about the time and place
of starting. The non-occurrence of this particular
Bluethroat in Germany may be due to defective
observation. Professor Newton gives an instance of
a bird making a flight of extraordinary length. A
kind of Cuckoo (*Eudynamis Taitensis*) that is found
almost throughout Polynesia, every year makes a
voyage to New Zealand to breed. A glance at the
map will show that it must pass great tracts of sea.
Still there are small islets, such as Norfolk Island
and the Lord Howe Islands, which it may possibly
use as resting places. Occasionally representatives
of American species are found in Europe and
undoubtedly they have crossed the Atlantic, which
has a breadth of over 2,000 miles at its narrowest
point. They cannot have crossed the Behring Strait
and flown over Asia to Europe, since they are hardly
ever found in Germany. But they may have either
rested on a ship on their way, or been borne along
involuntarily by violent gales. Such performances
cannot well be ranked with long flights voluntarily
and habitually undertaken. Setting such exceptional
phenomena aside, perhaps the longest known flight is
one which I have already mentioned. The American Golden Plovers breed in Arctic regions, from
Alaska to Greenland, above the limits of forest
growth, and when autumn comes they pass through
Nova Scotia, strike boldly out to sea, and, generally
leaving the Bermudas well to the west, sail on over

the ocean till they reach the West Indies. Even then, it is said, they will sometimes pass the first islands they reach and press on to more distant ones. From Nova Scotia to Hayti, the nearest West India Island available, is over 1,700 miles. Either, then, they fly at an almost incredible pace, or else they remain upon the wing an almost incredible time. But though it is easy to say that such a feat is incredible, it is very difficult to get over the evidence. One witness after another declares that he has seen flocks of them flying southward, several hundreds of miles to the east of the Bermudas, on which islands they alight only if the weather is unfavourable.[1]

The Beam-wind Theory.

Several very good observers, among them Herr Gätke himself, are of opinion that migratory birds dislike flying with a tail wind, *i.e.* with the wind directly behind them, and that what they prefer is a beam wind, *i.e.* a wind striking them upon the shoulder. A comical explanation of this supposed fact used to be given—that a wind from behind ruffled up the bird's feathers. But as he is moving with the wind, and necessarily at a greater pace, since in addition to that of the wind he has the velocity due to his own efforts, this explanation will not hold. Besides this, keepers of Homer Pigeons seem all to agree that their birds make much better times when

---

[1] See *The Naturalist in Bermuda*, by H. M. Jones, p. 72; and *North American Birds*, by Baird, Brewer, and Ridgway, vol. i. p. 140.

they fly with a tail wind. And a saving of time is a saving of effort. The best evidence in favour of the beam-wind theory is of the kind given by Herr Gätke, who says that he has seen birds heading, not towards their destination, but in a different direction.[1] But how is it possible to know exactly for what point they wish to steer? And how can we penetrate to their motives? Birds have been seen zigzagging as they flew down an estuary, and this, it is said, had for its object the avoidance of a tail wind. Before such evidence can be accepted, we want careful observations as to the direction of the wind, and then we must consider whether there is not some other perfectly simple explanation of their zigzag course. As a rule it seems that weather does not greatly affect migration. A great storm will, no doubt, sometimes prevent the progress of birds altogether. But the Puffin arrives here punctual almost to the day, and many other birds vary but little in the time of their coming, so that it is clear that they do not wait for some particular wind.

Wings shaped for Long Flight—From far South to far North.

Migrants whose two homes are widely separated have wings long and pointed as the necessary equipment for their arduous flights. Mr. Seebohm has taken our Great Reedwarbler and other birds of the same genus and shown how the form of the wing varies with the extent of the migration.[2]

---

[1] *Die Vogelwarte Helgoland*, p. 27.
[2] *Siberia in Europe*, p. 245.

Acrocephalus turdoides, our Great Reedwarbler, is found in summer as far north as the south of Sweden. Its winter migration takes it to the Transvaal and even further south.

A. orientalis differs little except in having a slightly less pointed wing. It migrates from Japan to Borneo.

A. stentorius. Wing much more rounded. It migrates only from Turkestan to India.

A. syrinx has the roundest wing of all. It does not migrate, but is resident in the Island of Ponape.

It is highly probable that among individuals of the same species similar differences exist, that those which travel furthest on migration are better fitted by the shape of their wings for long voyages than those which have a less extended range. This has actually been observed, it is said, in the case of the Wheatear and the Willow Wren. It is very natural that such variation should be found if there is truth in the theory that among the birds of a particular species those that winter furthest south pass the summer furthest north. Mr. Seebohm gives strong evidence of this. The Swallows at Natal start for the north the last week of March, only those that were hatched the previous spring setting out later, in the first half of April. But the swallow returns to southern Europe by the end of January, and in Spain Mr. Howard Saunders found many broods hatched by April 16th. It seems clear, then, that the Natal Swallows do not stop till they have made their way further north, and that our own, which arrive in the first half of April, when those which stop in Spain are well on with their nesting, have come from the far south. *A priori*, too, it is probable that birds which spend their summer in the cool northern climes

would avoid the great heat of equatorial regions and
seek further south a milder climate more similar to
that to which they have become accustomed.   But
though this seems likely, and though in the case
of some species definite evidence has been obtained,
it is unsafe to represent it as universally true.

The Height at which Migrants Fly.—Their Cries.

There is no doubt that birds usually mount to a
great height when about to start on a long voyage.
Homer Pigeons, when liberated, circle upward, in
order, apparently, to survey the country and take
their bearings.   But exact information as to the
altitude reached is very difficult to obtain, since it is
impossible to take trigonometrical observations of a
passing object.   The best evidence available has been
procured through the ingenuity of some American observers.   They have watched birds through telescopes
focussed upon the moon and have calculated the
height at which they were flying.   One of these
observers, Mr. F. M. Chapman, proceeded on the
assumption that the least distance at which a bird
could be seen was one mile (nearer than which it
would not be in focus), and the greatest, five miles.
The apparent altitude of the moon was calculated
at ten minute intervals, in order to discover the
angle formed by the telescope with the horizon.
When these two facts had been ascertained—(1) the
distance, within certain limits, of the bird from
the observatory, (2) the angle at which the telescope inclined upwards—it was easy to calculate

the altitude at which the bird was flying. Eleven birds were seen shortly before eleven o'clock and for these the lower limit was 3,000 feet above the earth's surface, and the higher 15,100—*i.e.* only just short of three miles. If they were one mile distant, they were flying at the lower altitude mentioned, if five miles, at the higher. It is probable that some of them were near the higher limit, since they passed far more slowly across the field of the telescope than others. So clear a view was obtained that Mr. Chapman confidently affirms that he recognised a Carolina Rail and a Snipe by their flight.[1]

Herr Gätke strenuously maintains that birds fly to enormous heights. He quotes Humboldt who, when himself 15,578 feet above the sea level, saw a Condor so high overhead that it looked like a small speck. Migratory birds often pass at so great a height that they altogether escape notice. When a Crane with a wing expanse of seven to eight feet rises so high that a good eye can hardly see it, the elevation attained must be, he calculates, not less than 15,000 to 20,000 feet, and though such unassisted observations cannot claim to be exact, yet they help us to the rough conclusion that the altitudes reached are very great. Nearly all migrants are high flyers, coming down only when compelled by the weather. Crows, Starlings, and Larks are exceptions and habitually fly low, only a few hundred feet above the sea.

It is usually on dark misty nights that the cries of migratory birds are heard. It is then that they

[1] See *The Auk*, 1888, p. 38; the Nuttall *Ornithological Bulletin*, vi., p. 97; and Newton's *Dictionary of Birds*, p. 563.

are most necessary, in order to keep the troop together, or, possibly, in clear weather the flight may be at too high a level for us to hear them. Around lighthouses, sometimes over inland towns, there is a perfect babel of sounds, among which a practised ornithologist can generally distinguish the notes of particular species. Superstition sometimes finds in the cry of the Wild Goose an omen of death.

Order of Departure.

In autumn the young birds, of many species at any rate, start first; then after an interval, sometimes extending to a month or two, follow the old birds, and after them some irregular flights, probably consisting mainly of cripples and young birds hatched late. Swallows often pass Heligoland in November, and in England stray specimens may be seen as late as that. About the same time as the great flights of young birds, often a little before them, there come to Heligoland a few old ones, still generally in their wedding plumage, which looks a trifle worn. These old birds, it is believed, are those who have not found mates and who, having no family ties to detain them, hurry to their winter homes. Every autumn there arrive there some Golden Plover (representatives of the bachelor birds just mentioned) still wearing the black breast plumage that is donned in spring; then, more than a month after, come flocks of young birds. The same order of departure is observed among Starlings. The young birds begin to arrive in Heligoland in the latter half of June, the old birds not appearing till the latter half of September. A few unmated old birds precede the young ones by two or three weeks. It is strange that the young and inexperienced should start, apparently, so much sooner than is necessary. Possibly, however, they have it strongly hinted to them by their elders that their room is wanted, since the supply of food is limited and the young second broods are voracious. There is a very remarkable exception to the general order of departure. The old Cuckoos are in the same position as the unmated birds of other species. They have no responsibilities to keep them in the north, and they go, leaving their young to find their way south as best they can.

These curious phenomena show how intimately migration is connected with nesting. Many birds who have paired stay late in order to bring up their young. Yet every year it happens that some Swallows and Housemartins start for the south, leaving their young to die in the nest. This seems unnatural ; still, parental affection keeps them in England longer than they would remain but for that. We may imagine a struggle within them between the love for their young and the migratory impulse, and the latter at last becomes overpowering and swamps the former. The unmated cock birds, in whom no such struggle between opposing motives goes on, have started long before. Many who have no young brood to tend are delayed by their moulting. It is possible that the unpaired migrants, like unpaired pigeons, have their moult delayed, and that their early departure southward takes place before it begins. This question affects only one migration, either that of spring or autumn, since the large quills are shed only once in the year. The Swallow having his one moult in early spring is detained in England by family cares only. The Swift leaves us much earlier, and as he rears only one brood, and as his main moult takes place in spring he is free to go. The old Cuckoos go, as a rule, before August ; like the Swift they moult chiefly in spring, and their young are in the charge of others. The majority of our migrants shed their wing feathers in autumn, and, if it were not for that, would, probably, start southwards earlier.

In spring the order of departure is reversed. First come the old cock birds, the finest of all it is said leading the van ; then old hen birds ; then old hen birds and young birds mixed ; then young birds alone ; and, lastly, cripples in every stage of dilapidation. In some cases it may be that two sets start together, but that the stronger birds outstrip the weaker and hence the different dates of arrival for the different sexes and ages. But Mr. Seebohm speaks of the young Swallows at Natal being later with their moulting than the old birds, and this necessitates a later start. Besides, if it were a race for which all started level, probably some of the hen birds would arrive with the first detachment, and this does not seem to happen.

Partial Migrants.

This name has been given to species some individuals of which migrate, while others remain resident throughout the year. In England the old Robins

drive away the young ones, in order, it is believed, to
avert the evils of over-population. If hard weather.
comes, the old birds also move southwards, till only
those that are fed by their human friends remain.
On the Continent almost all migrate, travelling as far
south as the Sahara or as far east as Turkestan. Thus
species which are resident in one country may be
migratory in another. In this respect England with
its mild winters is most fortunate, for the proportion
of residents is with us much greater than it is in
other countries where the cold is sharper. According
to Dr. Wallace, in Massachusetts less than one-third
of the birds are resident, in England more than two-
thirds. Among our partial migrants is the Thrush.
Every autumn our native Thrushes are joined by
large numbers from the north, which soon however
pass on further south and take many of the British-
born birds with them, leaving the species almost un-
represented in some parts of the country. In Germany
not one is left, but all go south. Our Blackbirds too
are perhaps partial migrants. Large flocks visit us
in autumn and it is probable that some of our native
birds leave our islands in winter. Starlings also come
to us in large numbers as autumn visitors and, as a
rule, continue westwards, leaving some parts of the
country untenanted, while the south of Ireland is
thickly peopled with them. The Wild Duck, the
Common Snipe, the Woodcock represent species
that are mainly migratory with us, only a few remaining to nest in Britain. Some birds which we do
not think of as travellers, such as the Moorhen, move
from the colder northern districts towards the south.

Woodpigeons come to us in thousands, attracted by
our green crops or by the large supplies of acorns to
be found in our woods. No one who in winter sees
the clouds of them in the sky can doubt that our native
birds have been reinforced from abroad. Hertford-
shire in the winter of 1893 was literally invaded by
Woodpigeons, and the acorns almost always to be
found in their crops showed what the attraction had
been.

It will be seen from what has been said that migration is far more general than is usually supposed, and
it is certain that even now ornithologists have not
succeeded in observing all the smaller movements
which change of season causes among our resident
species.

The Nesting-places of Migrants.

All migrants without exception nest in the coldest
part of their range. They pass the summer in the
north and the winter in the south. Birds that breed
in the tropics are resident there with the exception of
some that nest at great elevations among mountains.
It is quite possible that there is a migration to the
Antarctic regions and in this case too the breeding-
place is in the colder, though in the southern, part of
the range.[1] It has been thought that our birds on
reaching Africa nested a second time. When our
Swallows arrive at Natal, the resident birds are
beginning to build, for their summer is beginning.
But it is almost certainly untrue that the birds from

[1] See Hudson's *Naturalist in La Plata.*

the north follow their example. In the Transvaal are many resident Reedwarblers, and mingled with them during the southern summer are some of our Reedwarblers that nest in the north. How wonderful it is that these near relations should have formed habits so different and that those who have departed from the ancient traditions of the Reedwarblers (supposing it to be the migrants who are the innovators) should be present to watch the others maintaining the primitive customs of the race!

The Cause of Migration.

Two of the problems of migration rank in importance above the many others that meet us. These are (1) why birds migrate, (2) how they are able to find their way. The former of these two problems, though the easier of the two, is a difficult one. The Swallow would seem to be well enough off in South Africa. Why, then, start on a voyage which must be perilous even for an old and experienced traveller? Why adopt a plan of life which must mean frightful mortality among the young? For of the many Swallows hatched only a small proportion return, and the numbers washed up by the sea after a storm show what has become of them. These arguments sound forcible, but they will not stand investigation. Swallows and other migratory species maintain their numbers quite as well as those that are resident. Among all birds, whatever their habits, the death-rate is very high. It is true that migration has to answer for the deaths of a very large percentage, but there is a counterbalancing gain. The perilous flight over, they are in a genial climate with plenty of food. To say that Africa could support all the Swallows that come to us in spring is to speak positively on a subject of which we know very little. There may seem to be abundance of flies for all comers, but the large flocks of birds that fly northward, each with a voracious appetite requiring many hundreds of gnats or other small insects to satisfy its daily wants, might well get to the end of the supply. Over bird-population is certainly a possibility. Eagles will not allow their own young ones to stay within what they have marked out as their own domain. The same jealousy is found not only in other birds of prey, but in Robins, and probably other species. The Nightingales of the Jordan Valley seem to be in excess of what the country can support, for some remain there to nest while others fly northward. It has been well urged, too, that in the tropics in the height of summer the country becomes parched, whereas in the north there are hosts of succulent caterpillars and other grubs. Mr. Seebohm found abundance of insect life in the valleys of Asia Minor in May and June. But would the case have been the same a month or two months later? Flies would, of course, be there in plenty, but there might well be a dearth of juicy larvæ. And the mass of grub-eating migrants, it must be remembered, come from the parched regions near the equator. We have some direct evidence that food is the magnet that attracts. The Rice-bunting or Bobolink, an American bird which winters in Central and Southern America, is enlarging its northern range as the growing of rice and wheat is extended to new territories. Birds come wherever there is food for them. Mr. Seebohm mentions that when there has been a grass fire in South Africa, the scene is visited by Lapwings, Coursers, and Pratincoles eager to pick up the burnt grasshoppers. The Woodpigeon, as already mentioned, is attracted by the acorns and turnips of England.

These opportunist, gipsy migrations may supply a clue to enable us to find the cause of the grand migrations that admit of no irregularity. Where food is, there are animals to eat it. On mountains above the level at which grass or flowers grow, the scanty lichens upon the rocks support small wingless insects. On glaciers, if you lift a stone, you will often find upon the ice below numbers of " glacier fleas," [1] which seem to have nothing but the lichen on the stones on which they can live. Stagnant ponds teem with Hydras Rotifers, Amœbæ, Vorticellæ. The lowest depths of the Atlantic, where there is no kind of vegetable growth, are peopled with fish and crustaceans, supported directly or indirectly by the *débris* of animal life that descends from the surface waters. What wonder, then, that birds in spring are found hard at work upon the cranberries and crowberries that in Arctic regions have remained frozen during the winter, or that insect-eaters are attracted by the countless mosquitoes ? If there had been all this enormous supply of food and no demand, there would then have been a far more difficult problem. Climate may, no doubt, have been the cause in some cases. But, often, this must have acted only indirectly by

---

[1] *Isotoma Saltans*, an apterous insect.

cutting off the food supply. Birds are capable of standing a great deal of cold if only they are well fed. When we see them in winter apparently pinched by the frost, the real reason of their distress is generally that they cannot get worms or grubs from the frozen ground.

It is unnecessary, I think, to call in the assistance of the often-invoked glacial period. Though brief, geologically speaking, this period wrought enormous changes in the zoological world. It has the credit or discredit of having driven from Europe the gigantic animals that formerly peopled it. It may, possibly, be in part the cause of the migration of birds. Some theorists have gone back to pre-eocene times when according to geologists the climate in the north was mild, but for two or three months in the year the sun did not rise above the horizon. And this long Arctic night taught birds to go south. Theories of this kind have an interest, but they are impossible either to prove or disprove. Without attempting to see so far back into the history of birds, we may argue that the desire for food and a more genial climate can account for the phenomena. But, while refusing to invoke causes from the remote past, we must recognize the fact that birds are wonderfully conservative ; a habit once formed may be maintained for ages, though it may have ceased to be useful. Such an explanation, at any rate, seems best to account for the choice of a winter resort made by some migrants. I quote an instance from Mr. Seebohm.[1] The Petchora Pipit and the Arctic Willow Wren both winter in the Malay Archipelago.

[1] *Distribution of the Charadriidæ*, p 49.

They have extended their breeding-grounds from
Siberia to eastern Europe. But though they have
moved their summer residence so far west, in winter
they still return to their old haunts in the Malay
Archipelago, though Africa is more accessible and,
we might imagine, equally suitable.

When we descend to the details of this part of the
subject, it is easy to ask questions which it is impossible to answer. For instance, why does the Common
Snipe frequently remain to nest in Britain, the Jack
Snipe never? Why do Fieldfares never make our
island their nesting-place, while their near relatives
the Thrush and the Blackbird are mainly resident here?
The Gray Plover and the Golden Plover present us
with a similar problem. In thinking of these difficulties we must always bear in mind that there is
still much to learn about the lives even of those birds
with which we are most familiar

How migrants find their way.

In the whole subject of migration, in many ways
so mysterious, there is no such mystery as this.
Formerly it was supposed that the old birds guided the
young, but it is now known that the young birds start
on their adventurous voyage alone, their parents
following after an interval.[1] The bachelor birds that
migrate early cannot act as guides, since, though they
set out about the same time as the young birds, they

---

[1] Old Bernicle Geese, however, have been seen guiding
parties of young on leaving the Hebrides. Gray's *Birds of W.
Scotland*, p. 349.

do not as a rule come actually with them. We seem, therefore, forced to assume that there is some inborn faculty—whether we call it instinct or not, matters little—which guides them. The sense of direction varies infinitely among men. One man, to use an Americanism, is very easily "turned round," another never gets confused about the points of the compass and can always find his way home. Most civilized races have to a great extent lost this power, but the Swiss guide has it in a high degree. In savages it is often developed to a wonderful extent, and in some animals it is still more remarkable. A dog, when he is taken far from home, though he is shut up so that he cannot see where he is going, will often find his way back. A Homer Pigeon is put in a basket and without a chance of using his eyes is whirled along in the train to some distant place. When set free, he flies aloft, takes his bearings and sets off homeward. I cannot understand why Professor Newton has given up the opinion he had once formed, that we have in the "homing" faculty of Pigeons a hint as to the power by which a migratory bird finds his way. It is true, as he says, that the Pigeon depends largely upon sight to find the exact spot where his home lies. But those which flew from Rome to England cannot have depended upon the sense of sight alone. The circumstances of the Pigeon and the young migrant are not the same. The former is a trained specialist and finds his way to a place he is familiar with, the latter is young and inexperienced and has to steer for a place he has never seen. Still each depends, not on landmarks, but on some inborn faculty or instinct, to teach

him the general direction in which he is to travel.
This instinct is, no doubt, helped by the eyes, for instance in choosing the narrowest passage when a
voyage over sea has to be made. Flying at a great
height a Swift will be able on a clear night to see the
striking features of the country from a long way off,
and this will help him to keep his course. But the
eye cannot do more than assist and correct the instinct.
The migrant's faculty differs from that of the Pigeon,
in that it directs him to a place with which, not he,
but his parents, are familiar. Marvellous as this no
doubt is, we must be very careful not to exaggerate
the miracle. The young Swallow has only to make
for the south, not to find any exact spot. When he
returns in spring, he often steers for the particular
barn or chimney where his earliest days were passed.
Moreover, though the young birds are the first to
start, it is believed that there is much loitering on
the autumn migration, and it is possible that they
may be overtaken by the old birds and attach themselves to them. Whatever may be the power by which
they guide themselves, in many of them it is imperfectly developed and fails them in their need.
On no other supposition can we account for the fact
that so small a percentage ever return.

Though we decide that they find their way by instinct, we have not advanced far towards the understanding of the problem. An instinct is an inborn
faculty, distinct from reason, though reason may act
upon it and modify it, and this particular instinct we
cannot understand, because we have something only
very remotely similar to it in ourselves. In attempt-

ing to understand it, we are like a colour-blind man
who tries to see a colour to which his eye is not sensitive. But this is not the only fact in zoology that is
beyond our comprehension. How do certain wasps
know the exact point at which to sting a spider, whom
they wish to paralyse without killing, so that he may
not decay before their larvæ emerge hungry from the
egg ?

There has been great dispute as to the routes
followed by migrants, some authorities maintaining
that in almost all cases sea-coasts or river valleys form
the lines along which they steer. This view may
possibly have arisen from the fact that so much of
our knowledge of migration has been obtained from
lighthouses, and from the fact that waterbirds often
make for river valleys because they can find food there.
Herr Gätke thinks that a great deal too much has
been made of migration routes, and he very per-
tinently quotes the case of Richard's Pipit, which in
its journey westward from Lake Baikal crosses a
number of streams flowing north and south, and the
Ural Mountains into the bargain ! [1] On the other hand
the flocks of birds that alight on Heligoland seem
to show that that small island comes in a well-defined
migration track. And if there are tracks over sea,
they may well exist over land. On this subject we
must wait for further knowledge.

[1] The most elaborate attempt to trace the routes followed is
to be found in Palmen's *Zugstrassen der Vögel.*

Exceptional Migrations.

The Nutcracker, the Waxwing, the Shorelark, Pallas's Sandgrouse occasionally invade Western Europe. The Nutcracker is fond of pine forests, nests in Scandinavia, in the Black Forest and the Alps, and is not as a rule given to wandering. The Waxwing breeds in Arctic regions, and has a way of suddenly, for unknown reasons, forsaking a favourite breeding-ground and moving to another district. Five times during this century, in winter time, it has appeared in Britain in considerable numbers. The Shorelark's summer home is in Northern Scandinavia, Russia and Siberia. In its irregular migrations it sometimes reaches our east coast. Pallas's Sandgrouse lives in summer between the Caspian and Lake Baikal, in winter moves to Northern China, and there has been much speculation as to what caused large hordes to sweep westward in 1863 and 1888. The onward roll of the living wave from place to place on the Continent till at last it reached England excited the curiosity of people for whom, as a rule, the doings of birds have no interest. But in the absence of any facts to help us to explain these weird phenomena, it is well to let the reader's reason or fancy have free play without attempting to guide him.

Stray Wanderers.

American birds, as I have said, occasionally visit England, but no return visits are paid by English birds to America. Most of those that come to us are shore or marsh birds, a fact which suggests that they have been carried away involuntarily by storms. I have already (see p. 357) given reasons for believing that these birds travel over the Atlantic, not over Asia, to our shores. This being so, it is odd that the east of Great Britain claims most of the specimens obtained, the district of the Land's End ranking next, while Ireland has few to show. It has been suggested that they are first carried past the north of our islands to Norway, where observers are few and far between, and return thence with the stream of migrants to England. The subject has been fully discussed by Professor Newton.[1]

SOME OF THE LITERATURE OF THE SUBJECT.

(1) Gätke's *Die Vogelwarte Helgoland.*

(2) Newton's article on " Migration," *Dictionary of Birds,* vol. ii., pp. 547–572.

(3) Wallace's *Geographical Distribution of Animals.*

(4) Seebohm's *Geographical Distribution of the Charadriidæ.*

(5) Seebohm's *Siberia in Europe.*

(6) Palmen's *Zugstrassen der Vögel.*

(7) Articles and letters in *Nature* and the *Ibis ;* also papers referred to in footnotes in the course of this chapter.

(8) Howard Saunders' *Manual of British Birds.*

A NOTE ON GEOGRAPHICAL DISTRIBUTION.

Though birds are such travellers, yet different parts of the globe have their characteristic Avifauna. Mr. Sclater's division of the world into six ornithological regions has guided Dr. Wallace in his great work on the Geographical Distribution of Animals and Plants.

---

[1] *Dictionary of Birds,* vol. ii., p. 548.

It is very remarkable that the study of birds, of all animals the greatest wanderers, should have laid the foundation of animal geography. Though the subject of the geographical distribution of birds is one of great interest, a detailed account of it is beyond the scope of this book. It is only necessary to make it clear that it must be carefully distinguished from migration. The reader is referred to the article in Professor Newton's *Dictionary of Birds.*

CHAPTER XV

CLASSIFICATION

STRICTLY speaking, classification is not part of the subject of this book. But since it is based on structure, it cannot be entirely passed over. And, in fact, it cannot be properly studied without a great deal being learnt beyond the distinguishing marks of species, genera, and families.

The aim of the classifier is to discover the relationship of bird to bird and arrange them in natural groups. If the system be one that enables the learner easily to identify a specimen, so much the better, but that is not the object in view. The term relationship has gained a far more definite meaning, since the theory of evolution has been generally adopted. If two animals are described as related to one another, the meaning is that they are descended from the same ancestors. If taken in the broadest sense, this is a mere truism, since it is held that all species have been developed from one. It must be understood to mean that, if the two lines of descent be followed upward, the meeting-point will be, geologically speaking, soon reached.

In the animal kingdom birds constitute what is called a class, while reptiles form another. A smaller division is called a sub-class, and below that, dividing and subdividing, we have orders and sub-orders, families and sub-families, genera, species, varieties and sub-varieties. The last two are different in kind from all the other divisions. The differences which mark off one variety from another are considered not to be constant: a few generations hence its representatives may have lost their distinguishing characters. Any species may vary, but one that is worthy of the name has its characteristic features so far fixed, that it is not likely at any near date to change in a way that might be inconvenient to our systems of classification.

These divisions and subdivisions appear, at first sight, like complications. They are really a great assistance. Without them the field of ornithology, extending, as it does, over eleven thousand known species and some still unknown, would be a realm of chaos. The classification of birds has presented greater difficulties than that of any other class of animals. When the first attempts were made, wrong principles were adopted ; more importance was attributed to habits than to structure. And thus such names as " Scratchers," " Cooers," " Waders " " Swimmers," were given to various groups. Even now, in accordance with this wrong principle, the Swallow is sometimes put down as a near ally of the the Swift. In every case the aim should be to distinguish real marks of relationship from what is due merely to similarity of life and circumstances, or, to put it technically, to depend upon homologies and not upon mere analogies. The application of the true principles has caused the Horned Screamer, in spite of his arboreal habits, to be put near the Goose. In spite of his way of life and his long legs, which suggest that we should class him with wading birds, the Flamingo is allied to the Duck, as his webbed feet and his beak proclaim. Not only must structural and not functional characters, or mere habits, be studied for purposes of classification, but the concurrent testimony of a number of characters must in every case decide to which family a bird belongs. In botanical classification Linnæus made the mistake of taking into consideration nothing but the number of stamens. According to his system a wall-flower and a lily, a campanula and a dandelion, a buttercup and a rose, would belong to the same orders. The natural system produces results which may seem strange (*e.g.* the buttercup is put in the same order as the Traveller's Joy), but which will bear investigation. And in the same way the scientific classification of birds, startling as its results may often appear, yet gains more and more adherents as true principles come to be recognised. But, though the right method has now been adopted, the difficulties have not vanished. Many systems have recently appeared which differ in very important particulars, though the constant tendency is towards the narrowing of the divergencies. In Mr. Howard Saunders' *Manual of British Birds* the orders are not in all cases the

same as in Mr. Mivart's *Elements of Ornithology :* in
the one the owls form a separate order, in the other
they are a sub-order of the Raptores. Botanists are in
a very different position : the battles of their rival
classifiers are fought over far more minute points.
Ought a certain form of briar, willow, or rose to be
counted as a species or a variety? The question
whether a particular genus shall be included among the
rushes or the lilies is one that exceeds the ordinary
magnitude of the problems that beset the classification
of British flowers.

Reptiles also, from a classifier's point of view, present
a striking contrast to birds. They are divided into
great and unmistakable orders. There are the Tortoises,
the Lizards, the Crocodiles, the Snakes. With birds,
though the number of species is very great, the differences are very small ; it is only by a minute study of
many, often obscure, anatomical points that a sound
system of classification has been arrived at. Unfortunately a system founded on such a basis, however
true it may be, must always have this drawback—that
an amateur must accept a great deal of it on trust.
I shall try to make clear a few of the chief points on
which the best and more recent systems depend. And
these few will be selected not only for their importance
but because they may be understood without much
technical knowledge. If they seem insufficient, it
must be remembered that there is a great array of
equally telling, but less easily appreciable, facts in
reserve.

There are, as I have said, eleven thousand known
birds. The first step is easy : they can be divided

into two sub-classes. One is made up of those which have keels to their breastbones, the other of those which have a rounded breastbone with no keel. The former are called Carinatæ (*carina* = a keel); the latter, Ratitæ (*ratis* = a keelless boat). This separates off the Apteryx, and the Ostrich with its kin the

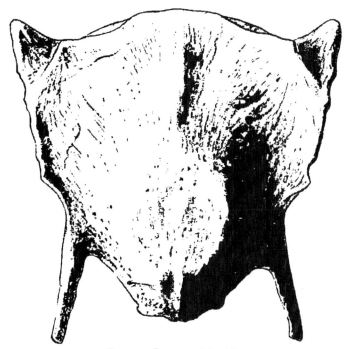

FIG. 75.—Sternum of Ostrich.

Rhea, the Emeu and the Cassowary. Thus some ten species out of the eleven thousand are disposed of.

I must now mention a few of the points that are most useful for deciding to which order one of the Carinatæ belongs. Very important are the following questions: the presence or absence of the first toe, and the arrangement of the four toes when all are

present; the relation of the branched tendon that
flexes the toes to that which flexes the hallux (see
p. 167); the presence or absence of the ambiens muscle
(see p. 169) which passes from the pelvis to the toes;
the distribution of the feathers on the neck and back
—whether there is a clearly defined tract of feathers
on the neck with bare spaces or apteria on either side,
and whether this tract forks, an apterion dividing it

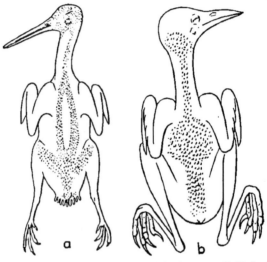

Fig. 76.—(*a*)—after Nitzsch—Snipe, spinal feather tract divided; (*b*) Blackbird, tract undivided.

into two arms, when it reaches the back; whether
there is an oil gland at the root of the tail, and whether
this, if present, is bare or tufted with feathers; whether
the young are helpless when born, whether they are
born naked or covered with down, and, if naked,
whether they pass through a down-stage before their
feathers grow; whether the hinder part of the sternum is *entire* or has notches or apertures; what is the
number of feathers in the tail.

The few species, the Ratitæ, which we have separated off from the rest, are held to have in them less of what constitutes a bird than any other. We will now go to the other end of the scale, the most highly specialized of the Carinatæ. These are the Passeriformes or sparrowlike birds, the largest order of all. Of the 367 birds which Mr. Howard Saunders counts as British, 125 belong to this order. This leaves 242 for the other sixteen. The Passeriformes may be known by these marks: (1) Their hallux or first toe is always turned backwards and is furnished with a larger claw than any of the other three; (2) there is no connection between the branched tendon and that which bends the hallux; (3) there is no ambiens; it is very curious that this muscle, whose duty is to help the toes to grip, should be absent in these perchers; (4) there is a well marked feather tract on the neck; (5) the young are born helpless, and hardly ever pass through a down-stage; (6) the oil gland is present and is naked; (7) they are without exception perchers. This last point is not, of course, a structural character, and is introduced only as supporting the others. To this order belong most of the very commonest of our birds; among them are none of much size except the Magpie, the Raven, the Crow, and the Rook. The Swallow is a Passerine, whereas the Swift belongs to a quite different order, what Mr. Mivart calls the Coraciiformes or crowlike birds. In this order the young are born with a little down upon them, the toes are united for some distance, and the first toe has not a larger claw than the others.

Among its representatives are the Kingfishers and the Nightjars, which thus are near relations of the Swifts. The Humming-birds are often put by themselves as a separate Passerine sub-order; but they are still a bone of contention, and it will probably be long before they are allowed to settle in a comfortable corner.

As affording a typical instance of difficulty, I mention two families, the Piciformes and Coccyges, to many representatives of both of which what is, perhaps, their most striking characteristic is common; they have zygodactyle or yoketoed feet.[1] How are they to be distinguished? The Piciformes—*i.e.* the Woodpeckers and their allies—have a well-marked feather tract on the neck with bare spaces on either side, while in our Cuckoo, who represents the Coccyges in Britain, the neck is all thickly covered with feathers.

Mr. Mivart's order, the Limicoliformes, illustrates well the difference between the older systems and the new. Most of the birds included were formerly put down as Waders because of their mode of life. These Waders are now grouped with a number of other species which do not wade. Their relationship is shown by the fact that they are born with down on them and are able almost at once to run; that they have a divided feather-tract on the forepart of the back; that they have an oil gland tufted with feathers. These and other characters cause the inclusion of the Gulls and Terns within the same order as the Waders.

[1] See p. 165.

I will now, taking a few typical cases, give the reasons why some birds which have a superficial resemblance should be separated from one another, and why others which at first sight are very unlike must be counted as near relations. What reason is there for putting Fowls and Pigeons in different orders, or at any rate in different sub-orders ? The young Pigeon is born blind and is helpless for about nine days ;[1] the young Chicken is able to run at once. In the Pigeon the tail has only twelve feathers, in the Chicken, eighteen. How is a Penguin to be distinguished from an Auk, a Puffin, or a Razorbill ? The Penguin has no apteria, or featherless spaces, a unique, or almost unique, characteristic. The Heron, the Stork, and the Adjutant are born helpless, then pass through a down stage, and are, therefore, to be distinguished from the Crane, which is born with down upon it, and runs a few hours after birth. The Petrel is related to the gigantic Albatross ; in each the nostrils may be seen as raised tunnels running for some distance along the top of the beak, and, hence, they are called Tubinares. The Water-ouzel is not distantly related to the Thrushes ; like them he has the first or outermost primary wing-feather very short, and the second shorter than the third or fourth. And yet he has the habits and look of a water-bird ; he dives and holds on to stones at the

---

[1] Mr. Seebohm and Mr. Mivart are in error when they state that no pigeons pass through a down stage. I have seen the down upon a young Stock dove, and also upon the young of *Columba Bolli.* See also Bronn's *Thier-Reich,* vol. "Aves," where Dr. Gadow figures the nestling down feather of a Pigeon.

bottom of streams as he searches for caddis-worms or insects, and his breast feathers are dense and impervious to water. The Rook may be known from the Crow by the absence of feathers on the beak ; they are worn away through his habit of digging in the ground for food. In the young bird they are still there, and to make sure whether you have a Rook or a Crow you have to look at the inside of the mouth ; in the Rook, it is deep flesh-colour, in the Crow, much paler.

Though some of these distinctions may appear trifling and insignificant, yet it is impossible to study classification without learning a great deal that is of real interest. There emerges, for instance, the very interesting fact that most birds, which for their size, lay large eggs, lay them on the ground, and that their young when hatched are covered with down, able to run at once or in a few hours, and, before long, to fend for themselves. There seems at the same time to be another principle at work side by side with that just explained—namely, that the eggs of a bird which lays a great number must be small, in order that she may be able to cover them. Certainly many of those whose eggs are largest lay only one, or at any rate very few, and their young are highly precocious.[1] No infant creature is more inde-pendent than the Maleo, a bird about the size of a small Turkey, native in the Island of Celebes. The mother buries her wonderful egg (weighing $8\frac{1}{2}$ to $9\frac{1}{2}$ ounces—*i.e*, about $\frac{1}{6}$th of the weight of a mature

[1] See the article on "Eggs" in Newton's *Dictionary of Birds.*

Maleo) in the sand, leaves the sun to hatch it, and, apparently, takes no care of her child.[1] The Crane lays her eggs upon marshland, and very soon after birth her young are running about ; the common Stork, which is about the same size, builds on house-tops, and her young for many days are helpless. The eggs of the latter measure only $2\frac{1}{5}$ by $2\frac{1}{10}$ inches, those of the former $3\frac{1}{5}$ by $2\frac{3}{5}$ inches. The Apteryx, of course, lays upon the ground, and her eggs are of astounding size. The Snipe's eggs are a great deal larger than the Blackbird's, though the two birds are about the same weight. The Curlew's egg is three times as big as that of the Raven, who equals her in bulk. It is very curious that some birds, which make their nests upon the narrow ledges of cliffs, in respect of the size of their eggs and the early activity of their young, resemble those which lay upon the level. Among them are the Gulls, the Razorbills, and Guillemots. Within a few hours from the time they emerge from the shell, these birds are able to run about, a serious danger one would have thought on a narrow ledge on which they must spend many days till at last they are able to fly, or in a burrow whose threshold overlooks a precipice. The Partridge's eggs are no larger than the Snipe's, and the nests of both birds are on the ground. Probably we have here an illustration of the second principle mentioned above—viz., that if the number laid be large, the size of the individual egg must of necessity be small.

---

[1] See Dr. F. H. Guillemard's *Cruise of the Marchesa*, p. 319.

The Partridge lays at least twelve eggs—sometimes over twenty—the Snipe only four.

This chapter which, as I have said, is only intended to give some idea of the general principles of classification, must now come to an end. Those who wish to make a study of the subject are referred to the books that deal specially with it.

SOME OF THE LITERATURE OF THE SUBJECT.

Elements of Ornithology. St. George Mivart. [The best book for beginners.]

Classification of Birds. Henry Seebohm.

Bronn's *Thier-Reich*, vol. "Aves." Dr. Gadow.

Vertebrate Anatomy. Professor Huxley.

CHAPTER XVI

THE HISTORY OF THE OSTRICH

WERE the ancestors of the Ostrich able to fly, and is the Ostrich, as we know him, an instance of " degradation "? Have his wings, after being large and strong enough for flight, been reduced till they are useless except to give some slight help in running? There are many examples of such degradation. Some moths, for instance the female Oakegger, have lost the power of flight. In the vegetable kingdom wheat is a good instance. It has three rudimentary calyx leaves and remnants of a corolla, which seem to show that it was once a perfect flower with its parts in threes like a lily. This is a clear case, for the corolla in its present form is useless, and " degradation " is the only principle on which we can account for its existence. But in many cases we cannot tell whether an organ is progressing towards a more perfect, or reverting to a less perfect, state. Those who maintain that the Ostrich and its allies are very far removed from the Carinatæ, or birds with keeled breastbones, and that their ancestors, like themselves, were incapable of flight, rely mainly on the following arguments :—

(1) The breastbone has no keel. There is no sign of one even in the embryo Ostrich.

(2) The clavicle is only rudimentary: in the Cassowary it almost vanishes as the bird grows to maturity; in the Emeu it persists in a much reduced state.

(3) The coracoid and scapula make a much larger angle than in birds that fly (pp. 13 and 34).

(4) The pelvis is very different from that of the Carinatæ. Except in the Rhea and the Cassowary, the ilium and ischium do not unite behind the thigh joint.

(5) The seams between the different bones of the skull persist much longer.   •

(6) Most of the feathers have no barbicels or hooklets. This really tells the other way, as I hope to show.

(7) There are, as it is maintained, no apteria or featherless tracts.

On the other side we have these arguments :

(1) In some of the Carinatæ, for instance in the Rails, the keel is much reduced, apparently reverting to a less developed state. The protuberance of the Rhea's rounded breastbone is not unlike a rudimentary keel.

(2) The clavicles are much reduced in some of the Carinatæ—e.g. in some Woodpeckers. In some of the Parrots the two bones do not even meet.

(3) The angle made by the coracoid and scapula varies very much in different species of the keel-less birds. Hence this point does not count for much.

(4) Rudimentary hooklets or barbicels have been found in the wing-feathers of the Rhea and some of the allied birds. This is a most important fact. If they did not help in flight, by making the feathers impervious to air, it is difficult to imagine what purpose they can have served.

(5) The fusion of the hand-bones in the Ostrich shows that the wing-feathers were once stronger and that the wing had work to do.

(6) Definite apteria have been found in some birds of the Ostrich kind. Even if this were not the case, we might urge that the point is one of little importance, since the Penguin has none.

On the whole the arguments seem to show that the progenitors of the Ostrich were birds of flight. But the question is a difficult one.[1]

---

[1] The whole question is discussed in Fürbringer's *Untersuchungen zur Morphologie und Systematik der Vögel*, p. 1481. See also Bronn's *Thier-Reich*, vol. " Aves."

CHAPTER XVII

OUTDOOR AND INDOOR ORNITHOLOGY

THE amateur ornithologist should study birds in every way that is open to him. A specialist whose life is devoted to classification and who takes notice only of the points that are important for this purpose, is doing work that must be done, and which requires a good man to do it. But after a time a bird may no longer be to him a living creature with wonderful powers and habits and character. He may come to look upon it as existing only to be put in its exact place in a system of classification. The outdoor ornithologist who knows nothing about birds but what he can learn by observation in the open, though he is, perhaps, the most to be envied of all specialists, yet has missed a great deal. He may not know that the most active and ethereal of all vertebrate animals is nearly related to a lizard. How the reptilian bones have been adapted to purposes of flight, how a cold-blooded torpid creature has become warm-blooded and full of life, is altogether out of the field of his observation. To another man a bird is only a flying machine illustrating profound mathematical principles. There is no reason why an amateur should be in bonds to any extreme form of specialisation. The amateur ornithologist should attack all parts of his subject in succession, or two or three parts at once, and he is certain to find that he is not losing so much in depth as he is gaining in breadth. All that he learns of one part of his subject is sure to throw light upon another.

Out of Doors.

It is best to begin with outdoor work. It is much more likely to generate a love of the subject than the alternative method. Instead of learning at the outset by dissection that a Wood Pigeon has a very strong gizzard and a Hawk nothing worthy of the name, it is much better first to gain the knowledge that a Hawk has only to digest flesh, while the pigeon has to grind acorns, and afterwards, when you can see the meaning of it, learn the difference in anatomy. But when a good start has been made, the two methods may well go hand-in-hand. A very good plan is to take a field-glass and look carefully at every bird that will submit to be looked at and not mistake it for a double-barrelled gun. The habit of observation wants cultivating. From our early years we are taught to acquire knowledge almost exclusively from books and lessons and lectures, so that, dulled by much reading and passive listening, we are slow in picking up facts direct from nature. Especially in a naturalist is power of observation

wanted. The older writers put down much that had
little foundation, believing a thing simply because it
was wonderful on the principle of *credo quia im-
possibile*. And some of these old stories are still
repeated and believed, while the real wonders of
nature, as startling, if not as grotesque, as anything
that can be invented, often remain unnoticed.
Examine every ird, then, with a field-glass or a
binocular telescope, and get to know the song that
each sings and, on getting home, take a good book
on birds and try to identify any you were not certain
of. The songs of birds are beautiful in themselves,
and it is, no doubt, delightful to listen to them without knowing in the least what birds are singing, or,
perhaps, even without distinguishing one song from
another. But it adds to the pleasure if the song
tells you of the bird and the bird of the song. When
you first learn to distinguish a Thrush's note from a
Blackbird's, and still more when you acquire the rare
accomplishment of knowing a Blackcap's song from
a Garden Warbler's, the delight in the song may, no
doubt, be at times alloyed with a certain baser feeling
of pride. But the baser feeling does not exclude the
higher, and it is difficult to be fond of a particular
song without wishing to know the songster. And
you come to like the Thrush's song all the better when
you find that he sometimes goes on for a quarter of
an hour without ever repeating himself exactly. You
become a partisan of particular birds, and, perhaps, hold
that the Thrush is a better singer than the Nightingale,
or the Blackbird than either. And you learn to take
pleasure in such minor things as call or alarm notes.

A good deal about flight may be learnt with a
field-glass.   When Gulls are playing in the air, or
when a Lark is rising, or when a Swallow is dashing
to and fro, you can often make out by the help of it
the movements of the head and tail.   Sometimes,
though, the naked eye is better, as it takes time to
aim with the glass, and the bird may be gone before
you have a good view of him.   A great many birds
may be known by their flight.   The Duck with its
outstretched neck, rapid wing pulsation, and lumber-
ing velocity, the slow and heavy stroke of the Heron,
the light easy beat of the Gull's finely-pointed wings,
the hovering of the Hawk, the sudden dashes and
acrobatic turns of the Swift or the Swallow are
things easy to remember.   A man who is much in
the open air, and brings an eye for what he sees,
notices many more varieties than these.

Most boys go through a birds'-nesting stage, and
to some of them it brings a good deal of valuable
knowledge.   At the same time they may get a liking
for birds that will introduce a spirit of humanity into
their birds'-nesting, and lead them to a study of the
lives and habits of creatures who have become their
friends but were formerly their victims.   But with
many it is, no doubt, only a form of greed and
rapacity, not so bad as that of the miser, since they
will probably either outgrow it or transform it to
something better, but, for all that, similar in its
nature.   Collecting anything, whether birds, eggs, or
postage stamps, or autographs, merely for the sake of
amassing, is a worse than barren employment.   But
if a birds'-nester makes a point of observing the

structure of each unfamiliar nest he finds and writing a description of it, of waiting about to see the old birds and listening to the song of the cock, if he does sing, and of verifying on getting home the one egg he has possessed himself of, by referring to books for an account of the eggs, nest, and bird; he is a rational being and little in danger of developing the greed that is the vice of the collector. Certainly he will never be guilty of the folly, that should be criminal, of buying rare eggs, and so raising their market value to the imminent danger of exterminating the species.

If you wish to look upon a scene of beauty, vigorous life and jostling sociability, you should go to some out-of-the-way cliff or island where seabirds nest —pay a visit to a colony of Puffins, most naïve, most comic of birds, sitting at the thresholds of their crowded nestholes—see the Guillemots lining long ledges that are perilously narrow for their eggs—see the Razorbills, the Oystercatchers, the flocks of Kitti-wakes and all the other winged things of loveliness. But, perhaps, nothing of the kind that Great Britain can show can equal the scene on some island in the Pacific, where acres of land are clothed with grave Albatrosses too busy with their eggs and their young to think of flying away from men and cameras.

Much may be learnt by shooting specimens, and if you either skin every bird you shoot, or pay for the skinning, you are likely to avoid indiscriminate slaughter. Many people are not content with a field-glass; they want more tangible results than it gives them. And some birds will not stop to be looked at.

FIG. 77.—Albatrosses nesting on Laysan Island in N. Pacific (from a photograph belonging to the Hon. Walter Rothschild, by his kind permission).

The gun must play an important part in ornithology till the world is far more depopulated of birds than it is at present, though no reasonable ornithologist will shoot a bird of a species that can with difficulty maintain itself and is in danger of extinction. Moreover, rarity does not in itself add to the interest of a bird. Great Auks, when plentiful, were just as interesting as at the present day when there are only a few dead specimens in museums. When shooting, you learn things that are not likely to come to your notice otherwise. You see how vigorous a bird is after his wing is broken ; a Cormorant, thus wounded, will dive and swim with undiminished activity. If you swim after a bird you think you have hopelessly crippled, he may lead you a terrible dance. There is no truth in the notion that a wounded bird never recovers. Brehm[1] says that he has often shot birds whose wing bones had evidently been previously shattered by a gunshot. You cannot help, while shooting, picking up a great deal of miscellaneous information as to the favourite haunts of particular species, their feeding times, their comparative shyness, their flight, their various notes, and many other things.

Every ornithologist, who can, should travel. Even if birds on their migration come to us, there is no reason why we should not travel in search of them. Those who have seen the nests of our Geese, Gray Plovers, Little Stints, Sanderlings, and Knots in the far north, are much to be envied. And the tropical

[1] See *Bird Life*, by Dr. A. E. Brehm, English translation, p. 89.

birds ought to be seen in their own countries. A
Humming-bird in a museum is a piece of wonderful
colour; in his own country he is something so wonderful that no one has ever yet described him. And
there are certain favoured islands to which it is worth
while to go and stop for a good long time, where
you may be able to realise the reign of system in
the great migrant world. Wherever you go, long
and patient observation is what is wanted. The
proverb "Everything comes to those that wait" is
one for all naturalists to bear in mind.

Indoors.

Though a live specimen, if you can see it well, is
worth twenty dead ones, it is seldom you can watch
a live bird near at hand for long together and make
out minute points. Museums, therefore, are wanted,
not only large ones in great towns, but smaller ones
scattered about the country. You often cannot get
to the large ones when you want. When you are
there, the amount of objects is distracting, and it
is difficult to concentrate your attention on one; and
you want specimens that you can handle, a skin that
you can take up and examine closely, count the wing
or tail feathers, measure the various parts, bare the
apteria, &c., &c. Even mounted specimens, unless
they are set up in costly style with elaborate
surroundings, it is well to have in cases that will
open, so that you can take them out and look at
them all round. Specimens of the common birds
and of the rarer ones are wanted; of the common

ones because you have seen them alive and want to
make out all the details of their plumage, of the
rarer ones because you, perhaps, have not seen them.
But, of the two, the common ones are the more important ; great rarities may well be dispensed with.
Museums, therefore, need not be such exterminators
as private slaughterers who often prize a specimen for
its rarity and nothing else.

An ornithologist should understand the art of bird-
skinning. Bird-stuffers, it is true, are many, and
there is nearly always one not very far off, but good
stuffers are rare. It is highly desirable, therefore, to
be able to make a good skin that can be mounted, if
you prefer it, afterwards. If he is travelling in an un-
civilised country, the ornithologist must, of necessity,
be a bird-skinner, if he wants to bring home any
specimens. You pick up a good deal in the process
of skinning besides learning patience. Patience is
highly necessary, since if you hurry too much or lose
your temper, there will soon be a rent that may be
difficult to conceal. You notice, as you go, the bare
patches or apteria which are so important in classification. You discover the powderdowns of the Heron.
You get a look at the wing muscles and notice the
depth of the breast. You appreciate the paper-like
thinness of the skull. You discover and wonder at
the extent of the air-cavities under the skin of the
Gannet. The Starling's skin, you find, is as tough
as leather, the Blackbird's delicate and easily torn.
You make a point of opening the gizzard to see
what the bird has been feeding on. The very
useful art of skinning can be learnt by means of a

lesson or two from some one who has mastered it, and a good deal of practice. Pace, which must be carefully distinguished from hurry, is a great desideratum. If you return in the evening with six birds that you wish to skin, you have some work before you.

The keeping of birds as pets ought only to be undertaken by people like Mrs. Brightwen, who are prepared to devote a great deal of care to them. And there are some that under the most favourable circumstances are always unhappy in confinement.

> A Robin Redbreast in a cage
> Puts all heaven in a rage.

Water birds with clipped wings if they have a pond and a moderate run are not unhappy. The Gulls at the Zoo evidently take the keenest pleasure in their morning wash. Some people regret that such a bird as an Eagle is ever cabined in an aviary. I think a zoological society may fairly do what an individual may not, for the animals which it keeps in captivity afford instruction to large numbers of people. In the same way with stuffed specimens, it is the private collectors upon whom a check should be placed, rather than upon public museums. Moreover it is comparatively inexpensive to build a large aviary in which birds may live happily, whereas boa-constrictors require much initial outlay of capital to build them a house, and considerable current expenditure to keep them warm.

Much as we should like to dispense with books and learn everything from nature, it is clear that on this system the field of our knowledge would be very limited. By our own observation we lay hold of isolated pieces of information, which, unaided, we should never be able to put in their proper setting. When we see a Golden Plover in autumn we want to know whence and whither he is travelling. When we find that the Gray Crow visits the realms of the Black Crow, but does not stay to nest there, we want a map to show us how these two, so alike that they may, perhaps, be considered to form one species, have divided the greater part of the Old World between them. When we see how our Cuckoos have perfected the parasitic habit, we, naturally, wish to know of other birds which are advancing towards or have attained the same unamiable perfection. Not only does the reading of books on natural history enable us to connect isolated observations and vastly extend the range of our knowledge ; it enables us also to observe more. Our power of seeing grows with our knowledge, if we only keep it alive and do not deaden it through want of exercise. When you travel in a country for the first time, if you have some previous knowledge of it gained from other travellers or from books, you will see far more than if you come to it quite raw.

If the study of birds is to have a solid foundation it must include some study of their anatomy. This, though we speak of it metaphorically as the foundation, need not necessarily come at the beginning. The point to be insisted on is, that to leave it out is to leave out what is indispensable. Flight is, in any case, a very difficult subject ; it is more difficult if you have no knowledge of a bird's anatomy. To know that a bird never tumbles off his perch during sleep is something ; it is well to go on to a knowledge of the machinery which keeps him there. When you see that a bird's neck is more supple than a snake, you wish to see the joint which allows such free play in all directions. An understanding of the problems of classification is impossible to an ornithologist who has not penetrated beyond the outside. The bird's whole life depends upon his anatomy, and to try to study the former without the latter is somewhat like attempting the study of a people's history without the study of the people themselves. It will not do to stop short at the skeleton. You must get dead specimens and dissect them ; see the enormous size of the great pectoral muscles ; inflate the air-sacks and see how spacious they are and how small in comparison are the lungs ; how the heart is far superior to a reptile's, different also from a man's, and yet equally efficient ; how the head is almost a feather-weight, and how the gizzard has taken the place of the grinders that would have burdened it ; see what a complexity of muscles serves to bring about the perfect adjustment of the wing to every need. These and hundreds of things besides can only be realised by the aid of dissection. You can only half understand what you read on a subject such as this. When you have seen a good deal with your own eyes, you can realise not that only, but more of the same nature that you learn from books. But to trust entirely to the eyes of others for your knowledge of anatomy is as foolish as it is to derive from books your knowledge of the Alps instead of going there to see them.

SOME BOOKS THAT ARE OF SERVICE TO THE PRACTICAL ORNITHOLOGIST.

Manual of British Birds. Howard Saunders.
British Birds. Seebohm.
Wild Nature won by Kindness. Mrs. Brightwen.
Practical Taxidermy. Montagu Browne.
Practical Zoology. Marshall and Hurst.
Bronn's *Thier-Reich*, vol. "Aves." Gadow.
Dictionary of Birds. Newton.
Field and General Ornithology. Elliott Cowes.
Summer Studies of Birds and Eggs. ⎱
A Year with the Birds. ⎰ Warde Fowler.

INDEX

The references in some cases are collected under heads, e.g. "Bones," "Muscles," "Authors quoted." Heavy type denotes that the reference is comparatively important. The Index includes the names of some only of the birds mentioned.

THE END